ARITHMETIC
FOR THE MODERN AGE

by

AARON BAKST

D. VAN NOSTRAND COMPANY, INC.
PRINCETON, NEW JERSEY

TORONTO   LONDON
NEW YORK

D. VAN NOSTRAND COMPANY, INC.

120 Alexander St., Princeton, New Jersey (*Principal office*)
24 West 40 Street, New York 18, New York

D. VAN NOSTRAND COMPANY, LTD.
358, Kensington High Street, London, W.14, England

D. VAN NOSTRAND COMPANY (Canada), LTD.
25 Hollinger Road, Toronto 16, Canada

03652a15

PRINTED IN THE UNITED STATES OF AMERICA
BY LANCASTER PRESS, INC., LANCASTER, PA.

Preface

Not long age we were thrust into the air age. Now we speak
of a space age and look forward to an interplanetary age. There
seem to be comparable advances or trends in instruction in
mathematics. The author, however, does not propose to take a
path that would relegate arithmetic to the museum just because
some theoreticians hold that mastery of mathematics (arithmetic is still a branch of mathematics) must be based on abstract
foundations. Arithmetic will be with us long after all the
computing devices, electronic or hand-driven, have been ac-
corded their proper place in the technology of computation, a
procedure that after all is based on arithmetic.

Here is a book in which the subject of arithmetic is presented
informally and without a single formal proof. The author be-
lieves that such a method of instruction can be extremely effective for the serious reader who seeks proficiency in the subject.
The impression that the usefulness of arithmetic was lessened
with the invention of electronic computing devices is as er-
roneous as the notation that electronic devices will displace
man's brains. We need and will always need arithmetic.
Those who work with electronic computers cannot escape this
fact.

Arithmetic is a subject which, like youth (to quote Bernard
Shaw) is usually wasted on young people; yet it is unsound
to relegate arithmetic to the memories of early school days. As
a matter of fact, arithmetic, or the utilization of arithmetic
skills, constantly permeates all fields of human activity, whether
science, engineering, mathematics, or matters more mundane.
But skill alone is insufficient for the intelligent use of arithmetic.
Proficiency calls for the use of reasoning processes as well.

A. B.

Table of Contents

1

The Decimal System

of Numeration

What is number?

Numbers have been used by men since prehistoric days. Men invented numbers because they needed them. Numbers were the result of counting. Counting was discovered because men found a need for correctly judging magnitudes of objects and collections of objects. The mastery of numbers is a good measure of the development of civilization. A primitive Pygmy tribesman in Africa can count to two only. Three is a very difficult number. He does not have an idea of three, and he has no word for it. Three is *many* to him.

As men became more civilized they felt a need for larger and larger numbers. Whereas ten or a hundred met the needs of Stone Age men, billions and numbers larger than billions are familiar and useful to nearly everyone today.

It is difficult to define a number. All of us use numbers; we have a fairly good idea what their purpose is, but defining them is so difficult that a knowledge of advanced mathematics is necessary in order to express precisely what a number is. We shall, therefore, examine the procedure by which we obtain any number, and thus define number for our present purposes.

We usually obtain a number when we count objects. When we want to record the result of counting we write a symbol, but this is *only* a symbol for a number. Thus 7 is the symbol for the number seven. At present we use a set of symbols which were introduced into Europe about a thousand years ago by the Arabs. Originally these symbols were invented in India by the Hindus. We call these symbols the Hindu-Arabic symbols or numerals.

The decimal system of numeration

Our method of counting is based on the use of the number *ten*. We arrange our counting in such a manner that there is a system

1

and method to it. We count up to ten, and then, instead of going on inventing special names for the numbers that follow, we stop at ten, use it as a base, and continue until we count ten more. Then we stop, call the result *two tens* and go on until ten more are counted. The next result is *three tens.* Extending this system, we can go on indefinitely.

There is an advantage in this method of counting. We do not need to have a very large supply of names for numbers. We also can arrange our writing of numbers in a very compact and simple manner.

Men have not always used this method of counting. The Pygmy, as has been mentioned, counts in *twos.* We have a special name that is still in use, which suggests that at some time in the distant past our ancestors likewise counted in twos; we often use the word *pair.* Other men counted in *fives;* the Chinese and Japanese still do so. Some counted in twelves; we have *the dozen* and *the gross* (a dozen dozen or twelve dozen). Some counted by twenties; we have the word *score,* which means twenty.

About 5,000 years ago, the Babylonians counted by sixties. We have inherited this method from them and we use it when measuring time. One hour is divided into sixty minutes, and one minute is divided into sixty seconds.

Names of numbers

Counting can be carried on indefinitely, if we are sufficiently patient in performing this task. This fact has a special meaning: after we reach some number we can name the next one, if we know how to do this. The sequence of numbers thus obtained is known as *the natural sequence of whole numbers* (or of *integers*).

The first ten numbers are:

one, two, three, four, five, six, seven, eight, nine, ten.

In order to indicate that there are no objects to be counted, we use the number

zero.

The names for other numbers up to one hundred are derived from the first ten. Thus we have:

> eleven, twelve, thirteen, fourteen, fifteen,
> sixteen, seventeen, eighteen, nineteen.

Then,

> twenty, thirty, forty, fifty, sixty, seventy, eighty, ninety.

Thereafter, we count by hundreds, thousands, millions, and so on.

Writing numbers

The symbols for numbers, also known as *the numerals,* are as follows:

zero	0	five	5
one	1	six	6
two	2	seven	7
three	3	eight	8
four	4	nine	9

With these ten numerals any number can be written.

The familiar principle that is used in the process of writing numbers in the decimal system of numeration is known as *the positional principle.* The value of each numeral in a number is determined by its position (judged from the right) in the number. The position on the extreme right is assigned to *units.* The position to the left of the units is assigned to *tens;* that is, the value of this position is ten times as great as the position on the extreme right (the units position). In the number 33 or thirty-three, for example, the 3 on the extreme right represents three units. The 3 to the left of the units position has the value of three tens. Thus 33 represents

$$30 \quad \text{and} \quad 3.$$

The value of the position immediately to the left of the tens has a value ten times as great as the position of the tens. This position, therefore, has the value of hundreds. In the number

444, the 4 on the extreme right represents four units, the 4 on the left of the units represents 40, or four tens, and finally the 4 on the left of the tens represents four hundreds.   Thus, 444 actually represents

400 and 40 and 4.

The positional values are arranged into groups by threes as follows:

Sixth group			Fifth group			Fourth group			Third group			Second group			First group		
Quadrillions			Trillions*			Billions*			Millions			Thousands			Units		
Hundreds of quadrillions	Tens of quadrillions	Units of quadrillions	Hundreds of trillions	Tens of trillions	Units of trillions	Hundreds of billions	Tens of billions	Units of billions	Hundreds of millions	Tens of millions	Units of millions	Hundreds of thousands	Tens of thousands	Units of thousands	Hundreds	Tens	Units

* This is the accepted language in the United States.   In England, the fifth group is called "billions."

We need not stop with quadrillions; we may go on coining names for other groups of threes: quintillions, sextillions, septillions, and the like.   As long as there may be a need, we can extend the limit of writing numbers and thus suit our purposes.

This arrangement enables us both to write and to read numbers easily.   Generally, when numbers are written the numerals are grouped by threes so that it becomes easy for the eye to distinguish them.   Thus five million, six hundred seventy-five thousand, four hundred ninety-two is written as

5 675 492.

Often the groups of threes are separated from one another by commas, thus:

$$5,675,492.$$

Either of the two methods of writing is correct.

Numbers, when written, are often described by the number of numerals they contain, that is, by *the number of places*. Thus 72 is a two-place number and 4,895 is a four-place number. Four-place numbers, especially dates, are often written without commas or spaces, as 1000, 1943.

PROBLEMS

1. Write the smallest three-place number. *Ans.:* 100.

2. Write the largest three-place number. *Ans.:* 999.

3. What three-place number does not change in value if the units and tens numerals are interchanged?

Ans.: Any three-place number in which these digits are the same. For example, 266, 300, 477, 522, 833.

4. What three-place number does not change if the units and hundreds numerals are interchanged?

Ans.: Any three-place number in which these digits are the same. For example, 141, 565, 282, 747, 939.

5. If in a given five-place number there is no unit number of hundreds, what numeral must be used to indicate this fact? *Ans.:* 0.

6. Write a six-place number which has five hundred-thousands, six thousands, and nine units. *Ans.:* 506,009.

7. How many hundreds are there in the number 12,091,732?

Ans.: 120,917.

8. What is indicated by the zeros in the number 60,108?

Ans.: That there are no units of thousands and no units of tens.

9. One foot contains twelve inches. What system of numeration is suggested by this fact? *Ans.:* Twelve.

10. How many thousands are there in six million? *Ans.:* Six thousand.

2

Addition and Subtraction
of Whole Numbers

Addition of whole numbers

The addition of two or more numbers is an arithmetic operation by means of which a new number is obtained. This new number contains as many units as are contained in all of the added numbers taken together.

The numbers that are added are known as *the addends*.

The number resulting from the addition of two or more numbers is known as *the sum*.

The sign for addition is $+$ (plus).

EXAMPLE. A factory employs 1,562 men and 1,891 women. How many people are employed in the factory?

In order to obtain the desired number (or, as we usually say, to solve the problem) we must add the two numbers, 1,562 and 1,891. The solution is written as follows:

$$1{,}562 + 1{,}891 = 3{,}453.$$

The symbol $=$ designates equality.

Addition is also employed when a certain number must be increased by some other number.

EXAMPLE. A factory worker's weekly wages of $92 were increased by $25. What are his new weekly wages?

In order to obtain the desired number we must add the two numbers, 92 and 25. The solution is written as follows:

$$92 + 25 = 117.$$

Thus we see that by means of addition two types of problems may be solved, namely:

6

    i. Problems wherein it is necessary to obtain the sum of two or more numbers.

    ii. Problems wherein a given number must be increased by some other number.

The columnar method of addition

Addition is best performed when the numbers that are to be added are written in columns so that units of the same denomination (units, tens, hundreds, thousands, and so forth) are aligned vertically. This arrangement simplifies the work and, as will be shown presently, permits easy checking of the correctness of the work.

For example, the sum of 1,562 and 1,891 is obtained as follows:

$$\begin{array}{r} 1,562 \\ +\ 1,891 \\ \hline 3,453 \end{array}$$

The addition is performed from right to left. First we add 2 and 1. Thus

$$2 + 1 = 3,$$

and 3 is written in the units column or place. Then we add 6 and 9. Thus

$$6 + 9 = 15.$$

Since only one numeral (some call it *digit* or *figure*) can be written down, we write 5 to the left of the 3 (in the place for the tens), and then we carry the 1 over in the next addition.

$$\begin{array}{r} {\scriptstyle 1} \\ 1,562 \\ 1,891 \\ \hline 53 \end{array}$$

We then add 1, 5, and 8. Thus

$$1 + 5 + 8 = 14.$$

Here, again we write 4 to the left of the 5 (in the place for the hundreds), and then we carry 1 over into the next addition. We then add 1, 1, and 1. Thus

$$1 + 1 + 1 = 3.$$

This 3 is written to the left of the 4 (in the place of the thousands). The sum of 1,562 and 1,891 is 3,453.

PROBLEMS

Add the following numbers:

11. 127, 642, and 396.

12. 583, 492, and 1,835.

13. 1,684, 3,489, and 497.

14. 34,671 and 89,483.

15. 1,765,789, 92,473, and 847,562.

16. 342, 679, 578, and 783.

17. Increase 47,892 by 11,765.

18. What number must be decreased by 8,947 in order to obtain 15,993?

19. The automobile touring mileage between Boston, Mass., and Albany, N. Y., is 184. The automobile touring mileage between Albany, N. Y., and Cleveland, Ohio, is 467. The automobile touring mileage between Cleveland, Ohio, and Chicago, Ill., is 354. What is the mileage between Boston and Chicago, by way of Albany and Cleveland?

20. The airway distance between London and Athens is 1,721 miles. The airway distance between London and Alexandria via Athens is 581 miles greater. What is the distance by air from London to Alexandria?

The commutative property of addition

We can easily observe that the addition of 8 to 35 gives the same result obtained when 35 is added to 8. In either of the additions the sum is 43. We then can write

$$8 + 35 = 35 + 8.$$

The same conclusion can be reached if three or more addends are in the computation. Thus

$$4 + 7 + 8 = 19,$$
$$8 + 7 + 4 = 19,$$
$$7 + 4 + 8 = 19,$$
$$8 + 4 + 7 = 19,$$
$$4 + 8 + 7 = 19,$$
$$7 + 8 + 4 = 19.$$

This property is known as the *commutative property* of addition.

It signifies that *the sum of two or more numbers does not change when the order in which the numbers are added is changed.*

This property is very important in addition, because its application enables us to check columnar addition. Also, by means of this property we may obtain some short cuts in addition.

When a column of several numbers is added, the addition may be performed by adding the numbers in the same column either by going upward or by going downward. If we add a column downward, we may then check our addition by adding it upward. If the two results agree, we may be reasonably certain that no mistakes were made. If we add upward, we check the addition by adding downward. For example, the addition

$$
\begin{array}{r}
36{,}782 \\
4{,}973 \\
64{,}583 \\
\hline
106{,}338
\end{array}
$$

is performed as follows, adding downward:

$$
\begin{aligned}
2 + 3 + 3 &= 8, &&\text{write 8;} \\
8 + 7 + 8 &= 23, &&\text{write 3 and carry over 2;} \\
2 + 7 + 9 + 5 &= 23, &&\text{write 3 and carry over 2;} \\
2 + 6 + 4 + 4 &= 16, &&\text{write 6 and carry over 1;} \\
1 + 3 + 6 &= 10, &&\text{write 10.}
\end{aligned}
$$

The checking is done by adding upward as follows:

$$
\begin{aligned}
3 + 3 + 2 &= 8, \\
8 + 7 + 8 &= 23, \\
2 + 5 + 9 + 7 &= 23, \\
2 + 4 + 4 + 6 &= 16, \\
1 + 6 + 3 &= 10.
\end{aligned}
$$

In some cases, when several numbers are to be added the addition may be made easier if the addends are transposed so as to simplify the addition. The following example will illustrate this procedure. Suppose we have to add the following numbers: 37, 85, and 63. Note that $37 + 63 = 100$. The addition of the three numbers is then performed as follows:

$$37 + 63 + 85 = 185.$$

The transposition can then be performed mentally.

PROBLEMS

21. Check the additions in Problems 11 to 20.

22. Obtain all possible arrangements of the three addends: 23, 15, and 28.

23. Check the correctness of

$$672 + 891 + 1{,}364 = 1{,}364 + 672 + 891.$$

24. Perform the following additions mentally:

$$47 + 54 + 53; \qquad 68 + 45 + 32; \qquad 73 + 35 + 27.$$

25. Perform the following addition mentally:

$$468 + 345 + 532.$$

The associative property of addition

In the preceding section we noticed that the application of the commutative property of addition enables us to simplify addition. However, the application of this property in the process of addition involved another property which will be examined now. Note that in the addition $37 + 85 + 63$ we combined 37 and 63, whose sum is 100, and then we added to this sum the third number, 85. In other words, we performed the addition by combining some of the addends, obtained a partial sum, and then added to this partial sum the third addend.

The fact that we can obtain partial sums leads to a simplification of the task of adding several numbers. Suppose that we have to add the following numbers: 42, 67, 28, 33, and 85. We can perform the addition as follows:

$$42 + 67 + 28 + 33 + 85.$$

In other words, we can write these numbers in a column and obtain the sum according to the processes described in the preceding section. However, the addition may be performed in another way. First we add 67 to 42. To the sum of these two numbers we add 28, then we add 33, and finally we add 85. We thus have

$$42 + 67 = 109,$$
$$109 + 28 = 137,$$
$$137 + 33 = 170,$$
$$170 + 85 = 255.$$

If we examine the numbers 42, 67, 28, 33, and 85, we may note that $42 + 28 = 70$, and $67 + 33 = 100$. Observe that $100 + 70 + 85$ can be performed with less effort than the addition of the five numbers as shown above. This illustration leads us to the conclusion that careful examination and correct combination of the various addends will always simplify addition. Furthermore, this combining of the various addends, after skill is developed, permits the performing of addition mentally. It should be noted that there is no restriction on the number of addends that can be grouped. The grouping is entirely dependent on the decision of him who performs addition. For example, the addition of 17, 42, 89, 41, 25, 63, and 12 leads to the following very advantageous groupings:

$$(17 + 42 + 41) + (25 + 63 + 12) + 89 = 100 + 100 + 89 = 289.$$

In order that there shall be no confusion as to what numbers are to be added separately they are enclosed in *parentheses* ( ). These parentheses indicate the procedure that is to be employed in the process of addition. Later on we shall learn of other uses of the method of parentheses.

We actually made use of the method of parentheses when we added numbers by the method of columns. Suppose that we wish to add the following numbers: 6,783 and 9,458. We can write them as

$$6{,}783 = 6{,}000 + 700 + 80 + 3,$$

and

$$9{,}458 = 9{,}000 + 400 + 50 + 8,$$

respectively. The addition may be then performed by grouping the numbers as follows:

$$6{,}783 + 9{,}458 = (6{,}000 + 9{,}000) + (700 + 400) + (80 + 50) + (3 + 8).$$

We then obtain the sums of the respective groups:

$$6{,}783 + 9{,}458 = 15{,}000 + 1{,}100 + 130 + 11.$$

Now, in order to make the addition easier we shall detach 10 from

11 and transfer it to 130.   We have then:

$$140 + 1.$$

Then we shall detach 100 from 140 and transfer it to 1,100.   We have then

$$1,200 + 40 + 1.$$

Finally, we shall detach 1,000 from 1,200 and transfer it to 15,000. We have then

$$16,000 + 200 + 40 + 1 = 16,241.$$

This 16,241 is the sum of 6,783 and 9,458.   Note that this associative procedure actually represents the columnar addition of these two numbers.

$$
\begin{array}{r}
6,783 \\
+ \ 9,458 \\
\hline
16,241
\end{array}
$$

We start the addition from the right.   Adding 3 and 8, we have $3 + 8 = 11$.   We write 1 and carry the other 1 into the next column (on the left).   Then $1 + 8 + 5 = 14$.   We write 4 and carry 1 into the next column.   Then $1 + 7 + 4 = 12$.   We write 2 and carry 1 into the next column.   Then $1 + 6 + 9 = 16$. We write 6 and carry 1 into the next column (on the left).   But this column is blank, aside from the carried 1; hence we write 1 in the sum.   Thus the sum is 16,241.

PROBLEMS

26. Perform the following additions mentally:

$21 + 37 + 79 + 63$
$29 + 37 + 71 + 53$
$7 + 83 + 14$
$47 + 43 + 68 + 12$
$36 + 42 + 84$

27. Perform the following additions mentally:

$2 + 30 + 400 + 7,000$
$800 + 1,400 + 2,000$
$8,200 + 740 + 60$
$12 + 868 + 220$
$6,000 + 3,800 + 162 + 38$

28. Perform the following additions by columnar method:

3,678 + 984 + 372 + 61

65,382 + 8,791 + 3,476 + 3,892

1,754 + 85,673 + 98,372 + 376

345,872 + 458,792 + 67,354

387,645 + 43,982 + 178,463 + 453,789

29. Increase 76,453 by 125,367.

30. What number must be decreased by 65,893 in order that 347,267 is obtained?

Subtraction of whole numbers

Subtraction is an arithmetic operation by means of which one of the addends is obtained when the sum and another addend are given. The resultant number is known as the difference of the two given numbers.

The number from which another number is to be subtracted is known as *the minuend*. In other words, this number is to be di*mini*shed.

The number that is *subtra*cted is known as *the subtrahend*.

Since in the case of subtraction the sum of two numbers is given and one of the addends is to be obtained, subtraction is actually an operation that undoes addition. In other words, subtraction is an operation opposite to addition.

EXAMPLE. In a factory there are 986 employees. Among them there are 354 men, and those remaining are women. How many women are employed in the factory?

The total number of employees is the sum of the numbers representing the men and women employees. The number of men employees is given. The number of women employees is obtained as follows:

$$986 - 354 = 632.$$

The symbol − is read *minus*. It is the sign for subtraction.

The procedure used in subtraction will be described presently.

Subtraction may be also encountered in the following situations:

i.   When a certain number must be diminished by some other number.

ii.   When it is required to find out by how many units one number is greater than another, or smaller.

EXAMPLE.   The delivery price of a certain automobile is $2,600.   The trade-in value of a car that is turned in is $650. The cash needed for the purchase of the car is

$$\$2600 - \$650 = \$1950.$$

EXAMPLE.   The selling price of a radio is $75.   The wholesale price is $50.   The gross profit (or also, the retail mark-up) is

$$\$75 - \$50 = \$25.$$

The process of subtraction

Subtraction of many-place numbers is best performed by the columnar method.   Thus the subtraction $986 - 354$ shown in the preceding section is performed as follows:

$$\begin{array}{r} 986 \\ - 354 \\ \hline 632 \end{array}$$

We begin the subtraction from the right, and we subtract the numbers in the same column.   Thus:

$$6 - 4 = 2,$$
$$8 - 5 = 3,$$

and

$$9 - 3 = 6.$$

Observe, in the above subtraction, that when we subtracted by columns we employed numbers all less than 10.   Thus, in order to be able to perform subtraction correctly, we must know the various differences of numbers up to and including 9.

However, subtraction is not always as simple as the illustration shown above.   Very often it happens that in a column the number to be subtracted is greater than the number from it is to be subtracted. The following example illustrates such a situation.

$$\begin{array}{r} 6{,}372 \\ -\ 2{,}896 \\ \hline \end{array}$$

The first subtraction, $2 - 6$, presents an obstacle. If we intend to subtract 6 from 2 we become confronted not only with an impossibility but with a meaningless procedure. Such an operation is impossible in beginning arithmetic.

In order to overcome this difficulty we proceed as follows. We *borrow* one of the units in the column on the left of the column in which the 2 is located. After this borrowing is completed we have 12, and we can subtract 6 from 12. Then

$$12 - 6 = 6,$$

and this 6 is written under the line in the column of the 2.

Since we borrowed 1 from the column on the left of 2, the number now standing in that column is not 7 but 6. In order that no mistake shall be made and that this borrowing shall not be forgotten, we usually place a dot over the 7. Our subtraction up to this moment appears recorded as follows:

$$\begin{array}{r} 6{,}\overset{\cdot}{3}72 \\ -\ 2{,}896 \\ \hline 6 \end{array}$$

Now, 9 cannot be subtracted from 6. We again borrow one unit from the column on the left. This borrowing leads to the subtraction

$$16 - 9 = 7.$$

Thus the subtraction is recorded:

$$\begin{array}{r} 6{,}\overset{\cdot\cdot}{3}72 \\ -\ 2{,}896 \\ \hline 76 \end{array}$$

Now in the third column we are left with 2.   Again 8 cannot be subtracted from 2.   We then borrow 1 from the column on the left.   This borrowing results in the subtraction

$$12 - 8 = 4.$$

We have then:

$$\begin{array}{r} \dot{6},\dot{\dot{3}}72 \\ - 2,896 \\ \hline 476 \end{array}$$

Finally, we perform the last subtraction

$$5 - 2 = 3.$$

Thus the subtraction of the two four-place numbers is:

$$\begin{array}{r} \dot{6},\dot{\dot{3}}72 \\ - 2,896 \\ \hline 3,476 \end{array}$$

Very often it happens that the borrowing from a column on the left may seem to be impossible because the numeral in such a column is zero (0).   This situation does not offer an obstacle, however.   If it occurs, the borrowing is done from a column where there is a numeral other than zero (0).   The subtraction below illustrates the procedure.

$$\begin{array}{r} \dot{\dot{2}}0,\dot{0}\dot{\dot{7}}4 \\ - 6,898 \\ \hline 13,176 \end{array}$$

The first subtraction is performed as

$$14 - 8 = 6.$$

The second subtraction is performed as

$$16 - 9 = 7.$$

To borrow from the two zeros is impossible.   We borrow from the 2.   Transferring the 1 to the column on the right of 2 we have 10.   Borrowing a 1 from it, we transfer this 1 to the right as 10, and we borrow 1 in turn from this 10.   This step permits the subtraction of 9 from 16.   The next two subtractions are

and

$$9 - 8 = 1,$$

$$9 - 6 = 3.$$

PROBLEMS

31. Perform the following subtractions mentally:

10,000 − 2,000	147 − 57
11,000 − 3,000	268 − 19
29,000 − 12,000	2,000 − 425
37,000 − 19,000	901 − 126
1,600 − 78	317 − 29

32. Perform the following subtractions: (a) 4,587 − 2,463; (b) 19,769 − 6,358; (c) 37,489 − 16,244; (d) 156,884 − 73,443; (e) 986,756 − 643,423.

33. Perform the following subtractions: (a) 879 − 397; (b) 1,543 − 688; (c) 4,873 − 2,986; (d) 41,673 − 13,986; (e) 617,482 − 349,695.

34. Perform the following subtractions: (a) 1,005 − 643; (b) 800,072 − 640,347; (c) 7,060,504 − 901,065; (d) 11,024,037 − 8,806,054; (e) 706,089,002 − 8,900,450.

35. How much must be added to 6,473 in order to get 15,892?

36. By how much is 34,657 smaller than 65,783?

37. By how much is 895,043 greater than 605,607?

38. What number exceeds 56,075 by 46,708?

39. Obtain the difference between the largest seven-place number and the largest six-place number.

40. The readings of an electric meter were as follows:

May 1	376,899 kilowatt-hours
June 1	380,673 kilowatt-hours
July 1	384,537 kilowatt-hours
August 1	389,975 kilowatt-hours
September 1	394,056 kilowatt-hours

How much electricity was consumed each month?   How much electricity was consumed during the entire period?

Problems in time

Problems in time generally refer to a number of days, years, months, hours, minutes, or seconds: How many days? How many years? How many months? How many hours? How many minutes? or How many seconds? or, sometimes, combinations of these.

Statements in problems involving time contain information that relates to *dates*, such as year, month, day of the month (or day of the week), and time of the day. In order to be able to solve problems in time we must be aware of the fact that time statements are not as simple as statements of, say weight, length, height, or the like. The following facts should be remembered.

> 1 year consists of 365 days.
> 1 leap year consists of 366 days.

(A leap year is one whose number can be divided by 4, such as 1944, 1948. A year whose number ends with two zeros, such as 1900, though divisible by 4, is not a leap year unless divisible by 400, by agreement.) February in a leap year has 29 days, while in any other year February has 28 days. The days of the months are as follows:

January	31 days	July	31 days
February	28 days	August	31 days
	(leap year 29)		
March	31 days	September	30 days
April	30 days	October	31 days
May	31 days	November	30 days
June	30 days	December	31 days

> 1 week has 7 days
> 1 day has 24 hours
> 1 hour has 60 minutes
> 1 minute has 60 seconds

A day begins immediately after midnight. In civil life a day is divided into two parts of 12 hours each. The hours from midnight to noon (meridian) are denoted by the letters A.M. (which means *ante* or before the meridian). Thus, 5 o'clock in the morning is 5 A.M. The hours from noon to midnight are denoted by

the letters P.M. (which means *post* or after the meridian).   Thus
3 o'clock in the afternoon is 3 P.M.   Midnight is denoted 12 P.M.;
noon is denoted 12 A.M. in common practice, such as railroad
timetables.

Our armed forces (Army and Navy) record time also from
midnight.   However, they do not divide the day into two parts,
and hours are numbered from 0 to 24.   Minutes are numbered
from 0 to 60; seconds are numbered from 0 to 60 (when seconds
are used).   Thus 3:25 A.M. is written as 03:25 or 0325.   But
3:25 in the afternoon is written as 15:25 or 1525.   Midnight is
recorded as 24:00 or 00:00, or 2400 or 0000.   1 minute after
midnight is written as 00:01 or 0001.

Problems involving the question: How many days elapse between two dates? are generally solved as follows (some business
organizations follow other rules): Unless otherwise specified, one
of the two dates is included in the elapsed interval.   For example,
the number of days that elapse between January 7 and January
25 of the same year is found by subtracting 6 (the day before
January 7) from 25, that is,

$$25 - 6 = 19.$$

Commercial practice varies so much that bank clerks and the
like usually depend on a table of the number of days between two
dates, and do not attempt computations.   Astronomical practice
is necessarily more sound and consistent in theory.   It may best
be learned from special texts on astronomy and navigation.

PROBLEMS

41. How many days are there between March 22 and September 17?

42. Someone was born on November 12, 1875, and lived 56 years 3 months
and 17 days.   What was the date of his death?   (How many leap years occurred during his life?)

43. The building of a house was started on February 15 (not in a leap year)
and completed 4 months and 18 days.   What was the date when the house
was completed?

44. A certain contract was completed on May 15, 1942.   It took 5 months
and 12 days to complete it.   The agreement called for 7 months and 20 days

for its completion. When was the work begun? When was it supposed to be completed?

45. How many days are there between the Fourth of July and Thanksgiving? Between the Fourth of July and Christmas?

Important information helpful in addition and subtraction

Whenever addition or subtraction is performed certain fundamental facts and relations between numbers are very helpful. These are the sums of numbers up to 10 inclusive and differences of such numbers. The tables below give all these facts. It is

ADDITION TABLE

	1	2	3	4	5	6	7	8	9	10
1	2	3	4	5	6	7	8	9	10	11
2	3	4	5	6	7	8	9	10	11	12
3	4	5	6	7	8	9	10	11	12	13
4	5	6	7	8	9	10	11	12	13	14
5	6	7	8	9	10	11	12	13	14	15
6	7	8	9	10	11	12	13	14	15	16
7	8	9	10	11	12	13	14	15	16	17
8	9	10	11	12	13	14	15	16	17	18
9	10	11	12	13	14	15	16	17	18	19

suggested that the reader study them and memorize these facts so that the simplest additions and subtractions may be performed at a glance and without any difficulty.

In the addition table, the sum of any of the two numbers shown in the first column on the left and in the upper row is

SUBTRACTION TABLE

	1	2	3	4	5	6	7	8	9	10	11	12	13	14	15	16	17	18	19	20
1	0	1	2	3	4	5	6	7	8	9	10	11	12	13	14	15	16	17	18	19
2	–	0	1	2	3	4	5	6	7	8	9	10	11	12	13	14	15	16	17	18
3	–	–	0	1	2	3	4	5	6	7	8	9	10	11	12	13	14	15	16	17
4	–	–	–	0	1	2	3	4	5	6	7	8	9	10	11	12	13	14	15	16
5	–	–	–	–	0	1	2	3	4	5	6	7	8	9	10	11	12	13	14	15
6	–	–	–	–	–	0	1	2	3	4	5	6	7	8	9	10	11	12	13	14
7	–	–	–	–	–	–	0	1	2	3	4	5	6	7	8	9	10	11	12	13
8	–	–	–	–	–	–	–	0	1	2	3	4	5	6	7	8	9	10	11	12
9	–	–	–	–	–	–	–	–	0	1	2	3	4	5	6	7	8	9	10	11
10	–	–	–	–	–	–	–	–	–	0	1	2	3	4	5	6	7	8	9	10
11	–	–	–	–	–	–	–	–	–	–	0	1	2	3	4	5	6	7	8	9
12	–	–	–	–	–	–	–	–	–	–	–	0	1	2	3	4	5	6	7	8
13	–	–	–	–	–	–	–	–	–	–	–	–	0	1	2	3	4	5	6	7
14	–	–	–	–	–	–	–	–	–	–	–	–	–	0	1	2	3	4	5	6
15	–	–	–	–	–	–	–	–	–	–	–	–	–	–	0	1	2	3	4	5
16	–	–	–	–	–	–	–	–	–	–	–	–	–	–	–	0	1	2	3	4
17	–	–	–	–	–	–	–	–	–	–	–	–	–	–	–	–	0	1	2	3
18	–	–	–	–	–	–	–	–	–	–	–	–	–	–	–	–	–	0	1	2
19	–	–	–	–	–	–	–	–	–	–	–	–	–	–	–	–	–	–	0	1

found in the cell where the column and the row of those two numbers intersect. Thus

$$5 + 7 = 12.$$

The top row of the subtraction table represents the minuends. The vertical column on the left represents the subtrahends. The differences of the respective numbers are found in the cells where the column and row lines intersect.   For example

$$13 - 7 = 6.$$

Note that in certain cells there are zeros.   When a number is subtracted from itself, the difference is zero.   For example,

$$17 - 17 = 0.$$

It should be also noted that the addition of zero to any number leaves the number unchanged.   For example,

$$11 + 0 = 11.$$

Likewise, the subtraction of zero from any number leaves the number unchanged:

$$15 - 0 = 15.$$

3

The Dependence of Sums and

Differences on the Data

The dependence of the sum on the addends

If several numbers are added, their sum is determined by their respective magnitudes. Any change in one or more addends must from necessity be reflected on the magnitude of their sum. Let us examine in detail how a change in the addends affects the sum.

EXAMPLE. Suppose that a shoe factory produces 1,000 pairs of men's shoes, 750 pairs of women's shoes, and 500 pairs of children's shoes a day. The daily production is then

$$1,000 + 750 + 500 = 2,250$$

pairs of shoes.

Now let us suppose that the production of men's shoes is stepped up to 1,500 pairs daily while the production of women's and children's shoes is not changed. The increase in the production of men's shoes is then $1,500 - 1,000 = 500$ pairs daily. The daily production of shoes is thus

$$1,500 + 750 + 500 = 2,750$$

pairs of shoes. The total increase in the daily production is

$$2,750 - 2,250 = 500$$

pairs. This total increase is equal to the increase in the production of men's shoes.

EXAMPLE. Let us take two numbers, 115 and 75. Their sum is

$$115 + 75 = 190.$$

Let us increase the first addend by 45.   We have then

$$(115 + 45) + 75 = 160 + 75 = 235.$$

The sum has thus increased by

$$235 - 190 = 45.$$

Similarly, let us decrease the second addend by 30.   We have then

$$115 + (75 - 30) = 115 + 45 = 160.$$

The sum has thus decreased by

$$190 - 160 = 30.$$

Thus we note that *when one of a group of addends is increased by some number, the sum is also increased by that number; when several addends are increased, the sum is increased by the sum of the increases.   If there is a decrease in one or several addends there is a corresponding decrease in the sum.*   This is a long and perhaps clumsy statement.   It will later be presented more briefly and neatly in a new form (see page 28).

Difference and its dependence on changes

The difference of two numbers is determined by the magnitudes of the minuend and of the subtrahend.   If either or both of them be changed, it is reasonable to expect a change in their difference.   Let us examine how a change in them affects their difference.

EXAMPLE.   Suppose that the weekly wages of a worker are $50, and that of this amount he spends $40 and saves the balance. Also suppose that his wages are raised $10 a week while his expenses remain the same.   How do these changes affect his saving?

Each week, he saves from his original earnings

$$\$50 - \$40 = \$10.$$

From his increased earnings, which are $50 + $10 = $60, he saves

$$\$60 - \$40 = \$20.$$

Thus he saves $20 − $10 = $10 more.   The increase in his wages leads to an increase in saving.

Suppose that his wages were not changed but his weekly expenses were increased by $5.   Thus his weekly expenses are

$$\$40 + \$5 = \$45,$$

and his weekly saving is

$$\$50 - \$45 = \$5.$$

In other words, an increase in his expenses leads to a corresponding decrease in his saving.

Now let us examine the change in the difference of two numbers if the minuend or subtrahend is diminished.

EXAMPLE.   Suppose we have the difference

$$74 - 29 = 45.$$

If the minuend (74) is diminished by 13, it becomes $74 - 13 = 61$, and the new difference is

$$61 - 29 = 32.$$

But 32 is the result of diminishing 45 by 13; that is, $45 - 13 = 32$. Thus we see that the decrease in the minuend results in a corresponding decrease (by the same number) in the difference.

If the subtrahend is decreased, say by 17, it becomes $29 - 17 = 12$, and the new difference is

$$74 - 12 = 62.$$

But 62 is the result of increasing 45 by 17, that is $45 + 17 = 62$. Thus we see that the decrease in the subtrahend results in a corresponding increase in the difference, equal in magnitude.

We may now make a rule for changes in minuends and subtrahends corresponding to the rule for changes in addends: *Whenever, in a subtraction, the minuend is increased or the subtrahend is decreased by any number, the difference is increased by an amount equal to that number; whenever the minuend is decreased or the subtrahend increased by any number, the difference is decreased by an amount equal to that number.*

This rule again is long and perhaps clumsy. Like the rule for addend changes, it will later be presented more briefly and neatly in a new form (see page 28).

PROBLEMS

46. Complete the following:

First addend	Second addend	The sum
Increased by 87	Increased by 43	?
Increased by 364	Decreased by 92	?
Decreased by 145	Increased by 62	?
Decreased by 73	Decreased by 54	?
Increased by 35	?	Increased by 67
Decreased by 45	?	Decreased by 32
Increased by 156	?	Increased by 98
Decreased by 58	?	Decreased by 87
?	Increased by 89	Increased by 142
?	Decreased by 68	Decreased by 189
?	Increased by 24	Increased by 10
?	Decreased by 98	Decreased by 127

47. A factory contracted to deliver on a certain date 24,500 large and small packing cases. On that date were delivered 1,545 more large cases than ordered and 1,763 fewer small cases than ordered. How many cases (large and small) were delivered?

48. How does a sum change if the first addend is increased by 379, the second addend is decreased by 116, and the third addend is increased by 75?

49. How does a sum change if the first addend is decreased by 75, the second addend is increased by 187, and the third addend is decreased by 137?

50. Complete the following:

The minuend	The subtrahend	The difference
Increased by 356	Increased by 78	?
Increased by 145	Decreased by 134	?
Decreased by 79	Increased by 154	?
Decreased by 42	Increased by 149	?
Increased by 125	Unchanged	?
Decreased by 37	Unchanged	?
Unchanged	Increased by 163	?
Unchanged	Decreased by 73	?
Increased by 49	?	Increased by 89
Increased by 178	?	Decreased by 365
Decreased by 164	?	Increased by 245
Decreased by 67	?	Decreased by 54
Unchanged	?	Increased by 134
Unchanged	?	Decreased by 243
Increased by 65	?	Unchanged
Decreased by 113	?	Unchanged
?	Increased by 135	Increased by 207
?	Increased by 231	Decreased by 467
?	Decreased by 187	Decreased by 125
?	Decreased by 94	Increased by 76
?	Increased by 457	Unchanged
?	Decreased by 43	Unchanged
?	Unchanged	Increased by 156
?	Unchanged	Decreased by 248

51. The profits of a store for a certain year were $2,567. The following year the expenses increased by $1,378 while the intake increased by $2,041. What were the profits for that year?

52. What must be done with the minuend so that the difference is increased by 35, if the subtrahend is increased by 42?

53. The minuend is decreased by 134. What should be done with the subtrahend so that the difference is increased by 78?

54. The subtrahend is increased by 65. What should be done with the minuend so that the difference is left unchanged?

55. The minuend is increased by 67. What should be done with the subtrahend so that the difference is decreased by 189?

A compact way of stating the above results

The results obtained above can be stated compactly by means of a method of writing commonly used in mathematics when it is desired to state certain facts in general form. Note that these results were stated in words; the facts referred to *any* number. In mathematics, when we imply or state that some property holds good for *any* number, this fact can be stated compactly by using letters in place of numbers. Thus, instead of stating that an increase in one of the addends results in a corresponding increase of the same magnitude in the sum, we write

$$(a + m) + b = c + m.$$

Here the two addends are a and b; their sum is

$$a + b = c;$$

and the fact referring to the change is stated as

$$(a + m) + b = c + m,$$

where m denotes the number by which the first addend was increased. In order to indicate that increase m was applied to the first addend, we enclosed this addend and the number m representing this increase in parentheses.

The facts concerning addition are then as follows:

$$(a + m) + b = c + m,$$
$$a + (b + m) = c + m,$$
$$(a - m) + b = c - m,$$
$$a + (b - m) = c - m.$$

The difference of two numbers a and b can be represented as

$$a - b = c,$$

and the facts concerning the changes in the difference are then as follows

$$(a + m) - b = c + m,$$
$$(a - m) - b = c - m,$$
$$a - (b + m) = c - m,$$
$$a - (b - m) = c + m.$$

The reader may, as an exercise, translate these statements and check the verbal statements obtained by him with those given on pages 24 and 26 above.

Reversing addition and subtraction

Very often we are faced with a problem in which we are given a sum of several numbers as well as all the addends but one, and we must find the missing addend.   In order to solve this problem we may reason as follows: We know the sum of all addends and we know all the addends but one.   We can obtain the sum of the known addends.   This sum will be smaller in magnitude than the sum of all the addends, and the difference between these two sums should give us the missing addend.

In the compact form, that is, using letters in place of numbers, the above reasoning can be written as follows: Let us take four addends, a, b, c, and d.   The sum of these is

$$a + b + c + d = s.$$

According to the statement of the problem we are given the sum s and three of the addends, say a, b, and c.   The problem is to find the remaining addend, d.   Since we know the three addends, we can obtain their sum,

$$a + b + c.$$

Subtracting this from the sum s, we obtain the fourth addend:

$$d = s - (a + b + c).$$

This expression states that any addend is equal to the sum of all the addends from which all the remaining addends are to be subtracted.   For example, let the sum be 346, two of the known addends being 98 and 76.   The third addend is

$$346 - (98 + 76) = 346 - 174 = 172.$$

A similar problem may arise in the case of subtraction.   Here, however, we must consider two cases.   We are given the difference and either the minuend or the subtrahend. In the *first case* (when the minuend is given) we are to find the subtrahend. In the *second case* (when the subtrahend is given) we are to find the minuend.

FIRST CASE. The difference and minuend are given, and we are to find the subtrahend. The difference represents a number that is obtained as a result of diminishing (taking away from) the minuend by the amount of the subtrahend. For example, $14 = 35 - 21$. The unknown number, the subtrahend, represents the number that is taken away from the minuend. If we add this number to the difference we ought to get the minuend. Thus $14 + 21 = 35$. We then observe that in order to obtain the subtrahend (21) we must subtract the difference (14) from the minuend (35). Thus we have

$$35 - 14 = 21.$$

This observation can be written down in compact and general form as follows: If the difference is d, and the minuend is m, then the subtrahend is

$$m - d = s.$$

SECOND CASE. While we have discussed the first problem we have incidentally obtained the answer to the second problem, when the difference and the subtrahend are given and the minuend is wanted. Note that the sum of the difference and the subtrahend ($14 + 21 = 35$) is equal to the minuend. We then can write our result at once as

$$d + s = m.$$

The reader may note that our selection of letters is somewhat obvious; we took the initial letters of the minuend (m), subtrahend (s), and difference (d). This initial method is often a very convenient way to select the appropriate letters while employing the compact writing. Another useful practice for indicating which letter is the unknown is to employ one of the last letters of the alphabet, x, y, or z.

PROBLEMS

56. The minuend is 187. The difference is 63. Find the subtrahend.

57. The difference is 89. The subtrahend in 46. Find the minuend.

58. By how much must we diminish 647 in order to obtain 459?

59. By how much must we increase 573 in order to obtain 947?

60. Find the unknown quantities in the following:

$457 + x = 679;$
$x + 359 = 891;$
$67 - x = 34;$
$789 - x = 478;$
$x + 34 + 67 + 189 = 376.$

Checking addition

The addition of several numbers may be checked in several ways.

If several numbers are added, and their sum is obtained, this sum can be checked by performing the addition once more.

This addition for checking may be performed in the same order, or (using the commutative property of addition) the order of the addends may be reversed. Thus, if the sum was originally obtained by columnar addition downward, then the checking is performed by means of columnar addition upward, as on page 7.

The second method of checking is based or a complete disarrangement of the order of the addends. This method is likewise based on the commutative property of addition. For example, the addition

$$\begin{array}{r} 34 \\ 17 \\ 29 \\ 42 \\ \hline 122 \end{array}$$

may be checked as follows:

$$\begin{array}{r} 29 \\ 34 \\ 42 \\ 17 \\ \hline 122 \end{array}$$

Finally, the addition may be checked by obtaining partial sums, that is, by taking a few addends at a time, and then adding these partial sums. This method is based on the associative property of addition (see page 10). For example, the above addition may be checked as follows:

$$\begin{array}{ccc} 34 & 17 & 63 \\ 29 & 42 & 59 \\ \hline 63 & 59 & 122 \end{array}$$

The combination of the addends in this case is left entirely to the discretion of the person who performs the addition and checking. The above example should not be accepted as the only and the best arrangement. Usually, the person who performs the addition will observe the numbers that are (or have been) added and he will select the most convenient combinations. Such usually are those that give partial sums that end with zeros. For example, the checking of the addition of 28, 62, 37, 43, 74, 36 may be performed as follows:

$$\begin{array}{cccc} 28 & 37 & 74 & 90 \\ 62 & 43 & 36 & 80 \\ \hline 90 & 80 & 110 & 110 \\ & & & \hline & & & 280 \end{array}$$

Checking subtraction

Subtraction may be checked in several ways also.

It may be checked by performing the operation on the same numbers again. However, this method may often be unreliable because a mistake in subtraction may easily be repeated.

The second method for checking subtraction is based on the results obtained on page 30. We check subtraction by means of addition. We obtain the minuend by adding the subtrahend to the difference; that is,

$$m = d + s.$$

For example, the subtraction $358 - 283 = 75$ is checked as follows:

$$358 = 283 + 75.$$

The third method for checking subtraction is also based on the results obtained on page 30. The subtrahend is obtained by subtracting the difference from the minuend, that is,

$$s = m - d.$$

For example, the above subtraction can be checked as follows:

$$283 = 358 - 75.$$

PROBLEMS

61. Check the following addition: $146 + 309 + 125$.

62. Check the following addition: $75 + 136 + 473 + 298$.

63. Check the following subtraction: $854 - 389$.

64. Check the following operations: $1,267 - 89 + 583$.

65. Check the following operations: $391 + 673 - 245 + 362 - 148$.

4

Multiplication of Whole Numbers

Multiplication

Before we define the arithmetic operation known as multiplication let us consider the following simple example. One pencil costs 5 cents. What will seven pencils cost? We can obtain the answer to this question as follows

$$5 + 5 + 5 + 5 + 5 + 5 + 5 = 35.$$

However, this long and repeated addition may be replaced by another arithmetic operation which is known as multiplication. The recording in writing of this operation is

$$5 \cdot 7 = 35.$$

Note that the dot between the two numbers is placed somewhat higher than the period point. This placement distinguishes this dot (which is the multiplication sign) from the period that denotes the end of a sentence and another dot whose function will be discussed later (page 108).

The above example enables us to obtain the definition of multiplication. *It is an arithmetic operation by means of which one number is repeated as an addend until it occurs as many times as is indicated by another number.*

There are two numbers involved in multiplication. The result of their operation on each other is known as *the product*.

That number which is repeated as an addend is known as the *multiplicand*.

That number which indicates the number of times the multiplicand is used as an addend—that is, the number by which the multiplicand is multiplied—is known as the *multiplier*.

Here again we can use the compact method of writing the above stated facts. If the multiplicand is denoted by a, and the

34

multiplier is denoted by b, then

$$a \cdot b = c,$$

if c denotes the product of the two numbers.

Some people prefer to use another multiplication sign, the $\times$. Thus the above fact may be recorded as follows:

$$a \times b = c.$$

We read either the $\times$ sign or the dot sign as "times": we say, "a times b equals c." This expression reminds us that the multiplicand can be regarded as an addend, and that this addend is to be written or mentally considered a certain number of times. If we multiply 7 by 5, the operation is equivalent to writing or saying $7 + 7 + 7 + 7 + 7 = 35$, that is, to using 7 just 5 times.

The result of multiplication by a whole number is to give us a product larger than the multiplicand, except in one case, namely, when the multiplier is 1. Then the product is equal to the multiplicand:

$$5 \cdot 1 = 5, \qquad \text{and} \qquad a \cdot 1 = a.$$

Thus we use the multiplicand, 5 or a, just 1 time in the operation; naturally enough, one 5 is 5, or one a is a.

Multiplication by zero will be examined soon.

It may help to keep the "feel" of multiplication if the two following facts are fixed in mind:

> *i.* By means of multiplication we actually obtain the sum of a certain number of identical (equal) addends.
>
> *ii.* By means of multiplication we add a certain number of identical numbers.

The commutative property of multiplication

Compare the two products

$$5 \cdot 7 = 5 + 5 + 5 + 5 + 5 + 5 + 5 = 35$$

and

$$7 \cdot 5 = 7 + 7 + 7 + 7 + 7 = 35,$$

The two products are identical (equal), and furthermore, we note that it is immaterial whether we use one or the other order of the two numbers whose product is obtained.   In other words,

$$5 \cdot 7 = 7 \cdot 5.$$

This equality represents the commutative property of multiplication: *in obtaining a product of two numbers it is immaterial which is taken as the multiplicand and which is taken as the multiplier.* We may as well as discard these two terms and talk of *the two factors* whose product is obtained.   We may then say that *a product remains the same and unchanged regardless of the order of the factors.*   This fact can be written in a compact form as

$$a \cdot b = b \cdot a.$$

The commutative property of multiplication can be extended to any number of factors.   We shall state this fact in general form for the case of three numbers.

$$a \cdot b \cdot c = a \cdot c \cdot b = b \cdot c \cdot a = b \cdot a \cdot c = c \cdot a \cdot b = c \cdot b \cdot a.$$

The reader may, if he wishes, check this fact by obtaining the products of some three numbers—say, 3, 6, and 9—after arranging them in the above orders.

As an illustration of the commutative property of multiplication let us consider the following problem.   A factory received a shipment of coal which was delivered on 5 trucks.   Each truck made 7 deliveries, and each time it carried 10 tons of coal.   How many tons of coal were delivered?

We may at first ask how many tons of coal were delivered by the 5 trucks during one delivery?   We find that

$$10 \cdot 5 = 50$$

tons of coal were delivered during one trip.   Since there were 7 such trips, we now may ask how many tons of coal were delivered altogether?   We find that

$$50 \cdot 7 = 350$$

tons of coal were delivered.

Now we may approach the same problem from another angle. Let us find out how many tons of coal were delivered by one truck during the 7 trips?   We find that each truck delivered

$$10 \cdot 7 = 70$$

tons.   Since there were 5 trucks delivering the coal, all the trucks delivered

$$70 \cdot 5 = 350$$

tons of coal.

Note that the two procedures of solution resulted in the same product.

PROBLEMS

66. Obtain the products of the following numbers: (*a*) 3, 6, and 8; (*b*) 4, 8, and 12; (*c*) 8, 7, and 2.

67. The hourly wage of a worker is \$2.   He worked 8 hours each day for 5 days.   What amount was he paid?

68. Obtain the products of the following numbers: (*a*) 3, 5, 2, and 5; (*b*) 3, 8, 9, and 4; (*c*) 8, 7, 3, and 4.

69. Write all the possible orders in which four factors *a*, *b*, *c*, and *d* can be arranged.

70. Could the commutative property of multiplication be used for checking the correctness of a product?   Why?

Multiplication by zero

We may apply the commutative property of multiplication to a special situation when one of the factors is zero (0).   Suppose that we have the following product:

$$7 \cdot 0 = 0 \cdot 7.$$

According to the definition of multiplication the product $0 \cdot 7$ signifies that 0 must be taken 7 times as an addend, that is,

$$0 \cdot 7 = 0 + 0 + 0 + 0 + 0 + 0 + 0.$$

But according to the property of zero in addition, the addition of zero to any number does not change the number; then

$$0 \cdot 7 = 0 + 0 + 0 + 0 + 0 + 0 + 0 = 0.$$

This result signifies that *the product of zero and any number (or of any number and zero) is always zero.*

The associative property of multiplication

When we examined the commutative property of multiplication we made use of another property. We shall examine this property now.

Let us obtain the product of the four numbers: 3, 5, 7, and 8. We may perform the multiplication as follows:

$$3 \cdot 5 = 15, \qquad 15 \cdot 7 = 105, \qquad 105 \cdot 8 = 840.$$

However, this consecutive multiplication is not necessarily the only way of obtaining the product of the four numbers. Note that above, every multiplication resulted in a partial product until we used up all the numbers but the last. The multiplication by the last number resulted in the final product.

Keeping in mind that according to the commutative property of multiplication the order of the factors does not affect the final product, we may take any other order of factors. However, we may combine the factors and obtain several partial products, then use these partial products as factors and thus, after all the numbers have been exhausted and all the partial products have been obtained, we may obtain the final product. For example, our multiplications may be

$$3 \cdot 7 = 21, \qquad 5 \cdot 8 = 40, \qquad 21 \cdot 40 = 840.$$

Note that the final product just obtained is the same, 840. Again, we may perform as follows:

$$3 \cdot 8 = 24, \qquad 5 \cdot 7 = 35, \qquad 24 \cdot 35 = 840.$$

Again we have arrived at the same final product, 840.

Thus we observe that *regardless of the arrangement and combination of the factors the product of several numbers remains unchanged.* This property is known as the *associative property* of multiplication.

We may state this property in compact form by means of letters as follows. Let a, b, c, and d be the factors (the number of factors is not necessarily restricted to four; this property holds for any number of factors). Then:

$$\begin{aligned}
a \cdot b \cdot c \cdot d &= (a \cdot b) \cdot (c \cdot d) \\
&= (a \cdot c) \cdot (b \cdot d) \\
&= (a \cdot d) \cdot (b \cdot c) \\
&= a(b \cdot c \cdot d),
\end{aligned}$$

and so on.

The associative property of multiplication enables us to simplify multiplication. There is no set rule of procedure in such situations. The computer must study the numbers he works with and combine them to suit himself.

Factoring a number

Just as by multiplying several numbers we obtain another number, their product, it is possible to reverse the procedure and represent a number as a product of several numbers. These are known as *the factors* of the number. For example, $18 = 3 \cdot 6$, or $18 = 2 \cdot 3 \cdot 3$, or $18 = 2 \cdot 9$. Such a procedure is known as the *factoring* of a number.

Factoring may be used in combination with the associative property of multiplication when simplification and speed are desirable. Let us illustrate with an example.

EXAMPLE. Obtain the product of 25 and 56. We proceed as follows: 56 is factorable into $56 = 4 \cdot 14$. Then, according to the associative property of multiplication, we have

$$25 \cdot 56 = 25 \cdot 4 \cdot 14 = (25 \cdot 4) \cdot 14 = 100 \cdot 14 = 1,400.$$

Note how simple this multiplication was.

PROBLEMS

71. Perform the following multiplications: (a) $50 \cdot 18$; (b) $25 \cdot 24$; (c) $21 \cdot 35$; (d) $50 \cdot 26$.

72. Five farm workers worked 200 days each, each working 8 hours a day. How many hours have they all worked?

73. Perform the following multiplication: $15 \cdot 35 \cdot 24$.

74. Perform the following multiplication: $8 \cdot 12 \cdot 30 \cdot 15$.

75. Write all the possible combinations for the product of the three numbers a, b, and c.

The distributive property of multiplication

Let us consider the following example. Two trucks are hauling sand. One carries 150 tons a day, the other 120 tons a day. How many tons of sand will they carry in 8 days?

We can solve this problem in two ways.

FIRST METHOD. The two trucks carry $150 + 120 = 270$ tons of sand each day. Then in 8 days they will carry

$$270 \cdot 8 = 2{,}160$$

tons of sand.

SECOND METHOD. The first truck will carry in 8 days

$$150 \cdot 8 = 1{,}200$$

tons of sand. The second truck will carry in 8 days

$$120 \cdot 8 = 960$$

tons of sand. Then the two trucks will carry in 8 days

$$1{,}200 + 960 = 2{,}160$$

tons of sand.

Note that the two methods yield the same final result. We observe that in the first case we added the two amounts and multiplied the sum by 8, while in the second case we performed the individual multiplications and added the products.

The above example and its solutions illustrate the distributive property of multiplication, that *the multiplication of a sum by some number may be performed by multiplying every addend by that number and then adding all the products.* The resultant sum is the required product. This fact may be stated in compact form as follows

$$(a + b) \cdot c = a \cdot c + b \cdot c.$$

The same property is applicable to the product of a difference of two numbers by some number. In compact form this property is

$$(a - b) \cdot c = a \cdot c - b \cdot c.$$

That the distributive property holds for the last case can be seen from the following example. Let $a = 8$, $b = 5$, and $c = 6$. Then

$$(8 - 5) \cdot 5 = 3 \cdot 5 = 15,$$

and

$$8 \cdot 5 - 5 \cdot 5 = 40 - 25 = 15.$$

PROBLEMS

76. Check the distributive property of multiplication on the expression

$$(a + b) \cdot c = a \cdot c + b \cdot c$$

by substituting the following sets of values:

$$a = 12, \ b = 7, \ \text{and} \ c = 3;$$
$$a = 17, \ b = 3, \ \text{and} \ c = 11.$$

77. Check the distributive property of multiplication on the expression $(a - b) \cdot c = a \cdot c - b \cdot c$ by substituting the following sets of values:

$$a = 26, \ b = 17, \ \text{and} \ c = 6;$$
$$a = 35, \ b = 21, \ \text{and} \ c = 9.$$

78. Check the correctness of the statement that

$$(a + b + c) \cdot d = a \cdot d + b \cdot d + c \cdot d$$

by substituting the values: $a = 5$, $b = 7$, $c = 11$, and $d = 4$.

79. Check the correctness of the statement that

$$(a - b + c) \cdot d = a \cdot d - b \cdot d + c \cdot d$$

by substituting the values: $a = 42$, $b = 13$, $c = 21$, and $d = 7$.

80. Check the correctness of the statement that

$$(a - b - c) \cdot d = a \cdot d - b \cdot d - c \cdot d$$

by substituting the values: $a = 53$, $b = 17$, $c = 19$, and $d = 11$.

Multiplication of many-place numbers

By means of the distributive property of multiplication we may derive the general method for multiplication of numbers.

Let us multiply 846 by 7. In order to do this we shall re-write 846 as $800 + 40 + 6$. Then our multiplication reduces to

$$
\begin{aligned}
846 \cdot 7 &= (800 + 40 + 6) \cdot 7 \\
&= 800 \cdot 7 + 40 \cdot 7 + 6 \cdot 7 \\
&= 5{,}600 + 280 + 42 \\
&= 5{,}922.
\end{aligned}
$$

We note that the multiplication of a many-place number by an integer less than 10 reduces to the multiplication of every digit (or figure) of the many-place factor by the multiplier, keeping in mind the positional value (see page 4) of each digit. Note that this positional value becomes evident when we represent 846 as a sum above, or as:

$$
\begin{array}{r}
846 = 800 + 40 + 6 \\
7 \\
\hline
42 \\
280 \\
5{,}600 \\
\hline
5{,}922
\end{array}
$$

In practice the multiplication is performed as follows:

$$
\begin{array}{r}
846 \\
7 \\
\hline
5{,}922
\end{array}
$$

We multiply (starting from right to left) 6 by 7; this operation gives $6 \cdot 7 = 42$. The 6 is in the units place. We write 2 under the units place and carry the 4 tens of the product, to be added to the next product. Next we multiply 4 by 7; this operation gives $4 \cdot 7 = 28$. To this 28 we add the 4 that we have carried, and we have $28 + 4 = 32$. We write 2 under the tens place, that is, to the left of the 2 that we wrote in the units place, and we carry the 3 (hundreds) until the next product is obtained. Next we have $8 \cdot 7 = 56$, and to this 56 we add the 3 that we have carried. This addition gives $56 + 3 = 59$. Since there aren't any more digits left in the multiplicand we write 59 to the left of the 22, and thus we obtain the product 5,922.

The same procedure may be applied to any number, regardless of how many digits it contains.   For example,

$$\begin{array}{r} 639{,}823 \\ 8 \\ \hline 5{,}118{,}584 \end{array}$$

After the above method of multiplication is mastered, the multiplication of a many-place number by a many-place number is readily seen to be just a further extension of the same method. Again we apply the distributive property of multiplication, that is, we spread out our work as shown in the example below.

Let us obtain the product of 6,357 and 483.   According to the distributive property of multiplication, we can write

$$6{,}357 \cdot 483 = 6{,}357 \cdot (400 + 80 + 3)$$
$$= 6{,}357 \cdot 400 + 6{,}357 \cdot 80 + 6{,}357 \cdot 3.$$

Using the scheme shown in the two examples above, we can then write:

$$\begin{array}{r} 6{,}357 \\ 483 \\ \hline 6{,}357 \cdot 3 \\ 6{,}357 \cdot 80 \\ 6{,}357 \cdot 400 \end{array}$$

Thus we see that we must obtain three products.   But note that each of these products has a special kind of multiplier.   It consists of a certain number of *units*, a certain number of *tens*, a certain number of *hundreds*.   In other multipliers there may be thousands, tens of thousands, and so on.   Before we can proceed with the actual multiplication, we must obtain a simple and speedy method of multiplying by such numbers.

When we multiply some number by 10 the resultant product actually states how many tens there are in it.   For example, $5 \cdot 10 = 50$.   When we multiply a number by 100 the resultant product shows how many hundreds there are in it.   For example, $6 \cdot 100 = 600$.   Thus we observe that there is a simple procedure for such multiplications. We simply append on the right of the multiplicand as many zeros as are in the multiplier. If we multiply a number by 10,000 we append four zeros on the right of the multiplicand. For example: $7 \cdot 10,000 = 70,000$; $6,734 \cdot 1,000,000 = 6,734,000,000$.

But suppose that the multiplier is 600. Here we shall make use of the associative property of multiplication and factor the multiplier so that one of the factors is of the form 10, or 100, or 1 with a greater number of zeros on its right. Thus, we change 600 into $6 \cdot 100$. The multiplication of some number, say 5,473 by 600, is then performed as follows:

$$5,743 \cdot 600 = 5,743 \cdot (6 \cdot 100) = (5,743 \cdot 6) \cdot 100.$$

We know how to multiply 5,743 by 6. When this product is obtained (the reader may do so as an exercise) we append two zeros on its right, and this result is the originally required product.

Now we can perform the multiplication of 6,357 by 483 according to the scheme shown above,

$$
\begin{array}{r}
6,357 \\
483 \\
\hline
19\ 071 \\
508\ 560 \\
2\ 542\ 800 \\
\hline
3,070,431
\end{array}
$$

and 3,070,431 is the required product.

Note the appearance of the scheme. It is known as the columnar form, and the multiplication so performed is known as *columnar multiplication*. We started to multiply from the right of the multiplier (483). When we multiplied by 3 we wrote its product so that the units (1) in it were directly below the units in the factors. When we multiplied by 8, we actually multiplied by 80. Thus a zero was appended on the right of the second product. For a like reason we appended two zeros in the product of 4. To avoid confusion, we refer to these three products as *partial products*. The product of the two factors, it should be remembered, is the sum of the three partial products.

However, the actual writing of these zeros is not necessary. They may be omitted, but we must remember that this omission is just a matter of convenience for the purpose of saving time and labor.   Thus the above multiplication can be written as follows:

$$
\begin{array}{r}
6{,}357 \\
483 \\
\hline
19\ 071 \\
508\ 56 \\
2\ 542\ 8 \\
\hline
3{,}070{,}431
\end{array}
$$

The examples below illustrate the multiplication of numbers as described above

$$
\begin{array}{r}
3{,}407 \\
590 \\
\hline
306\ 630 \\
1\ 703\ 5 \\
\hline
2{,}010{,}130
\end{array}
\qquad
\begin{array}{r}
15{,}879 \\
3{,}608 \\
\hline
127\ 032 \\
9\ 527\ 4 \\
47\ 637 \\
\hline
57{,}291{,}432
\end{array}
\qquad
\begin{array}{r}
6{,}780 \\
561 \\
\hline
6\ 780 \\
406\ 80 \\
3\ 390\ 0 \\
\hline
3{,}803{,}580
\end{array}
$$

Note that in the first example the multiplier ends with a zero. This fact, if taken into consideration, enables us to save one step. We write a zero on the right of the first partial product and then proceed with the multiplication.   In the second example there is also a zero in the multiplier.   When the multiplication process reached this zero (the second line) we took it into account and stepped the product by 6 one place to the left.   We did not write a zero on the right of the partial product 95,274 because it was not necessary.

PROBLEMS

Perform the following multiplications:

81. $378 \cdot 6$
    $8{,}091 \cdot 7$
    $995 \cdot 4$
    $8{,}903 \cdot 5$
    $11{,}603 \cdot 6$

82. $45 \cdot 10$
    $100 \cdot 17$
    $670 \cdot 100$
    $807 \cdot 1{,}000$
    $60{,}709 \cdot 100$

83. 58 · 400
780 · 90
3,090 · 800
600 · 573
780 · 9,000

84. 643 · 27
1,756 · 34
8,092 · 56
19,643 · 37
998,765 · 89

85. 7,764 · 345
8,503 · 567
75,983 · 254
13,589 · 734
87,453 · 987

86. 86,543 · 5,682
986,438 · 73,849
70,905 · 6,734
120,343 · 7,483
76,539 · 48,392

87. 76,893 · 6,072
86,007 · 7,001
340,102 · 5,503
110,178 · 8,005
50,607 · 20,603

88. 6,070 · 890
7,800 · 570
83,020 · 580
60,010 · 7,800
9,080,760 · 4,060

89. 156,032 · 3,456
780,435 · 6,040
710,023 · 4,009
5,505 · 6,709
78,093 · 65,060

90. 6,543 · 89,342
76,490 · 640,345
347 · 69,876
6,543 · 740,345
8,001 · 695,000

Important information useful in multiplication

Certain facts concerning numbers are always very useful if they are either consciously memorized or studied so long that they are just remembered. In multiplication it is very handy to know the products of numbers from 1 to 10. These products are shown in the Multiplication Table. The factors are in the upper line and in the vertical column on the left. The product of any two numbers appears at the intersection of the column and row in which the factors are found. For example, the product of 5 and 7 is found where the fifth row (with the number 5 on the left) intersects the seventh column (with the number 7); it is 35. The product of 7 and 9 is located where the seventh row (with the number 7 on the left) intersects the ninth column (with the number 9); it is 63. This table may be used as a reference, but to know it is of great help in computing. Most readers will already know it; any who do not may well memorize it.

MULTIPLICATION TABLE

	1	2	3	4	5	6	7	8	9	10
1	1	2	3	4	5	6	7	8	9	10
2	2	4	6	8	10	12	14	16	18	20
3	3	6	9	12	15	18	21	24	27	30
4	4	8	12	16	20	24	28	32	36	40
5	5	10	15	20	25	30	35	40	45	50
6	6	12	18	24	30	36	42	48	54	60
7	7	14	21	28	35	42	49	56	63	70
8	8	16	24	32	40	48	56	64	72	80
9	9	18	27	36	45	54	63	72	81	90
10	10	20	30	40	50	60	70	80	90	100

PROBLEMS

91. If 10 men can complete a certain job in 8 days, in how many days can 1 man complete the same job?

92. In a book there are 425 pages. On every page there are 32 lines. How many lines are there in the book?

93. There are 60 minutes in an hour and 24 hours in a day. How many minutes are there in a day?

94. In a minute there are 60 seconds. How many seconds are there in 2 days?

95. An automobile travels at the rate of 30 miles an hour for 3 hours. How many miles does it cover?

96. Sound travels at the rate of about 1,100 feet per second. How far will it travel in 25 seconds?

97. A stamping machine makes 58 contacts a minute. Each time it makes a contact it stamps a machine part. How many parts are stamped in 8 hours of uninterrupted work?

98. A Diesel engine uses 3 gallons of fuel oil for every horsepower per day. How much fuel oil is required for a 250-horsepower Diesel engine for 5 days?

99. The volume of the sun is about 1,300,000 times as great as that of the earth, and the volume of the earth is about 50 times as great as that of the moon. The sun's volume is how many times as great as that of the moon?

100. Two trains leave at the same time from two towns and travel so that they meet 5 hours after leaving. One train's speed is 45 miles an hour, the other's 55 miles an hour. What is the distance between the two towns?

5

Division of Whole Numbers

Division

Let us consider the product of two numbers, 7 and 9. We know that

$$7 \cdot 9 = 63.$$

In terms of a problem situation we may have any of three statements:

$$7 \cdot 9 = ? \quad \text{or} \quad 7 \cdot ? = 63 \quad \text{or} \quad ? \cdot 9 = 63.$$

The question mark (?) denotes the missing number that must be found by means of some arithmetic operation.

The answer to the first statement is obtained as the result of multiplying 7 by 9. To get the answers to the last two statements requires the employment of some other arithmetic operation.

Note that each of the two statements

$$7 \cdot ? = 63 \quad \text{and} \quad ? \cdot 9 = 63$$

contains a product and one of its factors, but the second factor is missing; it must be obtained. Thus we are confronted with an operation on two numbers. One of them is a product, and the other is one of the factors whose product is given. The operation to be applied is expected to result in obtaining the missing (unknown) factor.

The operation by means of which a factor is obtained when the product and the other factor are given is called *division*. In a sense, this operation undoes the result obtained by means of multiplication. (This statement is qualified because presently we shall consider another operation that also reverses multiplication.)

This arithmetic operation of division is performed on that number which we take as the given product. In division this

number is called the *dividend*,* or the number which is to be
divided.

The given factor is known as the number by which the dividend or product is to be divided. This number is called the *divisor*.

The result of the division of the dividend by the divisor is called the *quotient*.

There are several signs for division. This operation may be indicated by the sign $\div$. Thus $35 \div 7$ indicates the division of 35 by 7. Division may be also indicated by a horizontal bar — ; the dividend is then written above the bar, and the divisor is written below the bar. Thus the division of 35 by 7 may be recorded as $\frac{35}{7}$.

The actual division is usually performed according to some certain scheme in which the dividend, the divisor, and the quotient occupy definite places. Here are two of the many such schemes:

$$\begin{array}{c|c} \text{dividend} & \text{divisor} \\ \hline & \text{quotient} \end{array} \quad \text{or} \quad \begin{array}{c|c} 357 & 7 \\ \hline & 51 \end{array}$$

and

$$\begin{array}{c} \text{quotient} \\ \text{divisor} \overline{ \text{dividend}} \end{array} \quad \text{or} \quad \begin{array}{c} 51 \\ 7 \overline{ 357} \end{array}$$

The process of division will be described on page 53.

Some properties of division

From the description of division as a process by means of which an unknown factor is obtained when the product and the other factor are known, we can write the product of two numbers as follows

$$\text{quotient} \cdot \text{divisor} = \text{dividend}.$$

For example, if in division we have

$$35 \div 7 = 5,$$

---

* This definition is important. In financial jargon, "dividend" has another and mathematically incorrect significance.

then we can write

$$5 \cdot 7 = 35.$$

It is useful for getting the "feel" of division to think of it as a short-cut for accomplishing the subtraction from an original minuend of a series of identical subtrahends, reversing the adding of a collection of identical addends which we found equivalent to multiplication. Consider the operations

$$35 - 7 = 28,$$
$$28 - 7 = 21,$$
$$21 - 7 = 14,$$
$$14 - 7 = 7,$$
$$7 - 7 = 0,$$

and

$$35 \div 7 = 5.$$

Note that each subtrahend is the same number as the divisor, namely 7. Count the subtrahends; note that there are 5 of them, and that the number of identical subtrahends is the same number as the quotient, namely 5.

If the divisor is 1, the quotient is the same as the dividend:

$$8 - 1 = 7,$$
$$7 - 1 = 6,$$
$$6 - 1 = 5,$$
$$5 - 1 = 4,$$
$$4 - 1 = 3,$$
$$3 - 1 = 2,$$
$$2 - 1 = 1,$$
$$1 - 1 = 0$$

is the same as stating that

$$8 \div 1 = 8.$$

If we try to divide another number by zero, however, we can never get to the end of the subtraction process:

$$8 - 0 = 8,$$
$$8 - 0 = 8,$$

and so on forever, no matter how often we take 0 as a subtrahend.

Division by zero is impossible. In order to see further reason for this fact, let us examine the product of zero multiplied by any number, or the product of any number multiplied by zero (see page 37). We know that

$$0 \cdot a = 0, \quad \text{and} \quad a \cdot 0 = 0.$$

Now, from the two statements above we note that the number represented by the letter a may be any number; it may be 2, 3, 5, or it may be 1,000. From these two statements we can obtain division of zero by any number, that is,

$$0 \div a = 0.$$

Note, however, that at no time can we obtain a multiplication situation in which a product of some number by 0 (zero) will result in any number other than zero. That is, no multiplication

$$a \cdot 0$$

is ever possible (unless the product is zero). From this it becomes obvious that division by zero such as

$$b \div 0 = a$$

is impossible. Such statement as $b \div 0 = a$ is meaningless. That is, a quotient of $5 \div 0$ cannot be expressed as a number.

The problems that are solved by means of division may be concerned with any of several types of questions, all of them in a sense equivalent in meaning. The following are typical:

i. Find a factor when a product and the other factor are given.

ii. Find how many times a known number is contained in another known number.

iii. Find what number is contained in another and known number a stipulated number of times.

iv. Compare two numbers and find how many times one number is as great as the other.

The process of division

When two numbers are multiplied we obtain their product, as for example $5 \cdot 7 = 35$; if we use this product as a dividend and one of the factors as a divisor, the quotient of the division will be a whole number, while the division is performed completely. The completeness of the division is checked by multiplication which will give the dividend. Thus, if $35 \div 5 = 7$, then $5 \cdot 7 = 35$.

However, such a situation is not always possible. Very often the dividend is not equal to the product of a whole number and the divisor. For example, the indicated division $45 \div 7$ cannot be performed exactly. If we take 6 as a quotient we obtain $6 \cdot 7 = 42$, and if we take 7 as a quotient we obtain $7 \cdot 7 = 49$.

The general practice in such situations is to take for the quotient that number which when multiplied by the divisor will give a product slightly smaller than the dividend. Thus the quotient in the division of 45 by 7 is 6. But $6 \cdot 7 = 42$, and $45 - 42 = 3$. This difference (which is always smaller than the divisor) is called the *remainder* of the division. The division is recorded as follows:

$$45 \div 7 = 6 + \text{remainder } 3,$$

or it may be recorded as

$$45 \div 7 = 6 \text{ (remainder 3)}.$$

By this time the reader may raise, and justly so, a very important question: How is the division performed?

We have considered division as a continued subtraction. That this approach to division is correct can be further seen from the application of continued subtraction to the division $45 \div 7$. We have then

$$45 - 7 = 38,$$
$$38 - 7 = 31,$$
$$31 - 7 = 24,$$
$$24 - 7 = 17,$$
$$17 - 7 = 10,$$
$$10 - 7 = 3.$$

Note that we have here 6 subtractions, that is, a number represented by the quotient 6 obtained above. The remainder is the last difference obtained.

However, one more point must be cleared up before we take up the actual division of large numbers. If we view division as a continued repeated subtraction, we can apply subtraction and thus obtain the required quotient. This repeated subtraction is exactly what happens when division is performed on calculating machines. Such mechanical instruments can perform this subtraction rapidly. When division is performed by means of a pencil and paper, repeated subtraction is lengthy and tiresome. Hence we must devise some other method which will speed up the operation.

Before we set out to devise this method, it is a good idea to learn some important sets of dividends, divisors, and quotients. They are shown in the Division Table; when any two of the three numbers are known, the other can be found—if necessary, and if the set is in the table. The table contains the quotients and divisors from 1 to 9 and the dividends which are products of these numbers. In short, it is a Multiplication Table, reorganized.

Now let us develop a process for division when the dividend is large and the divisor small. Consider the division problem

$$60 \div 2 = ?$$

The number 60 does not appear in the Division Table opposite divisor 2. Perhaps rewriting it will help. We know that 60 means 6 tens. Hence we write

$$60 \div 2 = 6 \text{ tens} \div 2 = ?$$

We know that $6 \div 2 = 3$. Hence

$$6 \text{ tens} \div 2 = 3 \text{ tens} = 30.$$
$$60 \div 2 = 30.$$

In the forms shown on page 50:

$$\begin{array}{r|r} 60 & 2 \\ \hline 30 \end{array} \qquad\qquad \begin{array}{r} 30 \\ 2 \overline{\smash{)}60} \end{array}$$

DIVISION TABLE

	Dividend									Divisor
1	2	3	4	5	6	7	8	9		**1**
	2	4	6	8	10	12	14	16	18	**2**
	3	6	9	12	15	18	21	24	27	**3**
	4	8	12	16	20	24	28	32	36	**4**
	5	10	15	20	25	30	35	40	45	**5**
	6	12	18	24	30	36	42	48	54	**6**
	7	14	21	28	35	42	49	56	63	**7**
	8	16	24	32	40	48	56	64	72	**8**
	9	18	27	36	45	54	63	72	81	**9**
Quotient	**1**	**2**	**3**	**4**	**5**	**6**	**7**	**8**	**9**	

Note that the 6 and the 3 are in the tens column, where their meaning is 6 tens and 3 tens. Our process of division, then, is merely to divide 6 (tens) by 2 and write the partial quotient 3 (tens). This process will find correct quotients for problems of this sort, no matter how great the dividend.

$$\begin{array}{r} 300 \\ 2\,\overline{|\,600} \end{array} \qquad \begin{array}{r} 2{,}000{,}000{,}000 \\ 2\,\overline{|\,4{,}000{,}000{,}000} \end{array}$$

But we may be confronted with a problem like this one:

$$68 \div 2 = ?$$

We do not find 68 in the Division Table opposite the divisor 2. But we can rewrite the problem:

$$68 \div 2 = (60 + 8) \div 2 = (60 \div 2) + (8 \div 2) = ?$$

We have just found that $60 \div 2 = 30$, and we know that

$8 \div 2 = 4$.   We make use of this knowledge:

$$(60 \div 2) + (8 \div 2) = 30 + 4 = 34.$$

The 30 and the 4 are partial quotients.   They can be combined in the form

$$\begin{array}{r} 34 \\ \hline 2 \mid 68 \end{array}$$

in which the 3, being in the tens column, signifies 3 tens or 30. Our process permits us to perform the division in the form shown. We divide 60 (6 in the tens column) by 2 and get a partial quotient 30 (3 in the tens column).   Next we divide 8 (ones) by 2 and get a partial quotient 4 (ones), which we write in the ones or units column of the quotient beside the partial quotient 3 (tens).   The steps are:

$$\begin{array}{r} 3 \\ \hline 2 \mid 68 \end{array} \qquad \text{and} \qquad \begin{array}{r} 4 \\ \hline 2 \mid 68 \end{array}$$

The process can be applied to large numbers:

$$\begin{array}{r} 342 \\ \hline 2 \mid 684 \end{array} \qquad \begin{array}{r} 2,313 \\ \hline 3 \mid 6,939 \end{array} \qquad \begin{array}{r} 120 \\ \hline 4 \mid 480 \end{array}$$

We can show the separation of our dividend 68 into $60 + 8$ if we find it makes the process clearer, but it should not be necessary:

$$\begin{array}{r} 30 + 4 \\ \hline 2 \mid 60 + 8 \end{array}$$

Now let us study a very simple problem:

$$9 \div 2 = ?$$

By repeated subtraction:

$$9 - 2 = 7, \quad 7 - 2 = 5, \quad 5 - 2 = 3,$$
$$3 - 2 = 1 = \text{remainder}.$$

There are 4 subtrahends 2, hence

$$9 \div 2 = 4 + \text{remainder } 1.$$

Can we avoid the repeated subtractions?   Consider:

$$\begin{array}{r} 4 \\ \hline 2 \mid 9 \\ 8 \\ \hline \text{remainder } 1 \end{array}$$

We have found that 4 2's can be subtracted from 9. But 4 2's make 8, or $4 \cdot 2 = 8$. So we write the quotient 4, multiply it by the divisor 2 and get 8, which is the same as the sum our 4 subtrahends 2. Hence we subtract this 8 from the dividend 9, just as we subtracted the 4 2's, and the result is the remainder 1.

The process is successful in other examples:

```
        2              2              3              2
    3 ⌐7           4 ⌐9           2 ⌐7           3 ⌐8
        6              8              6              6
       ──             ──             ──             ──
remainder 1    remainder 1    remainder 1    remainder 2
```

The remainder need not be labeled, for its position makes it obvious. It may be zero, that is, there may be no remainder·

```
        3              2
    3 ⌐9           4 ⌐8
        9              8
       ──             ──
        0              0
```

When there is no remainder, we may show the multiplication and subtraction, or we may omit them.

```
        4
    2 ⌐8
```

Now re-examine our problem which was solved by separating a large dividend into smaller numbers:

$$68 \div 2 = ?$$

We can show its solution in three steps:

FIRST		SECOND	COMBINED	
30	(3 tens)	4	30 + 4	(3 tens + 4)
2 ⌐60 + 8		2 ⌐60 + 8	2 ⌐60 + 8	
60	(6 tens)		60	(6 tens)
──		──	──	
00 + 8		8	00 + 8	
		8	8	
		──	──	
		0	0	

There is no real need for such a separation, however, once we

understand firmly that 68 means $60 + 8$ and 34 means $30 + 4$.
Then we write the problem in the form:

$$2 \overline{\smash{)}68}$$

We show this solution in three steps, equivalent to those above:

FIRST	SECOND	COMBINED
3 (3 tens)	4	34 (3 tens + 4)
$2\overline{\smash{)}68}$	$2\overline{\smash{)}68}$	$2\overline{\smash{)}68}$
6 (6 tens)		6 (6 tens)
08	8	08
	8	8
	0	0

In the first step, since the 3 is in the tens column it is really a 30;
its product 6, placed beneath the 6 (6 tens or 60) of the dividend,
is by the same reasoning really a 60. Consequently, bringing
down the 8 from the dividend to the remainder is really a
subtraction.

Our division process, as we now have it, permits us to solve
problems with large dividends; for example:

412	231
$2\overline{\smash{)}824}$	$3\overline{\smash{)}695}$
8	6
2	9
2	9
4	5
4	3
0	2

But we have not yet considered one situation. A common
type of problem is

$$58 \div 2 = ?$$

We had better go back to fundamentals to solve this one:

2 tens + 9 ones	29
$2\overline{\smash{)}\text{5 tens + 8 ones}}$	$2\overline{\smash{)}58}$
4 tens	4
1 ten + 8 ones	18
or	18
18 ones	0
18 ones	
0	

Note that we add the remainder (1 ten) from the partial division of the number 5 in the tens column to the number 8 from the ones column. This sum becomes the partial dividend; we write its partial quotient in the ones column of the quotient, then multiply and subtract.

Now we have developed a division process that will allow us to deal with a dividend of any size and any arrangement of numbers in its units, tens, and higher columns. For example:

$$
\begin{array}{r}
2{,}643{,}823 \\
2\ \overline{\smash{)}5{,}287{,}647} \\
4 \\
\overline{1\,2} \\
1\,2 \\
\overline{08} \\
8 \\
\overline{07} \\
6 \\
\overline{1\,6} \\
1\,6 \\
\overline{04} \\
4 \\
\overline{07} \\
6 \\
\overline{1}
\end{array}
$$

It does not matter if there is a zero in some column of the dividend:

$$
\begin{array}{r}
1{,}672 \\
3\ \overline{\smash{)}5{,}016} \\
3 \\
\overline{2\,0} \\
1\,8 \\
\overline{21} \\
21 \\
\overline{06} \\
3 \\
\overline{0}
\end{array}
\qquad
\begin{array}{r}
1{,}720 \\
3\ \overline{\smash{)}5{,}160} \\
3 \\
\overline{2\,1} \\
2\,1 \\
\overline{06} \\
6 \\
\overline{00} \\
0 \\
\overline{0}
\end{array}
$$

Neither does it matter if no partial quotient can be found for the first number in the dividend:

$$
\begin{array}{r}
031 \\
7 \overline{\smash{)}\, 217} \\
0 \\
\hline
21 \\
21 \\
\hline
07 \\
7 \\
\hline
0
\end{array}
$$

Ordinarily we do not write the zeroes that do not affect the value of the quotient:

$$
\begin{array}{r}
31 \\
7 \overline{\smash{)}\, 217} \\
21 \\
\hline
7 \\
7 \\
\hline
\end{array}
$$

Now before we develop our process further to enable us to handle two-place divisors, one more point should be noted. We have built up our quotients place by place or column by column—a partial quotient in the tens column, for example, and another partial quotient in the ones column. We can only put one number in a column, 0 or 9 or some number between them. The one-place divisor must likewise be no larger than 9. The partial dividend which enters into the calculation of the quotient may therefore occupy either one or two of the places in the dividend, but not more, since there is no three-place number into which any one-place divisor can be divided without yielding at least a two-place quotient. And as was demonstrated above, a two-place partial quotient cannot be written in a single place or column. The limitation here established has counterparts in respect to two-place divisors, three-place divisors, and so on; the recognition of them aids in performing division operations.

Many times a division can be performed without writing the multiplications and subtractions. Division so performed is called *short division.* In *long division*, the multiplications and subtractions are written, as we have written them in developing our process of division from the study of a series of increasingly intricate examples.

If our divisor is a two-place number the partial division is performed in the same manner. Here again we must keep in mind that in every partial division the quotient must be a one-place number. Let us divide 9,826 by 34. The division is as follows:

```
                              289
    9,826 | 34          34 | 9,826
    6 8     289              6 8
    ─────                    ─────
    3 02                     3 02
    2 72                     2 72
    ─────                    ─────
      306                      306
      306                      306
      ───                      ───
```

In this example the divisor is a two-place number, and the partial division is not as simple as in the case with a one-place divisor, where we made use of the Division Table. Note that in the division 9,826 ÷ 34 the partial division 98 ÷ 34 gave the partial quotient 2. How was this partial quotient obtained? Generally the procedure is as follows. We note that the first digit of 98 is 9, and the first digit of 34 is 3. These digits give a clue to a possible first digit for the partial quotient. We try then the partial quotient 3, because $9 \div 3 = 3$. However, a trial multiplication shows that $34 \cdot 3 = 102$, and 102 is greater than 98; our trial digit is too large. We try then the partial quotient that is 1 less than 3, namely 2. The product $34 \cdot 2 = 68$ shows that this digit is the correct choice.

Note that in the dividend 9,826 the first two digits (98) are sufficient to start with because 98 can be divided by 34 (though not exactly). This division gives us a quotient 2 and a remainder 30. Bringing down the next digit (2) we have 302. After 302 is divided by 34 we obtain the quotient 8 and the remainder 30.

Bringing down the last digit (6), we have 306, and the division by 34 gives us the quotient 9.   Thus the division of 9,826 by 34 gives the quotient 289.

The following example represents another situation.   Let us divide 36,594 by 57.   The division is performed as follows

```
                                            642
        36,594 | 57            57 | 36,594
        34 2     642                34 2
        ─────                       ─────
          2 39                        2 39
          2 28                        2 28
          ─────                       ─────
           114                         114
           114                         114
           ─────                       ─────
```

Note that if we take two places only, we have 36; 36 is less than 57.   Thus, before we proceed with our division, we must extend our partial dividend by one more digit (5).   We then have 365, and this number, when divided by 57, gives the quotient 6 and the remainder 23.   Bringing down the next digit (9), we have 239. When 239 is divided by 57 we have the quotient 4 and remainder 11.   Finally, bringing down the last digit (4) we have 114. Dividing 114 by 57 we have the quotient 2.   Thus the division of 36,594 by 57 gives the quotient 642.

In this example, the division $36,594 \div 57$, the first partial division is $365 \div 57$.   Note that here we must use the first two digits in the dividend in estimating a trial quotient, because 3 (the first digit of the dividend) is less than 5 (the first digit of the divisor).   We note that $36 \div 5$ should give the partial quotient 7.   We try this 7, and the trial multiplication $57 \cdot 7 = 399$ gives a product which is greater than 365; the trial quotient is too large. We try then the next quotient, which is 1 less than 7, that is, 6. The product $57 \cdot 6 = 342$ shows that this 6 is the correct partial quotient.

Some special cases of long division

Consider the following example in division:

$$365,940 \div 57 = ?$$

```
                        6,420
365,940 | 57        57 | 365,940
342       6,420        342
 ____                  ____
 23 9                  23 9
 22 8                  22 8
 ____                  ____
  1 14                  1 14
  1 14                  1 14
  ____                  ____
```

Note that a zero (0) must be brought down as the last digit. But no remainder is left after 114 is divided by 57. This zero, however, indicates that the last partial dividend 114 actually represents 114 tens. Thus the last quotient is actually 2 tens. Hence this zero may be written as the last digit on the right of the partial quotient 642 obtained thus far. Hence, our quotient is 6,420.

Very often we bring down a digit, and still it is impossible to perform a partial division because the partial dividend remains smaller than the divisor, as illustrated in the example below:

```
                            509
653,047 | 1,283      1,283 | 653,047
641 5     509                641 5
 _____                       _____
 11 547                      11 547
 11 547                      11 547
 _____                       _____
```

Note that when 4 is brought down we have 1,154, and 1,154 is less than 1,283. We must bring down another digit. But before we do so we must write a zero after the 5 in the quotient, which indicates that the partial quotient in such a case is less than 1.

PROBLEMS

101. Perform the following divisions: (a) $13,179 \div 3$; (b) $31,475 \div 5$; (c) $564,372 \div 6$; (d) $4,893,568 \div 8$; (e) $837,819 \div 9$.

102. Perform the following divisions: (a) 941,160 ÷ 60; (b) 78,436,050 ÷ 50; (c) 6,458,910 ÷ 3; (d) 25,060 ÷ 7; (e) 1,865,250 ÷ 9.

103. Perform the following divisions: (a) 24,185 ÷ 35; (b) 32,037 ÷ 59; (c) 64,622 ÷ 79; (d) 25,628 ÷ 86; (e) 50,344 ÷ 58.

104. Perform the following divisions: (a) 94,430 ÷ 190; (b) 335,960 ÷ 370; (c) 146,560 ÷ 32; (d) 3,658,400 ÷ 68; (e) 73,827,600 ÷ 770.

105. Perform the following divisions: (a) 4,858,263 ÷ 237; (b) 379,472 ÷ 592; (c) 3,217,206 ÷ 402; (d) 11,584,618 ÷ 7,209; (e) 5,381,872 ÷ 592.

106. Perform the following divisions: (a) 6,223,312 ÷ 31; (b) 23,722 ÷ 818; (c) 1,981,557 ÷ 79; (d) 61,555 ÷ 65; (e) 43,688 ÷ 508.

107. What number must be multiplied by 37 so that the product is equal to 18,389?

108. What number is contained 23 times in 18,216?

109. What number is contained 77 times in 29,106?

110. Find one-third of the following numbers: (a) 789,315; (b) 93,456,720; (c) 1,975,491; (d) 8,845,122; (e) 1,020,306,711.

111. Find one-fourth of the following numbers: (a) 796,548; (b) 9,087,012; (c) 100,236; (d) 776,532; (e) 964,064.

112. Find one-fifth of the following numbers: (a) 45,675; (b) 1,357,590; (c) 89,745,300; (d) 10,124,565; (e) 870,056,000.

113. Find one-sixth of the following numbers: (a) 6,924; (b) 41,538; (c) 56,034; (d) 41,832; (e) 37,638.

114. Find one-seventh of the following numbers: (a) 40,579; (b) 33,432; (c) 173,670; (d) 547,442,280; (e) 227,882,956.

115. Find one-eighth of the following numbers: (a) 196,241,784; (b) 118,085,904; (c) 1,482,864; (d) 3,759,856; (e) 26,502,624.

116. Find one-ninth of the following numbers: (a) 59,778; (b) 35,028,873; (c) 864,723,546; (d) 118,926,432; (e) 90,762,849.

117. Find one-twelfth of the following numbers: (a) 318,727,968; (b) 3,054,018,324; (c) 596,889,948; (d) 970,867,956; (e) 598,817,964.

118. Find one-sixteenth of the following numbers: (a) 234,885,872; (b) 7,336,044,016; (c) 1,176,070,560; (d) 4,576,018,304; (e) 247,686,192.

119. Into how many parts must we divide 42,768 so that each part is equal to 81?

120. What number must be divided by 1,467 to obtain the quotient 648?

121. What number, divided by 649, gives a quotient 43 and a remainder 336?

122. What number, divided by 8,903, gives a quotient 143 and a remainder 663?

123. An airplane left an airport at 9:30 A.M. and landed at another airport at 2:30 P.M., covering a distance of 1,675 miles. What was its speed?

124. What number, multiplied by 483, gives 18,837 as a product?

125. What number must be divided by 893 in order to get a quotient 478?

6

Dependence of Products and

Quotients on the Data

The dependence of the product on the factors

When two numbers are multiplied, their product is determined by their respective magnitudes. Any change in one of them or in both must affect the magnitude of their product. Let us examine in detail how a change in the factors changes the product:

$$36 \cdot 20 = 720.$$

Suppose that one of the factors, say 36, is doubled; that is $36 \cdot 2 = 72$. Our product then becomes

$$72 \cdot 20 = 1,440.$$

But

$$1,440 \div 720 = 2.$$

Thus we see that doubling one factor results in doubling the product.

If instead we double the second factor, 20, we have $20 \cdot 2 = 40$. Our product then becomes

$$36 \cdot 40 = 1,440.$$

This 1,440 is double the original product. Thus we see that it is immaterial which of the factors is doubled; the product is doubled in either case.

Now suppose that one of the factors is multiplied by 7. Let $20 \cdot 7 = 140$. Then the product is

$$36 \cdot 140 = 5,040,$$

and

$$5,040 \div 720 = 7.$$

In other words, the product has been multiplied by the same number that has multiplied the factor.

Suppose that each factor is multiplied by a certain number. Let one factor be doubled and the other factor quadrupled (multiplied by four). Let $36 \cdot 2 = 72$, and $20 \cdot 4 = 80$. Then the product becomes

$$72 \cdot 80 = 5,760.$$

But $2 \cdot 4 = 8$, and

$$5,760 \div 720 = 8.$$

Thus we see that the initial product (720) is in effect multiplied by a number (8) which is equal to the product of the numbers (2 and 4) that were the multipliers of the initial factors (36 and 20).

Consider a product of three factors, say

$$36 \cdot 20 \cdot 12 = 8,640.$$

If each of the three factors is multiplied by some other factor, say

$$(36 \cdot 2) \cdot (20 \cdot 3) \cdot (12 \cdot 5) = 259,200,$$

and the new product then divided by the first product, we find a quotient equal to the product of the second set of three factors:

$$259,200 \div 8,640 = 30 = 2 \cdot 3 \cdot 5.$$

In a similar manner we may examine the effect on the product if one or both factors are divided by any number.

Let one of the factors, say 36, be divided by 3; then $36 \div 3 = 12$, and the product becomes

$$12 \cdot 20 = 240.$$

But

$$720 \div 240 = 3.$$

Thus we see that the product has likewise been divided by 3.

If both factors are divided, say one by 3 and the other by 4, then $36 \div 3 = 12$ and $20 \div 4 = 5$.   The product then becomes

$$12 \cdot 5 = 60.$$

But

$$720 \div 60 = 12.$$

Note that $3 \cdot 4 = 12$.

The above observations may be stated in a compact form as follows.   Let the product be

$$a \cdot b = c.$$

If a is multiplied by m, then

$$(a \cdot m) \cdot b = c \cdot m.$$

If b is multiplied by m, then

$$a \cdot (b \cdot m) = c \cdot m.$$

If a is multiplied by m and b is multiplied by n, then

$$(a \cdot m) \cdot (b \cdot n) = c \cdot (m \cdot n).$$

If a is divided by m, then

$$(a \div m) \cdot b = c \div m.$$

If b is divided by m, then

$$a \cdot (b \div m) = c \div m.$$

If a is divided by m and b is divided by n, then

$$(a + m) \cdot (b \div n) = c \div (m \cdot n).$$

Note one particular situation.   Let one factor be multiplied by a certain number and let the other factor be divided by the same number.   What will be the effect on the product?   Let this number be 4.   Then in the product

$$36 \cdot 20 = 720$$

there will be the following changes:

$$36 \cdot 4 = 144, \quad \text{and} \quad 20 \div 4 = 5,$$

and the new product

$$144 \cdot 5 = 720.$$

Thus we note that such a change produces no effect at all on the product.

If we have a product

$$a \cdot b \cdot c = h,$$

and each factor is multiplied by some other factor, then

$$(a \cdot x) \cdot (b \cdot y) \cdot (c \cdot z) = h \cdot x \cdot y \cdot z.$$

PROBLEMS

126. How does the product change if one factor is multiplied by 12?

127. How does the product change if the multiplier is divided by 9?

128. How will a number change if it is first multiplied by 5 and the changed number is then multiplied by 7?

129. How will a number change if it is first multiplied by 5 and the changed number is then multiplied by 15?

130. How will the product change if the multiplicand is multiplied by 9 and the multiplier is multiplied by 3?

131. How will the product change if the multiplicand is divided by 6 and the multiplier is divided by 5?

132. How will the product change if the multiplicand is multiplied by 12 and the multiplier is divided by 4?

133. How will the product change if the multiplicand is divided by 18 and the multiplier is multiplied by 9?

134. Describe the changes that will take place in the product $45 \cdot 60$ if (a) the multiplicand is multiplied by 5; (b) the multiplier is multiplied by 10; (c) the multiplicand is divided by 15; (d) the multiplier is divided by 20; (e) the multiplicand is divided by 5, and multiplier is multiplied by 10.

135. Complete the following:

Multiplicand	Multiplier	Product
Multiplied by 4	Multiplied by 3	?
Multiplied by 8	Divided by 2	?
Divided by 5	Multiplied by 10	?
Divided by 4	Divided by 5	?
?	Multiplied by 7	Multiplied by 21
?	Multiplied by 9	Multiplied by 3
?	Multiplied by 10	Divided by 3
?	Divided by 5	Multiplied by 3
?	Divided by 2	Divided by 12
?	Divided by 14	Divided by 7
Multiplied by 15	Divided by 30	?
Divided by 25	Multiplied by 5	?
Multiplied by 6	?	Multiplied by 18
Multiplied by 12	?	Multiplied by 4
Multiplied by 8	?	Divided by 4
Multiplied by 7	?	Unchanged
Divided by 5	?	Unchanged
Divided by 14	?	Divided by 28
Divided by 7	?	Multiplied by 21

The dependence of the quotient of two numbers

The quotient of two numbers is determined by the magnitudes of the dividend and the divisor, that is, by the magnitudes of the numbers on which the operation of division is performed. Any change in one of them or in the two must necessarily be reflected on the magnitude of their quotient.

Let us examine the quotient

$$72 \div 18 = 4.$$

Suppose the dividend is multiplied by 5; that is, $72 \cdot 5 = 360$ is substituted for 72. The quotient then becomes

$$360 \div 18 = 20.$$

But

$$20 \div 4 = 5.$$

Thus we see that when the dividend is multiplied by 5 the quotient is also multiplied by 5.

Suppose the divisor is multiplied.   Let us double it; that is, substitute $18 \cdot 2 = 36$ for 18.   The quotient then becomes

$$72 \div 36 = 2.$$

But

$$4 \div 2 = 2.$$

Thus, doubling the divisor results in halving the quotient.

Let us suppose that both the divisor and the dividend are each multiplied by a certain number.   For example, let the dividend be quadrupled (multiplied by 4) and the divisor be doubled: $72 \cdot 4 = 288$, and $18 \cdot 2 = 36$.   The quotient is then

$$288 \div 36 = 8.$$

But

$$8 \div 4 = 2.$$

Thus, in this case, the quotient is doubled, because $4 \div 2 = 2$.

Let the dividend be divided, say halved: $72 \div 2 = 36$.   The quotient is then

$$36 \div 18 = 2.$$

But

$$4 \div 2 = 2.$$

That is, halving the dividend results in halving the quotient.

Suppose that the divisor is divided, say by 6.   Then $18 \div 6 = 3$.   The quotient is then

$$72 \div 3 = 24.$$

But

$$24 \div 4 = 6.$$

Thus, when the divisor is divided by 6, the quotient is multiplied by 6.

The above observations show that a change in the dividend leads to the same change in the quotient.   A change in the divisor, however, leads to an opposite change in the quotient.   If the dividend is multiplied by a certain number the quotient is multiplied by the same number. If the dividend is divided by a certain number, the quotient is also divided by the same number. On the other hand, when the divisor is multiplied by a certain number the quotient is divided by the same number. When the divisor is divided by a certain number, the quotient is multiplied by the same number.

All these results may be stated in compact form using letters. In all the following statements a represents the dividend, b represents the divisor, and the c represents the quotient. Thus the statement for division is

$$a \div b = c.$$

If a is multiplied by m, then

$$(a \cdot m) \div b = c \cdot m.$$

If a is divided by m, then

$$(a \div m) \div b = c \div m.$$

If b is multiplied by m, then

$$a \div (b \cdot m) = c \div m.$$

If b is divided by m, then

$$a \div (b \div m) = c \cdot m.$$

PROBLEMS

136. The dividend is multiplied by 5. How does the quotient change?

137. The divisor is divided by 7. How does the quotient change?

138. The dividend is divided by 6. How does the quotient change?

139. The divisor is multiplied by 8. How does the quotient change?

140. Describe the changes in the quotient of $1,152 \div 54$ if (a) the dividend is multiplied by 4; (b) the dividend is divided by 6; (c) the divisor is multiplied by 3; (d) the divisor is divided by 9; (e) the dividend is multiplied by 4 and the divisor is multiplied by 5; (f) the dividend is divided by 9 and the divisor is divided by 4; (g) the dividend is multiplied by 4 and the divisor is multiplied by 3; (h) the dividend is divided by 8 and the divisor is multiplied by 2.

141. Complete the following:

Dividend	Divisor	Quotient
Multiplied by 5	?	Multiplied by 15
Multiplied by 4	?	Divided by 8
Divided by 5	?	Divided by 10
Divided by 4	?	Multiplied by 12
Multiplied by 6	?	Unchanged
Divided by 4	?	Unchanged
?	Multiplied by 4	Multiplied by 12
?	Multiplied by 3	Divided by 3
?	Divided by 4	Multiplied by 8
?	Divided by 3	Multiplied by 6
?	Multiplied by 4	Unchanged
?	Divided by 3	Unchanged
Multiplied by 3	Multiplied by 9	?
Multiplied by 4	Divided by 3	?
Multiplied by 5	Multiplied by 5	?
Divided by 3	Multiplied by 3	?
Divided by 6	Divided by 12	?
Divided by 4	Divided by 4	?

142. The quotient of two numbers is 45. What will be the quotient if the dividend is doubled?

143. The quotient of two numbers is 75. What will be the quotient if the divisor is tripled?

144. When the dividend is multiplied by 7 the quotient is 56. What was the original quotient?

145. When the divisor is divided by 15 the quotient is 105. What was the original quotient?

Checking multiplication and division

Multiplication may be checked in several ways.

We may repeat the multiplication once more. However, this method of checking is not reliable. If some mistake has been made it is very likely that it will be repeated.

We may make use of the commutative property of multiplication and interchange the positions of the factors and then repeat the multiplication. This method of checking is highly reliable.

For example:

MULTIPLICATION	CHECK
35,617	579
579	35,617
320 553	4 053
2 493 19	5 79
17 808 5	347 4
20,622,243	2 895
	17 37
	20,622,243

If we make use of the definition of division, we may check multiplication by turning the product into a dividend and one of the factors into a divisor. After performing the division we obtain a quotient which should be equal to the other factor (if the multiplication was performed correctly). Thus the above multiplication may be checked as follows:

$$20,622,243 \mid 35,617$$
$$17\ 808\ 5 \qquad 579$$
$$2\ 813\ 74$$
$$2\ 493\ 19$$
$$320\ 553$$
$$320\ 553$$

$$20,622,243 \mid 579$$
$$17\ 37 \qquad 35,617$$
$$3\ 252$$
$$2\ 895$$
$$357\ 2$$
$$347\ 4$$
$$9\ 84$$
$$5\ 79$$
$$4\ 053$$
$$4\ 053$$

Division may be checked in several ways.

We may repeat the process. However, this method of checking is not reliable, because if some mistake has been made it is very likely that the same mistake will be repeated.

However, if we consider the definition of division we may obtain two methods for the checking. If we take the quotient as one of the factors and the divisor as the other factor, then their product will give the dividend. For example:

DIVISION	CHECK
39,858 | 438	438
39 42 91	91
438	438
438	39 42
	39,858

Another method for checking is to interchange the quotient and the divisor, that is, to keep the same dividend and divide it by the quotient.   This division should give us as the quotient the original divisor.   Thus:

$$
\begin{array}{r|l}
39{,}858 & 91 \\
36\ 4 & \overline{438} \\
\hline
3\ 45 & \\
2\ 73 & \\
\hline
728 & \\
728 & \\
\hline
\end{array}
$$

If the original division resulted in a quotient and remainder, then, if the multiplication method of checking is used, this remainder must be added to the product.   The sum is then equal to the original divisor, if all operations were correctly performed. For example:

DIVISION	CHECK

$$
\begin{array}{r|l}
26{,}384 & 598 \\
23\ 92 & 44 \\
\hline
2\ 464 & \\
2\ 392 & \\
\hline
72 & = \text{remainder} \\
\end{array}
\qquad
\begin{array}{r}
598 \\
44 \\
\hline
2\ 392 \\
23\ 92 \\
\hline
26{,}312 \\
72 = \text{remainder} \\
\hline
26{,}384 \\
\end{array}
$$

If the division method of checking is used, then this remainder must first be subtracted from the original dividend.   The difference should be divided by the original quotient.   For example:

$$
\begin{array}{r}
26{,}384 \\
72 \\
\hline
\end{array}
$$
$$
\begin{array}{r|l}
26{,}312 & 44 \\
22\ 0 & \overline{598} \\
\hline
4\ 31 & \\
3\ 96 & \\
\hline
352 & \\
352 & \\
\hline
\end{array}
$$

PROBLEMS

146. Perform the following multiplications and check: (*a*) 4,572 · 643; (*b*) 89,635 · 4,783; (*c*) 799,403 · 706; (*d*) 10,564 · 80,043; (*e*) 1,187,452 · 345.

147. Perform the following divisions and check: (*a*) 65,676 ÷ 842; (*b*) 387,182,868 ÷ 717; (*c*) 52,521,861 ÷ 861; (*d*) 232,171,308 ÷ 327; (*e*) 46,198,728 ÷ 513.

148. Perform the following divisions and check: (*a*) 45,993 ÷ 728; (*b*) 52,782 ÷ 67; (*c*) 22,387 ÷ 358; (*d*) 16,185 ÷ 583; (*e*) 52,162 ÷ 78.

7

More Facts Concerning

Multiplication and Division

Repeated multiplication

Let us recall that we described multiplication as repeated addition (see page 34). Very often we are faced with a problem of multiplication in which all the factors are the same, for example,

$$3 \cdot 3, \quad \text{or} \quad 3 \cdot 3 \cdot 3 \cdot 3, \quad \text{or} \quad 4 \cdot 4 \cdot 4 \cdot 4 \cdot 4 \cdot 4 \cdot 4.$$

Just as multiplication is a simplification of the repeated addition of the same number, the repeated multiplication of the same number may be simplified by agreeing upon an arithmetic operation known as *raising to a power*.

The recording of the raising to a power must take into account the number which is repeated as a factor as well as the number of times it is repeated. In order that we do not confuse the significance of these two numbers it is necessary to agree on a method for writing them. The number of times the factor is repeated is always written to the right of the factor and above it as shown below:

$$3 \cdot 3 = 3^2,$$
$$4 \cdot 4 \cdot 4 = 4^3,$$
$$5 \cdot 5 \cdot 5 \cdot 5 \cdot 5 \cdot 5 \cdot 5 = 5^7.$$

The number that is repeated as a factor is called the *base*.

The number of times the factor is repeated is called the *indicator* or the *exponent*.

The result of the raising to a power is called the *power* of the number or base.

The statement

$$2^2 = 4$$

states that two, raised to the second power, is equal to four.

The statement

$$3^3 = 27$$

states that three, raised to the third power, is equal to twenty-seven.

Later, when we learn about logarithms, we shall develop a very simple method for raising a number to a power. For the time being, the computational work of raising a number to a power will actually be performed as repeated multiplication. Thus:

$$4^2 = 4 \cdot 4 = 16, \qquad 6^3 = 6 \cdot 6 \cdot 6 = 216.$$

PROBLEMS

149. Compute:

7^2	8^3	9^2	12^2
3^4	4^5	6^4	2^6
3^5	8^4	15^2	16^3
20^2	25^3	30^2	45^2

Some properties of raising to a power

It is often necessary to perform arithmetical operations with numbers raised to powers. Suppose we are required to multiply two such numbers having the same base, for example,

$$2^2 \cdot 2^3 = ?$$

This computation may be performed thus:

$$2^2 \cdot 2^3 = 2 \cdot 2 \cdot 2 \cdot 2 \cdot 2 = 2^5.$$

But note that our exponents have the relation

$$2 + 3 = 5.$$

We thus observe that this kind of multiplication may be simplified. Its recording is reduced to the addition of the exponents. The general rule for this kind of multiplication may be expressed in compact letter form:

$$b^m \cdot b^n = b^{m+n}.$$

The letter b represents any base, and the letters m and n are indicators of powers.   The powers may be different or they may be the same.   Any attempt to state this rule in words is difficult.

To simplify future discussion, let us agree on a term for such expressions as 2^2, 3^4, b^m, and the like.   We may simply call them powers.

Suppose that we have the product of two powers whose bases are different but whose exponents are the same, for instance,

$$3^3 \cdot 5^3 = ?$$

This computation can be written as follows:

$$3^3 \cdot 5^3 = 3 \cdot 3 \cdot 3 \cdot 5 \cdot 5 \cdot 5.$$

If we make use of the associative property of multiplication we can arrange the factors as follows:

$$(3 \cdot 5) \cdot (3 \cdot 5) \cdot (3 \cdot 5) = 15 \cdot 15 \cdot 15 = 15^3.$$

Note that in this case we multiplied the bases and retained the same exponent.   This practice is the general rule for this kind of multiplication:

$$a^n \cdot b^n = (a \cdot b)^n.$$

The $(a \cdot b)^n$ indicates that the multiplication $a \cdot b$ is to be performed and the product then raised to the nth power.   The use of the parentheses is fully explained on page 81.

We shall examine the division of powers in a later chapter.

PROBLEMS

150. Perform the following multiplications: (a) $5^2 \cdot 5^4$; (b) $4^4 \cdot 4^3$; (c) $10^2 \cdot 10^3 \cdot 10^4$; (d) $6^3 \cdot 6^4$; (e) $2^5 \cdot 2^7$.

151. Perform the following multiplications: (a) $4^2 \cdot 5^2$; (b) $6^3 \cdot 7^3$; (c) $3^4 \cdot 5^4$; (d) $6^2 \cdot 7^2$; (e) $10^3 \cdot 12^3$.

The order of arithmetic operations

When several (and different) arithmetic operations must be performed, confusion may easily arise as, for example, in the problem

$$4 \cdot 5 + 12.$$

Here we have two operations, namely multiplication and addition. If we perform the multiplication first and addition afterwards we obtain

$$20 + 12 = 32.$$

If we perform addition first and multiplication afterwards we obtain

$$4 \cdot 17 = 68.$$

Until a general agreement is made as to which operations are given preference we cannot be certain which of the two results is correct.

In order to eliminate any possible confusion it is generally agreed to adhere to the following order of operations. If we have several operations indicated, they are always to be performed in the sequence:

1. Raising to a power.
2. Multiplication and division.
3. Addition and subtraction.

If this rule is observed there will never be any confusion.

For example,

$$2^2 \cdot 12 - 7 + 3 \cdot 6 - 10$$

is computed as follows:

$$2^2 = 4, \qquad 2^2 \cdot 12 = 4 \cdot 12 = 48, \qquad 3 \cdot 6 = 18.$$
$$2^2 \cdot 12 - 7 + 3 \cdot 6 - 10 = 48 - 7 + 18 - 10 = 49.$$

Note that in the computation of $48 - 7 + 18 - 10$ we proceeded from one number to the next one, that is, $48 - 7 = 41$, $41 + 18 = 59$, $59 - 10 = 49$. If any other order is desired it should be indicated. The method for such indication will be explained in the next section.

If several operations of the same kind are to be performed, the order is a matter of indifference in the case of addition or multiplication. For example,

$$3 + 5 + 9 + 7 = 24 = 7 + 3 + 5 + 9,$$

and

$$3 \cdot 5 \cdot 9 \cdot 7 = 945 = 9 \cdot 3 \cdot 5 \cdot 7.$$

In a mixed series of operations involving both addition and subtraction, the result is likewise not affected by the order in which the operations are performed:

$$16 - 5 + 3 - 4 = 10 = 16 + 3 - 5 - 4.$$

In a series of divisions, the intended order is very important. Consider

$$1,050 \div 105 \div 5 = ?$$

If we perform the operation $1,050 \div 105$ first, and divide the resulting quotient by 5, the answer is 2. If we perform the operation $105 \div 5$ first, then divide 1,050 by the resulting quotient, the answer is 50. Hence it is the convention that division operations are to be performed in the order presented; thus

$$1,050 \div 105 \div 5 = 2.$$

In careful practice, it is customary to avoid "stringing out" series of divisions. Instead, the various methods of indicating the order of operations are used.

PROBLEMS

152. Perform the following computations:

$$120 + 3 \cdot 10$$
$$150 - 60 \div 5$$
$$180 + 75 \div 3 - 10 \cdot 5$$
$$200 - 25 \cdot 4 + 45 \div 9$$
$$100 + 15 \cdot 5 \div 3 + 10 \div 2 \cdot 5 - 75 \div 25$$
$$480 \div 6 - 4 \cdot 5 + 75 \div 15 - 144 \div 24 + 5 \cdot 20 \div 4$$
$$3^3 \cdot 5 + 80 \div 2^4 - 56 \div 2^3 + 5^4 \div 5^2 + 10^2$$

The use of parentheses

Very often the set-up of a problem may require an order of arithmetic operations which is not in conformity with the order stated on page 80. In order to indicate this fact, as well as to indicate the desired order of operations, we use special symbols known as parentheses.

We have already used parentheses in order to separate a complex operation into simpler operations and to indicate the order in which operations must be performed. We stated the distributive property of multiplication (page 40) in the form

$$(a + b) \cdot c = a \cdot c + b \cdot c,$$

which in numbers might be

$$(7 + 5) \cdot 3 = 7 \cdot 3 + 5 \cdot 3.$$

If it were not for the parentheses, we should have had to write this latter as

$$7 + 5 \cdot 3 = 7 \cdot 3 + 5 \cdot 3,$$

which would lead normally to the absurd statement that

$$7 + 15 = 21 + 15.$$

But the parentheses indicate that the operation enclosed within them is to be performed before any other:

$$(7 + 5) = 12;$$

then

$$12 \cdot 3 = 21 + 15 = 36.$$

There are several kinds of parentheses, for we often need to write a parenthetical expression inside another parenthetical expression. Hence we find:

( )   parentheses,
[ ]   brackets,
{ }   braces.

If more than one of these must be used, they are usually arranged in the relation shown here:

$$\{ [( )] \}.$$

That is to say, brackets [ ] are used to enclose an operation of which a part is already enclosed in parentheses ( ), and braces

{ } are used in turn, when necessary, to enclose an operation of which a part is already enclosed in brackets. In solving a problem presented according to this plan, we dispose first of the operation inside the parentheses ( ), then of the operation inside the brackets [ ], then of the operation enclosed in the braces { }, and finally of the greater operation of which all the smaller parenthetical operations are parts.

For example,

$$5 \cdot \{2 + [6 + (8 - 3) \cdot 7] \cdot 3\}$$

is computed as follows:

$$(8 - 3) = 5,$$
$$[6 + 5 \cdot 7] = 6 + 35 = 41,$$
$$\{2 + [6 + (8 - 3) \cdot 7] \cdot 3\} = 2 + 41 \cdot 3 = 2 + 123 = 125.$$
$$5 \cdot 125 = 625.$$

Note that the order of operations within each pair of parentheses was the normal order as stated on page 80, and that the normal order was likewise followed after each pair of parentheses was removed. This normal order is evident in the computation of

$$[6 + 5 \cdot 7]$$

as well as in the computation of the numbers enclosed in the braces { }.

When the computation of numbers enclosed by some parentheses is completed, these parentheses are removed and they are not written. This procedure is known as the *removing of parentheses*.

PROBLEMS

153. Perform the following computations:

$(2,307 + 345) \cdot 15$

$67 \cdot (4,673 - 379 + 1,098 - 3,487)$

$20,000 + 125(1,200 - 8 \cdot 125)$

$(2,500 - 1,367) \cdot (300 - 256)$

$[6,453 - (8,907 - 8,899)] \cdot 3,003$

$[895 \cdot 11 - (5,000 - 4,899) \cdot 55] \cdot 40$

$3 \cdot \{2 + 45 \cdot [865 + (1,000 - 998) \cdot 25]\}$

154. Perform the following computations:

$(3,345 - 675) \div 15$

$18 \cdot (340 \div 17 + 13)$

$(360 \div 12 + 45) \div 3 + (561 \div 17 + 88) \div 11$

$[8,235 \cdot (150 - 144) + 915] \div 61$

$360 \div \{1,500 \div [30,363 + (8,098 + 1,911) + 1,485]\}$

$[(18,789 + 13,372) + (347,567 + 418)] \cdot [(5,427 - 3,989) + (5,634 \div 18)]$

155. Perform the following computations:

$(2^6 + 32) \div 12$

$3^2 \cdot (5^3 - 3^4)$

$4^4 \div (128 - 2^6) \cdot 3^2$

$15 \cdot [10 + (7^3 - 17^2)]$

$16^2 + \{45 + [2^3 + (25^2 - 24^2)]\}$

156. Multiply half the sum of 457 and 341 by half the difference of these two numbers.

157. Raise to the second power one-tenth of the sum of 64 and 36.

158. Divide the fourth power of 6 by the fourth power of 3.

159. Subtract from the sum of the second powers of 12 and 8 twice the product of 12 and 8.

160. Obtain the difference of the third powers of 11 and 9.

Divisibility of numbers

When a number divides another and no remainder is obtained, then the first number is called a divisor of the second. We examined the relation between the dividend and divisor on pages 49–50. Thus 427 can be divided exactly by 7, and 7 is a divisor of 427.

A number may have several divisors. For example, 240 can be divided by 1, 2, 3, 4, 5, 6, 8, 10, 12, 15, 16, 20, 24, 30, 40, 48, 60, 80, 120, and 240.

There are numbers that have no divisors except 1 and themselves, for example, 2, 3, 5, 7, 11, 13, 17, 19, 23, 29, 31, 37, 41, 43, and so on. Such numbers are known as *prime numbers.*

The above facts are very important because we can apply them to the study of the divisibility of numbers. Very often it may become necessary, in the course of the solution of a problem, to ascertain whether a number is divisible by some other number, although the computation of the quotient is not required.

In order to examine the various tests for divisibility of numbers we shall first examine two very important properties of sums and products.

We sometimes add several numbers, all of them divisible by the same number. Naturally we may ask the question: Will the sum of these numbers be divisible by that number? Let us examine an example of such a sum, having each addend divisible by 7:

$$(14 + 35 + 63 + 147 + 224) \div 7 = 483 \div 7 = 69.$$

Note that

$$(14 + 35 + 63 + 147 + 224) \div 7 = 2 + 5 + 9 + 21 + 32 = 69.$$

Thus we observe that the sum is also divisible by 7.

The following rule always holds: *The sum of several numbers, each addend of which is divisible by the same divisor, is also divisible by this divisor.*

If, however, one of the addends is not exactly divisible by the divisor—that is, if there is a remainder after the division—then the sum is also not divisible by that divisor. For example, in the expression

$$(14 + 35 + 63 + 147 + 223) \div 7,$$

$223 \div 7 = 31 +$ remainder 6; the sum within the parentheses is 482; and $482 \div 7 = 68 +$ remainder 6.

If we multiply several numbers, and one of them (at least) is divisible by some number, we may ask whether the product will be divisible by this same number. Let us consider the following example. The factor 34 of the product

$$15 \cdot 34 \cdot 63 \cdot 7$$

is divisible by 17. The product of the four numbers is 224,910. This product is divisible by 17:

$$224,910 \div 17 = 13,230$$

—as might be expected, since

$$15 \cdot 34 \cdot 63 \cdot 7 = 15 \cdot 63 \cdot 7 \cdot 2 \cdot 17 = 13{,}230 \cdot 17.$$

The following rule always holds: *The product of several numbers, one of which (at least) is divisible by some number, is divisible by this same number.*

PROBLEMS

161. Write all the divisors of the following numbers: (*a*) 246; (*b*) 368; (*c*) 479; (*d*) 108; (*e*) 1,248.

162. Compute the sums of the divisors of the following numbers (exclude the numbers themselves and the number 1): (*a*) 6; (*b*) 28; (*c*) 496.

163. Why is the sum $698 + 1{,}076 + 894$ divisible by 2?

164. Is the product $456 \cdot 225$ divisible by 2, 3, 4, 5, 6, 8, 9, 15? Do not perform the multiplication.

165. Write the prime divisors (divisors that are prime numbers) of the following numbers: (*a*) 180; (*b*) 400; (*c*) 2,464; (*d*) 612; (*e*) 5,220.

Tests for divisibility

It is often desirable to know, without performing the entire operation, whether some number is exactly divisible by another. For instance, is 1,096 exactly divisible by 15? We have a number of tests that will, either at a mere glance or with very little work, give us this information. These tests for divisibility depend in part on the fact (see Chapter 1) that our number system is decimal and positional. Related to this fact, and also of importance in establishing tests for divisibility, are two further facts:

The divisors of 10 are 1, 2, 5, and 10.
The divisors of 100 are 1, 2, 4, 5, 10, 20, 25, 50, and 100.

The test for divisibility by 2. If, in any number, the number in the units place is 2, 4, 6, 8, or 0, the entire number is divisible by 2. Now let us find why. Note that 10 is divisible by 2, and any product in which 10 is a factor is also divisible by 10;

for example, $152 \cdot 10 = 1,520$. We have just learned that the sum of two numbers, each of which is divisible by the same number, is also divisible by this last number. Now, every number can be represented either as a number of tens or as the sum of a number of tens and a number of units; for example, $6,735 = 6,730 + 5$. The first addend, 6,730, is divisible by 2. If 5 is divisible by 2, the sum of $6,730 + 5 = 6,735$ is also divisible by 2. But 5 is not divisible by 2; hence 6,735 is not divisible by 2. On the other hand, 8,346 is divisible by 2 because 6 is divisible by 2. A number divisible by 2 is called *even*. A number not divisible by 2 is called *odd*.

The test for divisibility by 5. For the same reasons that the divisibility of a number by 2 is determined by the number that is located in the units place, the divisibility of a number by 5 is also determined by the number located in the place of units. Every number may be represented as a sum of two addends, one of which gives the number of tens and the other the number (possibly zero) of units; for example, $14,675 = 14,670 + 5$. The first addend, 14,670, is divisible by 5, and the second addend, 5, is also divisible by 5. Thus the sum, 14,675, is also divisible by 5. On the other hand, 56,848 is not divisible by 5, because 8 is not divisible by 5.

The test for divisibility by 10. By this time, it will have become obvious that the test for divisibility by 10 is very simple. If the number has a zero on its extreme right, as 670 or 89,100, it is divisible by 10. Otherwise it is not divisible by 10. Thus 1,367 is not divisible by 10.

The test for divisibility by 4. Note that 100 is divisible by 4. Also, any number of hundreds is also divisible by 4, as for example, 300, 5,600, 87,900. In order, then, to determine whether a number is divisible by 4, we must separate it into two addends, one of which represents the number of the hundreds and the other of which is represented by the last two digits (figures) on the right, as, for example, $543,789 = 543,700 + 89$. If the second addend is divisible by 4, the entire number is divisible by 4.

Now, 543,700 is divisible by 4, but 89 is not divisible by 4; hence 543,789 is not divisible by 4.   On the other hand, 364,784 is divisible by 4, because 84 is divisible by 4.   The test for divisibility by 4, therefore, is: If the tens and units digits of a number, in order, form a number divisible by 4, then the entire number is divisible by 4.

The test for divisibility by 25.   If the tens and units digits of a number, in order, form a number divisible by 25, then the entire number is divisible by 25.   We know that 100 is divisible by 25. Thus, in order to determine whether a number is divisible by 25 it is necessary to break it up into two addends; one of them should represent the number of hundreds, and the other the last two digits (figures) on the right of the number, as, for example, 642,675 = 642,600 + 75.   Now, 642,600 is divisible by 25, and 75 is divisible by 25.   On the other hand, 809,246 is not divisible by 25 because 46 is not divisible by 25.

The tests for divisibility by 3 and by 9.   In order to obtain the method for determining divisibility by 3 we must note that 3 is divisible by 3 and 9 is divisible by 3.   Furthermore 99, 999, 9,999, 99,999 and all other numbers made up of 9's are all divisible by 3 and 9.   This fact is very important, as we shall observe presently.

Now, we may represent the following numbers as sums:

$$10 = 9 + 1,$$
$$100 = 99 + 1,$$
$$1,000 = 999 + 1,$$
$$10,000 = 9,999 + 1,$$
$$100,000 = 99,999 + 1,$$

and so on.

Note that in each sum the first addend is divisible by 3 and by 9.

In order to determine whether a number is divisible by 3 or 9 we must represent this number as a sum of several addends; these should be the number of units, the number of tens, the number of hundreds, and so on.   Thus 351 is represented as 300 + 50 + 1.   Each addend should then be represented in the form shown above:

$$300 = 3 \cdot (100) = 3 \cdot (99 + 1) = 3 \cdot 99 + 3,$$
$$50 = 5 \cdot (10) = 5 \cdot (9 + 1) = 5 \cdot 9 + 5,$$
$$1 = 1 = 1 = 1.$$

Then

$$351 = (3 \cdot 99 + 5 \cdot 9) + 3 + 5 + 1.$$

Note that $(3 \cdot 99 + 5 \cdot 9)$ is divisible by 3 and by 9. Thus the divisibility of 351 by 3 or by 9 depends on whether the sum $3 + 5 + 1$ is divisible or is not divisible by 3 or 9. Accordingly, if such a sum of the digits is divisible by 3 or by 9, then 351 is also divisible. If the sum of the digits is not divisible by 3 or by 9, then 351 is also not divisible by 3 or by 9. Note that $3 + 5 + 1$ is the sum of the digits of the number 351.

The sum of the digits $3 + 5 + 1 = 9$, which is divisible by 3 and by 9; hence 351 is divisible by 9.

Consider the following example: The number 68,544 can be represented as

$$60,000 + 8,000 + 500 + 40 + 4,$$

and also as the sum of

$$60,000 = 6 \cdot 10,000 = 6 \cdot (9,999 + 1) = 6 \cdot 9,999 + 6,$$
$$8,000 = 8 \cdot 1,000 = 8 \cdot (999 + 1) = 8 \cdot 999 + 8,$$
$$500 = 5 \cdot 100 = 5 \cdot (99 + 1) = 5 \cdot 99 + 5,$$
$$40 = 4 \cdot 10 = 4 \cdot (9 + 1) = 4 \cdot 9 + 4,$$
$$4 = 4 = 4 = 4.$$

Here again we observe that the divisibility of 68,544 by 3 or by 9 is determined by the divisibility of the sum $(6 + 8 + 5 + 4 + 4)$ by 3 or by 9. Again, this sum is the sum of the digits of the number 68,344. This sum is 27, and 27 is divisible by 3 and 9. Thus 63,844 is divisible by 3 and by 9.

If the sum of the digits of the number is not divisible by 3, then the number is not divisible by 3. If the sum of the digits of the number is not divisible by 9, then the number is not divisible by 9. For example, 763,925 is not divisible by 3 or by 9 because $7 + 6 + 3 + 9 + 2 + 5 = 32$, and 32 is not divisible by 3 or by 9. The number 85,395 is divisible by 3, but is not divisible by 9 because the sum of the digits is $8 + 5 + 3 + 9 + 5 = 30$, and 30 is divisible by 3, but is not divisible by 9.

PROBLEMS

166. List all the even numbers from 40 to 60.

167. List all the odd numbers from 75 to 90.

168. Which of the following numbers are divisible by 2, 4, and 5?

| 11,210 | 7,638 | 992,536 | 773,645 | 809,234 |
| 10,635 | 8,876,458 | 3,426,378 | 445,672 | 6,095,432 |

169. Which of the following numbers are divisible by 3, 9, and 25?

67,775,895	11,345,675
7,096,052	2,538,756,225
99,563,587	

170. Write a five-place number that does not end with a zero and that is divisible by 3 but is not divisible by 9.

171. Replace the zero of the number 74,980 with a digit such that the resultant number will be divisible by 2, 3, and 9 (all at the same time).

172. Using the numerals 0, 4, 6, and 8, write all possible numbers that are simultaneously divisible by 2, 3, 4, 5, 9, and 10.

173. Write a five-place number that is divisible by both 4 and 9.

174. Write a four-place number that is divisible by both 3 and 5 but not divisible by 2, 4, and 9 simultaneously.

175. Is the difference $1,398 - 738$ divisible by 2? by 3? by 9? Do not perform the subtraction.

More tests for divisibility

If we wish to ascertain whether a number is divisible by a number that is a product of two or more numbers, as for example, $6 = 2 \cdot 3$, $12 = 3 \cdot 4$, $15 = 3 \cdot 5$, $18 = 2 \cdot 9$, we must determine whether this number is divisible by the individual factors of the divisors. For example, if we wish to determine whether 45,732 is divisible by 6 we examine whether this number is divisible by 2 and 3. We note that this number ends with a 2, that is, it is divisible by 2. The sum of the digits of the number is 21, hence the number is also divisible by 3. Then 45,732 is divisible by 6.

In a similar manner, if we wish to determine whether 864,558 is divisible by 18 we examine it in order to ascertain whether it is divisible by 2 and also by 9.   It is divisible by 2 because it ends with 8, an even number.   The sum of the digits of 864,558 is 36, which is divisible by 9, hence this number is divisible by 9 also. Thus 864,558 is divisible by 18.

PROBLEMS

176. Which of the following numbers is divisible by 12? by 18? by 15?

| 4,789,325 | 87,498 | 645,312 | 57,870 | 1,536,725 |
| 489,276 | 5,089,572 | 73,845 | 94,367,232 | 748,926 |

177. Which of the numbers given in Problem 176 are divisible by 45?

178. Replace the question mark in 648,93? with a digit such that the six-place number is divisible by 18.

179. With the digits 0, 3, 6, 7, and 2, write a number divisible by 30.

180. With the digits 0, 4, 6, 7, 5, 2, and 3, write a number divisible by 90, also a number that does not end with a zero and is divisible by 45.

8

Applications of
Arithmetic Operations

General remarks

There is no general rule of thumb for solving problems by means of arithmetic. The solution of a problem depends entirely on the following:

> *i*. Knowledge of the arithmetic operations, that is, what every operation is for and what it does.
>
> *ii*. Understanding of the conditions set forth in the problem, that is, what information is given and what is wanted.
>
> *iii*. The combination of (*i*) and (*ii*) just stated, that is, the determination of the proper procedure and the proper arithmetic operations, as well as the order in which they must be applied.

Generally, the most important fact that should be constantly kept in mind when solving an arithmetic problem is that common sense is the best and safest road to a solution. The understanding of a problem is of primary importance, and this means that a problem should be read, and if necessary reread, until it is perfectly understood. No problem is difficult if and when it is understood.

Before starting with the solution of a problem always ask the question, "What is given?" If possible, write it:

Given: (Here state the numerical facts.)

Then ask the question:

What is wanted? (If possible, write this also.)

92

Then examine the given information in relation to what is wanted. Determine what relation exists between these two. This relation should give a hint as to what arithmetic operations must be used in order to obtain the desired information. Finally, arrange the given numerical facts to indicate the operations that must be performed. Perform the indicated arithmetic operations, and thus obtain the solution.

In order to be certain that the solution obtained is the correct one, and that it satisfies the conditions set forth in the statement of the problem, always check this solution by complying with these conditions. A check is very important because there is no other way to determine the correctness of the solution. Moreover, even if the plan of solution has been correct and the set-up of the operations likewise correct, mistakes in computation will give the wrong answer. The only way to detect a mistake or an error is to check.

Everything that was said so far is general. In the following sections of this chapter we shall examine certain typical problems which will illustrate the procedures used in their solution.

Problems in addition

On page 7 it was stated that problems involving addition are concerned with two situations, namely

> *i.* Problems wherein it is necessary to obtain the sum of two or more numbers.
>
> *ii.* Problems wherein a given number must be increased by some other number.

The computation of the sum of two or more numbers, and problems involving this operation and this alone, do not require any special illustration or examination. The statement of such a problem is always direct. In practical experience of everyday life such problems arise in adding expenditures, measurements, billed amounts, weights, and the like.

The increase of one number by a given amount represents an operation of a single step. A problem of this type is Problem 20 (see page 8). Generally a problem of this type reads in substance as follows: "One number is 234 and another number is 56 units greater than the first number. What is the second number?" or, "What is the sum of the two numbers?" The solution of this problem is obtained by means of addition. The required number is $234 + 56 = 290$, and the sum of the two numbers is $234 + 290 = 524$.

Some problems of this type may require several additions before the final solution is obtained. For example, consider the following problem: At the beginning of its operations a factory employed 1,200 workers. After one week 150 additional men were hired. After another week 200 more men added. How many men were employed at the end of the third week? Here we have

$$1,200 + 150 + 200 = 1,550.$$

Still other complications may arise in connection with problems in addition. For example, the following problem requires repetition of one addend. On Monday a coal mine yielded 2,452 tons of coal. On Tuesday 453 more tons were mined than on Monday. On Wednesday the increase over Monday's yield was 537 tons. On Thursday the increase over Monday's yield was 485 tons. How much coal was mined during the four days? Here we have the following numbers:

Monday's yield.........		2,452 tons
Tuesday's yield.........	$2,452 + 453 =$	2,905 tons
Wednesday's yield......	$2,452 + 537 =$	2,989 tons
Thursday's yield.......	$2,452 + 485 =$	2,937 tons
Total yield.........		11,283 tons

Problems in subtraction

On page 14 it was stated that problems involving subtraction are concerned with two situations, namely *i.* When a certain number must be diminished by some other number.

ii. When it is required to find by how many units one number is greater than another, or smaller.

Problems that require subtraction for their solution, and subtraction only, are generally simple in their statements. In practical experience and everyday applications such problems arise in connection with the determination of balances (bank, stock room), readings of meters (gas, electricity, automobile mileage).

Problems in addition and subtraction

More complicated situations arise when two or more different arithmetic operations are necessary for the solution.

Problems requiring both addition and subtraction do not propose any other questions than those stated in the two sections above. However, these questions are interconnected in one manner or another. Whenever such problems are proposed the reader will immediately observe the fact that sums or differences are to be found, or both. This situation is illustrated in the following problem: A piece of ground is 146 feet long. Its width is 58 feet less. What length of fencing would be required to enclose this piece of ground?

First, we must find the width of the ground. To do so requires the subtraction

$$146 \text{ feet} - 58 \text{ feet} = 88 \text{ feet}.$$

The answer to our problem is then obtained by addition:

$$146 \text{ feet} + 146 \text{ feet} + 88 \text{ feet} + 88 \text{ feet} = 468 \text{ feet}.$$

PROBLEMS

181. In a warehouse there were 7,274 boxes. Three shipments were made from this stock. The first shipment was 2,965 boxes. The second shipment was 1,565 boxes fewer than the first. The third shipment was 894 boxes fewer than the first. How many boxes were left in the warehouse?

182. A rectangular field is 3,665 feet long. Its width is 923 feet shorter. What length of fencing would be required to enclose the field?

183. The expenditures of three factories were as follows: the first $825,642, the second $75,668 less than the first, and the third $45,781 more than the first. What was the total expenditure of the three factories?

Problems in multiplication

According to the definition of multiplication, the result of this operation is a product which represents the sum of a number repeated as an addend until it occurs a certain number of times (see page 34).

Problems which require only multiplication represent situations which lead to the determination of a number whose magnitude is increased to a certain number of times the original number. Such a situation may be concerned with the weight of several objects of the same size, the cost of several objects whose price is the same, the combined length of several objects of the same size, and so on. The problems below represent illustrations of this type.

PROBLEMS

184. A railroad passenger fare is computed on the basis of 3 cents per mile. What is the price of a ticket for a trip of 157 miles?

185. How many seconds are there in a week?

186. On a railroad line there are 8 trains, each of 60 freight cars. Each freight car can carry 100 tons of freight. How much freight can the 8 trains haul?

187. A blast oven at a steel mill produces 1,724 tons of pig iron a day. How much pig iron will be produced in 30 days?

Problems in addition, subtraction, and multiplication

The solution of the problems following this section involves three different arithmetic operations. Since such problems are somewhat more complicated than those described in the preceding sections, it would be well to use care in arranging the solutions systematically. The illustrative problem will present a systematic arrangement.

EXAMPLE. A factory had 60 pieces of cloth, each 45 yards long, to be cut for men's and women's garments. In all, 14 dozen men's and 10 dozen women's garments were cut. It took 3 yards of cloth for a man's garment and 2 yards for a woman's garment. How much cloth was left? The solution of the problem is as follows.

A dozen is equal to 12. Thus, the number of garments cut was

$$12 \cdot 14 \text{ men's garments and } 12 \cdot 10 \text{ women's garments,}$$

and the number of yards of cloth used was

$$3 \cdot 12 \cdot 14 + 2 \cdot 12 \cdot 10 = 12 \cdot (3 \cdot 14 + 2 \cdot 10).$$

Thus the amount of cloth left was

$$60 \cdot 45 - 12 \cdot (3 \cdot 14 + 2 \cdot 10)$$

yards. Performing the computations, we find that $2{,}700 - 744 = 1{,}956$ yards of cloth were left uncut.

PROBLEMS

188. Two trains leave two stations and travel toward one another. One train makes 56 miles an hour, and the other train makes 64 miles an hour. After 8 hours they meet. What is the distance between the two stations? How many miles apart were the trains after 6 hours?

189. A tank contains 4,000 gallons of water. Three pipes are attached to the tank, and the water is allowed to flow from the tank through them. The water flows out at the following rates: through the first pipe 15 gallons per minute, through the second 18 gallons per minute, and the third 22 gallons per minute. If the water begins to flow through the three pipes at the same time, how much water is left in the tank after 18 minutes?

190. Two pumps were used to draw water from a flooded basement. One pump draws 2,500 gallons per hour; the second pump draws 4,800 gallons per hour. After 3 hours the basement was cleared of water. How much water was there in the basement?

191. A store sold 1,045 yards of cloth. In a check-up of the cloth left on hand, it was found that 1,567 yards were left. A yard of cloth was priced at $2 per yard. What was the total selling price of all the cloth, including the part of it that was sold?

192. Three gangs of workers were assigned to grade a highway 19,745 feet long. The first gang worked 146 hours and graded 32 feet per hour. The second worked 268 hours and graded 38 feet per hour. What was assigned to to the third gang?

Problems in division

According to the definition of division, the result of this operation is a quotient which represents a factor in a multiplication wherein the dividend and the other factor are known (see page 49).

Problems which require only division represent a variety of situations, discussed on page 52. Division finds numerous applications in many fields. The problems below involve the application of division.

PROBLEMS

193. A factory completed an order for 600 tables and was paid $6,600. Afterwards it received another $9,185 order for the same kind of tables. How many tables were ordered?

194. A wheel makes 4,620 revolutions in 77 minutes while a second wheel makes 1,080 revolutions in 54 minutes. The rate of the first wheel's revolution is how many times that of the second?

195. A potato crop of 11,020 bushels was collected from 76 acres. From how many acres were 12,760 bushels of potatoes collected if the average yield was the same?

196. A train leaves a station and travels at the rate of 62 miles per hour. How long will it take to arrive at another station 248 miles away?

197. The speed of a typical airplane in 1917 was 100 miles per hour. The speed of a typical airplane in 1965 was 400 miles per hour. How many times as fast as the planes of 1917 did the planes of 1965 travel?

Problems in multiplication and division

In the following problems both multiplication and division must be applied. Generally, it is impossible to state which of the two processes should be applied first. The decision concerning the order of operations applied must be based upon the examination of the statement of the problem. For example, the amount of heat obtained by burning 60 pounds of coke is equal to the heat obtained from burning 100 pounds of coal. How much coal will be required to replace 720 pounds of coke?

In order to solve this problem we reason as follows: We shall take 60 pounds of coke as a unit. Then in 720 pounds of coke there are

$$720 \div 60 = 12$$

units. Each 60-pound unit of coke is equivalent to a 100-pound unit of coal. The 12 units of coke are equal to 12 units of coal, or 1,200 pounds. The arithmetic statement of this reasoning is:

$$100 \cdot (720 \div 60) = 100 \cdot 12 = 1,200$$

pounds of coal.

PROBLEMS

198. A train traveled a distance of 456 miles in 8 hours. What distance will it go in 3 hours if the speed is the same?

199. An army unit received 45 cartridge boxes containing 360 cartridges each. The cartridges were distributed among the soldiers, 150 to each soldier. How many soldiers received cartridges?

200. It took 72 men to dig a ditch in 15 days. How many would be needed to dig a ditch of the same size in 10 days?

201. One wheel makes 17 revolutions while another wheel in the same time makes 11 revolutions. How many revolutions will the first wheel make while the second makes 352 revolutions?

202. Out of every 100 tons of crude oil, 30 tons of gasoline are refined. How many tons of gasoline will be refined from 785,430 tons of crude oil? How many tons of crude oil will be required for obtaining 45,630 tons of gasoline?

203. In 60 days, 48 lumberjacks felled a certain number of trees. How many days would be required to complete the same work if 96 men were employed?

Areas and volumes

The computation of areas and volumes is based on the results obtained from raising a number to a second power (in the case of areas) and the third power (in the case of volumes).   In order to know how to compute either areas or volumes we must have some knowledge concerning geometric figures.   However, a study of geometric figures is beyond the scope of this book; we shall have to accept the rules obtained in geometry for the computation of areas and volumes.   All these rules are found in the Appendix, where they are stated as formulas.

The Appendix also contains tables of units of measure, both for areas and volumes.

If we have a unit for linear measure we can derive units for areas and volumes, as described below.

Figure 1 shows a rectangle.   All the angles of a rectangle are right angles.

FIGURE 1

A special rectangle all of whose sides are equal is a square. A square is shown in Figure 2.   Now, the unit taken for the measure of areas is the area of a square having its sides equal to

FIGURE 2

one unit of length.   The area of any square is the product of two numbers, one representing the length of the square, and the other its width.   The area of the square of 1-unit side is then

$$1 \cdot 1 = 1^2 = 1.$$

Now this product is actually the second power of 1.   We borrow the name of the square to indicate that it represents a unit of measure for areas, and we call it a square unit.   Likewise, the second power of any number may be called the *square* of a number.   *To square* a number means *to raise it to the second power.*

The unit of area thus developed from the linear unit (the unit which is used for measuring lengths) is known as the *square* unit. If we use inches, then the area unit is a *square* inch.   If we use feet, then the area unit is a *square* foot.

In order to compute the area of a rectangle we must multiply the number of units in its length by the number of units in its width.   The formula for the area of a rectangle is represented as a product

$$\text{Area} = \text{length} \cdot \text{width},$$

or, when shortened, as

$$A = l \cdot w.$$

For example, if the width of a rectangle is 6 inches and the length is 8 inches, then the area is

$$A = 6 \cdot 8 = 48 \text{ square inches.}$$

For brevity we may write square inches as in.^{2}, and square feet as ft.^{2}

By means of the properties of division the formula $A = l \cdot w$ for the area of a rectangle may be used for the computation of the width (if the area and the length are given) or of the length (if the area and the width are given) of any rectangle.   Thus we have two more formulas: for the width,

$$w = A \div l,$$

and for the length,

$$l = A \div w.$$

Thus, if the area of a rectangle is 75 square feet and the length is 5 feet, then the width is $75 \div 5 = 15$ feet. If the area of a rectangle is 84 square inches and the width is 7 inches, then the length is $84 \div 7 = 12$ inches.

The volume of a boxlike object is that portion of space that is enclosed within this figure (Figure 3). A special "box" used

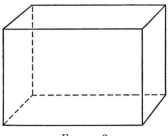

FIGURE 3

in the derivation of the unit for measuring volumes is the cube (Figure 4). In Figure 3 all the faces are rectangles. In a cube all the faces are squares. The edges of a cube are all equal. The

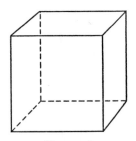

FIGURE 4

volume of any cube is computed as the product of three numbers representing the measures of its length, width, and height; all these are the same. If we take a cube that has its edges equal to one unit of linear measure, the volume of this cube is

$$1 \cdot 1 \cdot 1 = 1^3 = 1.$$

Now this product is actually the third power of 1. We borrow the name of the cube to indicate that it represents a unit of measure for volumes, and we call it a cubic unit. Also, the third power of any number may be called the *cube* of the number. *To cube* a number means *to raise it to the third power*.

The unit of volume thus developed from the linear unit (the unit which is used for measuring lengths) is known as the cubic unit. If we used inches, then the volume unit is the cubic inch. If we use feet, then the volume unit is the cubic foot.

In order to compute the volume of a box like Figure 3, we must multiply the number of units in its length by the number of units in its width and also by the number of units in its height. The word formula for the volume of a box is represented as a product:

Volume = length · width · height,

or, when shortened, as

$$V = l \cdot w \cdot h.$$

Notice in this product the factors $l \cdot w$, and recall that $l \cdot w = A$, that is, the area of the base of the box. Hence the volume of the box may also be computed as the product

$$V = A \cdot h,$$

the product of the number of square units in the base multiplied by the number of linear units in the height.

For example, if the measurements (also known as the *dimensions*) of a box are length 10 inches, width 7 inches, and height 8 inches, then the volume is

$$V = 10 \cdot 7 \cdot 8 = 560 \text{ cubic inches.}$$

For brevity we may write cubic inches as in.[3] and cubic feet as ft.[3]

Note also that if we had the area of the base of the box (which is $10 \cdot 7 = 70$ square inches) we could compute the volume of the box as

$$V = 70 \cdot 8 = 560 \text{ cubic inches.}$$

If the volume of a box and any two of its dimensions are given, we can compute the third missing dimension. Thus we may have the following three formulas.

For the length:

$$l = V \div (w \cdot h).$$

For the width:

$$w = V \div (l \cdot h).$$

For the height:

$$h = V \div (l \cdot w).$$

The reader should note that when computing areas as well as volumes in each case, all the dimensions should always be stated in the same units. If the length is stated in inches, then the width should also be stated in inches for the purpose of computing an area. If, when a volume is to be computed, the length is stated in feet, then the width and height should also be stated in feet.

PROBLEMS

204. Compute the areas of the squares whose sides are: (*a*) 5 feet; (*b*) 10 inches; (*c*) 15 yards; (*d*) 15 inches; (*e*) 30 feet.

205. Compute the areas of the rectangles whose dimensions are:

	Length	Width
a	15 in.	25 in.
b	24 ft.	18 ft.
c	15 in.	3 ft.*
d	3 yd.	4 ft.
e	11 ft.	21 in.

* *Hint:* Change feet into inches.

206. Change 3 cubic feet into cubic inches.

207. Change 5 square yards into square feet.

208. Compute the volumes of the cubes whose edges are: (a) 15 inches; (b) 3 feet; (c) 2 yards; (d) 8 inches; (e) 10 feet.

209. The area of a rectangle is 96 square inches. Its length is 16 inches. What is its width?

210. What is the area of a room whose dimensions are 13 feet by 18 feet?

211. Compute the volumes of the boxes whose dimensions are:

	Length	Width	Height
a	20 in.	15 in.	8 in.
b	24 in.	2 ft.	4 ft.
c	12 in.	18 in.	3 ft.
d	1 yd.	4 ft.	2 ft.
e	2 yd.	2 ft.	18 in.

212. What is the volume of a room whose dimensions are length 15 feet, width 10 feet, and height 8 feet?

213. Compute the areas of the walls in the room mentioned in Problem 212.

214. Change 3 cubic feet into cubic inches.

215. Change 2 cubic yards into cubic feet.

216. Change 5 cubic yards into cubic inches.

Problems involving all arithmetic operations

The solution of problems that involve all arithmetic operations requires no additional explanation. The reader is again advised to read each problem carefully. Then he should ascertain what is definitely given and what is to be found. Finally, he should determine what arithmetic operations are to be used and then set up the correct procedure of operations on numbers. The following will illustrate the above in detail.

EXAMPLE. The amount of coal in one coal yard is 3 times as great as in another. If 1,100 tons are removed from one and 100 tons from the other, then the two yards will have an equal amount of coal. How much coal was there in each yard?

Note that from the first yard $1,100 - 100 = 1,000$ tons of coal was removed over the amount removed from the second yard. Furthermore, for every 3 tons of the first yard there was only 1 ton in the second. That is, if we take 3 tons and 1 ton as units, then for every unit the first yard had $3 - 1 = 2$ tons in excess over the second yard. Altogether there were 1,000 tons in excess; then the first yard contained

$$(1,100 - 100) \div (3 - 1) \cdot 3 = 1,000 \div 2 \cdot 3 = 1,500 \text{ tons,}$$

and the second yard contained

$$1,500 \div 3 = 500 \text{ tons.}$$

Check:

$$1,500 - 1,100 = 400, \quad \text{and} \quad 500 - 100 = 400.$$

PROBLEMS

217. One repair shop could retread 3,900 tires in 6 days. Another could complete this job in 5 days. How long would it have taken the two shops to retread 14,300 tires?

218. Water is being pumped out from a mine. In 36 hours all the water is pumped out. How long will it take to pump out 3 times as much water with a pump that can draw out 4 times as much water as the first pump?

219. If 100 trees cost $250, how much will 250 trees cost?

220. A train leaves a station and travels at the rate of 50 miles per hour. Two hours later another train leaves the same station and travels at the rate of 60 miles per hour. How long will it take the second train to overtake the first?

221. An airplane flies at the rate of 200 miles per hour. If the speed of the plane were increased to 240 miles per hour it would take it 1 hour less to complete a certain flight. What is the distance that the plane had to fly?

222. In two cases there are 856 books. If 72 books were removed from one case, each case would contain the same number of books. How many books were in each case?

223. Three stones weigh 1,560 pounds. The first weighs 180 pounds more than the second, and the second is 150 pounds lighter than the third. What were the weights of the three stones?

224. At a gathering there were 672 persons.   There were 4 times as many men as children and twice as many women as children.   How many men, women, and children were there?

225. In a factory there were 6,240 workers.   In one section there were 5 times as many as in the second.   In the third there were 3 times as many as in the first two combined.   How many workers were there in each section?

226. On one side of a balance scale 5-pound weights are placed.   On the other 3-pound weights are placed.   The scale is balanced.   Altogether 24 weights are used.   How many are 5-pound and how many are 3-pound weights?

227. 9,600 books had to be bound in the shortest time possible.   Three binderies submitted bids.   The first undertook to complete the job in 16 days, the second undertook to do the work in 24 days, and the third undertook to do the job in 48 days.   The work was distributed between the three bidders. How many books were bound by each and in how many days was the work completed?

228. Three diemakers completed 5,847 dies.   The first two completed the same number of dies.   The third delivered 45 fewer dies.   How many dies were delivered by each?

229. A farmer has feed for chickens for 18 days.   For how many days will he have feed if this supply is increased tenfold and the number of chickens is quadrupled?

230. A car and a truck cost $8,460.   How much does each cost if the truck cost $60 more than twice what the car cost?

231. One cubic yard of coal weighs 1 ton.   How much coal can be stocked in a bin whose dimensions are 2 yards, 3 yards, and 4 yards?

9

Decimal Fractions

General remarks

We observed in Chapter 1 that our system of numeration is a decimal and positional system. According to this system we can, with only ten numerals, write any whole number we wish. In this chapter we will extend the method of writing numbers, as explained in Chapter 1, so that we can also write fractions as well as whole numbers.

The numbers obtained by us in Chapter 1 and with which we have been working so far do not completely satisfy the needs of our everyday life. In practical situations, especially whenever we use measurements, we cannot work solely with whole numbers. Whole numbers arise only when we count. All other activities give rise to some numbers that are not whole. We call such numbers *fractions*. The simplest way to describe a fraction is to say that it represents a part of a whole number, a subdivision of a whole number.

The decimal and positional system of numeration can be easily, almost mechanically, extended to include the writing of fractions. Furthermore, all the properties obtained by us for whole numbers, after we firmly establish the method of writing fractions, can be easily and automatically extended to include fractions.

In order to indicate a whole number we shall agree on a modification that is very simple, but useful (as will be presently seen). Let us agree to place a period or point (.) after the units, that is to the right, of a whole number. Thus we shall write

$$7. \, , \quad 56. \, , \quad 896. \, , \quad 1{,}873. \, ,$$

and all these expressions will represent as usual whole numbers. In other words, the writing of a point after a whole number will not affect the whole number in any way or manner. This point at the extreme right of a whole number will just indicate where the units' place is (to its immediate left) as well as signify the fact that the number is a whole one.

But this introduction of a point allows us at once to introduce more places for writing numbers. This seemingly insignificant point turns, as we shall now see, into a very powerful tool that enables us to extend the number system with which we have so far worked.

According to the properties of our positional system of numeration, the decimal system, a number in the units place (2. , for example) has a value ten times that of the same number in the place to its right (.2 for example):

$$2. \text{ is ten times } .2 \quad \text{or} \quad 2. = 10 \cdot .2$$

Just as we say 200 is two hundreds, or 20 is two tens or 2 is two units, we say that .2 is two-tenths. The place to the right of the units is called the tenths place. If we were to take one thing—one stick, one pound, one anything—and divide it into ten equal parts, these parts would be tenths.

If we move a number from the tenths place to the place on its right (for example, from .2 to .02, the zero serving to fill the vacated place), the number in the tenths place has ten times the value of the same number in the place to the right. If we consider the value of the same number in the units place, the unit-place number has one hundred times the value of the same number two places to its right:

$$2. \text{ is one hundred times } .02 \quad \text{or} \quad 2 = 100 \cdot .02$$

Numbers in the place at the right of the tenths are in the hundredths place. We read .2 as two-tenths and we read .02 as two one-hundredths or two-hundredths.

Thus we have obtained a method for writing and reading fractions, *decimal* fractions.

For example, if we want to write *twelve and three-tenths* we write 12.3. Note that the point, called hereafter the *decimal point*, separates the whole part of a number from the fractional, decimal part. Thus we have 12. as the whole part of the number and .3 as the decimal (fractional) part.

The expression 456.78 is read as four hundred fifty-six and seventy-eight hundredths. The expression 68.834 is read as sixty-eight and eight hundred thirty-four thousandths.

Note that the number of places to the right of the decimal point determines the kind of the decimal fraction:

> The first place denotes tenths.
> The second place denotes hundredths.
> The third place denotes thousandths.
> The fourth place denotes ten-thousandths.

The rule for the determination of the kind of a fraction is simple. Recall how many zeros there are in 10, 100, 1,000, 10,000, 100,000, etc. *Ten* has *one* zero; a number *one* place to the right of the decimal point denotes *tenths*. *One hundred* has *two* zeros; a number *two* places to the right of the decimal point denotes *hundredths*. *One thousand* has *three* zeros; a number *three* places to the right of the decimal point denotes *thousandths;* and so on.

Very often we may have a number that has no whole part. This is often indicated by writing one zero to the left of the decimal point, as for example, 0.345. This expression is read as three hundred forty-five thousandths. A number of this kind is called a *pure decimal fraction.*

If a number has a whole part and a fractional (or decimal) part, for example 765.34892, it is called a *mixed decimal fraction.*

PROBLEMS

232. Read the following decimal fractions:

6.3	67.4	89.45
9.576	489.563	48.4673
0.15	9.8057	0.13769
0.00035	42.30789	

233. Write the following fractions: (*a*) one hundred five and sixty-seven hundredths; (*b*) four thousand six hundred and thirty-one ten-thousandths;

(c) eleven thousandths; (d) fifty-seven ten-thousandths; (e) seven and six hundred eighty-two thousandths.

Moving the decimal point

We now know that the decimal point indicates where the units place is on its left as well as the tenths place on its right. Now, suppose that in the number 456.8346 we move the decimal point one place to the left; our new number is 45.68346. Let us examine how this moving of the decimal point affected the first number. Note that in 456.8346 the 5 is in the *tens* place. In 45.68346 the 5 is in the units place. In other words, the value of the 5 was divided by 10. An examination of every numeral will disclose the same fact. In other words, the moving of the decimal point one place to the left divided the number by 10.

Suppose we have moved the decimal point two places to the left instead of one. We then have another number, 4.568346. Now note that in 456.8346 the numeral 4 was in the hundreds place. In the new number, 4.568346 the numeral 4 is in the units place. In other words, its value was divided by one hundred, and this, if every other numeral in the two numbers is examined, is exactly what happened to all the other numerals. Thus, the moving of the decimal point two places to the left divides the number by 100.

If we move the decimal point three places to the left of its original position we divide the number by 1,000. If we move the decimal point four places to the left of its position we divide the number by 10,000.

Now suppose that we move the decimal point in the number 456.8346 one place to the right. We then have 4,568.346. Note that in the original number 456.8346 the numeral 8 was in the tenths place while in the new number 4,568.346 this numeral 8 occupies the units place. In other words, the value of the numeral 8 was multiplied by 10. An examination of every other numeral in the two numbers will disclose the same fact. Thus, by moving the decimal point one place to the right of its original position we multiply the number by 10.

Suppose that we move the decimal point two places to the right of its original position in the number 456.8346. We then have 45,683.46. Note that in the first number 456.8346 the numeral 4 was in the hundreds place. In the new number 45,683.46 this numeral 4 occupies the ten-thousands place. Thus the value of this numeral was multiplied by 100. This same fact may be observed if we examine all the remaining numerals. Thus, by moving the decimal point two places to the right of its original position we multiply the number by 100.

If we move the decimal point three places to the right of its original position we multiply the number by 1,000. If we move the decimal point four places to the right of its original position we multiply the number by 10,000.

The reader will recall (see page 43) that the writing of an additional zero on the right of a number multiplies this number by 10. For example, by writing a zero on the right of 45 we obtain 450, and 450 is ten times as great as 45. In the case of decimal fractions this procedure does not hold true any longer. The zero at the right of 45 has the effect of pushing the 5 from the units into the tens place, and so on. But the writing of an additional zero or additional zeros on the right of a decimal fraction does not change its value, since the decimal point fixes the positions of the places. For example, if we write two additional zeros on the right of the fraction 34.25, making it 34.2500, the value of the fraction remains unchanged. In a later chapter (see Chapter 16) we shall discuss a very valid reason for writing such zeros, but this reason has no relation to the value of the number.

The writing of an additional zero on the left of a fraction or on the left of a number produces no effect on the value of either the fraction or the number. As a matter of fact such writing is meaningless and unnecessary. For example, no one would write 056 or 000.325. Some people prefer not to write the one zero on the left of a pure decimal fraction such as 0.462, and they write .462. We shall, however retain the writing of one zero, using such forms as 0.462.

PROBLEMS

234. Multiply the following numbers by 10:

4372	9.8	87.54	0.123	0.046
0.00036	56.002	892.304	41.7809	0.0000045

235. Multiply the following numbers by 100:

56	809	1.2	12.3	0.135
7.0089	0.00025	0.00562	890.072	0.000076

236. Multiply the following numbers by 1,000:

8	789	3.4	15.67	0.13
0.0045	0.000743	89.765	70.0305	0.00000642

237. Divide the following numbers by 10:

5	56	783
4.7	56.87	678.352
0.165	0.0754	0.000056
809.00045	2.000001	

238. Divide the following numbers by 100:

4	73	934
3.4	5.47	89.354
5,173.9023	0.57	0.683
0.00453	0.0000723	80.00035

239. Divide the following numbers by 1,000:

7	35	702
8,365	7.3	89.4
463.24	36.872	4080.756
0.634	0.00809	
0.0005072	0.0000063	

240. By how much must we multiply 6.0789 in order to obtain 6,078.9?

241. By how much must we divide 70.734 in order to obtain 0.0070734?

242. By how much must we multiply 0.000042 in order to obtain 4.2?

243. By how much must we divide 0.5 in order to obtain 0.000005?

244. What must be done to 0.567 to obtain 56.7?

245. What must be done to 4.073 to obtain 0.0004073?

Addition and Subtraction of Decimal Fractions

The addition and subtraction of decimal fractions is performed in the same manner as the addition and subtraction of whole numbers.

There is one limitation imposed on the kind of numbers that can be added or that can be subtracted, and it is a very important limitation.   The reason for this limitation will be fully explained in Chapter 16.

> *i.* When we add two or several decimal fractions all of these numbers should have the same number of places to the right of the decimal point.
>
> *ii.* If we subtract one decimal fraction from another, the two should have the same number of places to the right of the decimal point.

To simplify discussion, we will hereafter refer to places at the right of the decimal point as *decimal places*.

In a set of addends or in a minuend or subtrahend, one or several of the numbers may have more decimal places than do the others.   In such situations, we note the number having the fewest decimal places and discard the digits which are to the right of these decimal places in the other numbers.   For example, in adding

$$45.6723$$
$$156.78$$

we discard the digits 2 and 3.   But we do not simply ignore these discarded digits.   They may cause a change in one of the digits we intend to use.   If we have

$$45.6723$$
$$156.7$$

we must rewrite it as

$$45.7$$
$$156.7$$

according to the following rule:

> *If the first digit (figure) at the left of the portion that is to be discarded is either 0, 1, 2, 3, or 4, then the last digit on the right that is to be retained should be left unchanged. If the first digit (figure) at the left of the portion that is to be discarded is either 5, 6, 7, 8, or 9, then the last digit on the right that is to be retained should be increased by 1.*

Such discarding of the unnecessary decimal places is known as the *rounding* of numbers. For example, 45.6723 rounded to two places after the decimal point, or, as we often say, rounded to hundredths was 45.67, because the first digit of the portion discarded was 2. When 45.6723 was rounded to one decimal place, that is, to tenths, we obtained 45.7 because the first digit of the discarded portion was 7, and therefore, the last digit on the right (the 6) was increased by 1, and we thus obtained 7.

The actual addition and subtraction of decimal fractions is performed in the same manner as in the case of whole numbers, subject to one simple rule: Arrange the numbers so that the decimal points are all in a vertical column as shown below:

$$
\begin{array}{r}
56.983 \\
123.784 \\
25.075 \\
\hline
205.842
\end{array}
\qquad \text{or} \qquad
\begin{array}{r}
875.728 \\
-\,648.917 \\
\hline
226.811
\end{array}
$$

PROBLEMS

246. Round the following numbers to tenths: (*a*) 15.6256; (*b*) 706.0725; (*c*) 18.256; (*d*) 0.7105; (*e*) 1.0675.

247. Round the following numbers to two decimal places: (*a*) 9.2045; (*b*) 66.5734; (*c*) 0.0273; (*d*) 0.0089; (*e*) 8,345.2056.

248. Perform the following additions:

15.89 + 1.7098   9.008 + 8.91

1.37 + 3.405   7.38 + 8.13

5.398 + 16.27734 + 24.5016

17.25478 + 0.56709 + 11.056 + 9.1243

249. Perform the following subtractions: (a) 67.456 − 18.92; (b) 101.23 − 75.345; (c) 2.0752 − 1.86; (d) 12.746 − 0.487; (e) 8.000 − 2.476.

250. Perform the following computations:

7.65 + 2.34 − (6.15 − 3.78)

6.77 − 2.34 − (16.98 − 15.67) + (1.24 + 2.85)

18.753 − (3.789 + 1.476) − [2.365 + 1.782 − (13.088 − 9.899)]

251. What change will take place in a difference if the minuend is decreased by 13.67 and the subtrahend is increased by 15.25?

252. A train traveling at the rate of 58.45 miles per hour overtakes a train going at the rate of 48.56 miles per hour. How many miles apart were they 1 hour before?

253. A freely falling body that was dropped from a height falls 16.1 feet the first second, and its speed increases 32.2 feet every succeeding second. Through how many feet will it fall in 4 seconds?

254. Add to the number 4,763.456 its one-thousandth, and then from this sum subtract 2,987.462.

Multiplication of decimal fractions

The multiplication of numbers in which there are decimal fractions is performed in the same manner as the multiplication of whole numbers.

The only difference between the multiplication of whole numbers and of decimal-fraction numbers is that we must take into consideration in the latter case the fact that some portion of one or both factors is fractional, as indicated by the decimal points. The question is: Where shall we locate the decimal point in the product?

The reader will recall that on page 111 we examined the effect of moving the decimal point. Now, we shall use this effect in order to obtain the rule for locating the decimal point in the product of two numbers having decimal fractions. Let us obtain the product:

$$3.672 \cdot 2.85$$

Now, instead of multiplying decimal fractions, let us for the time being multiply whole numbers 3,672 and 285. To obtain 3,672 from 3.672 we move the decimal point 3 places to the right, that is, we multiply the number by 1,000, and to obtain 285 from 2.85 we move the decimal point two places to the right, that is, we multiply it by 100. Thus, the product $3,672 \cdot 285$ is $1,000 \cdot 100 = 100,000$ times the product $3.672 \cdot 2.85$. When the product of the whole numbers 3,672 and 285 is obtained, we must divide it by 100,000, that is, move the decimal point 5 places to the left. The multiplication of the whole number is:

$$
\begin{array}{r}
3,672 \\
285 \\
\hline
18\ 360 \\
293\ 76 \\
734\ 4 \\
\hline
1,046,520
\end{array}
$$

The decimal point (not written) is at present on the extreme right of the product, that is, we have 1,049,520. , and after moving it 5 places to the left we have 10.49520.

Notice that one factor had 3 decimal places, and the second factor had 2 decimal places. The product has 5 decimal places; that is: *The number of the decimal places in the product is equal to total number of decimal places in the factors.* This statement is the rule for the number of decimal places in the product of factors containing decimal fractions.

If one of the factors is a whole number this situation does not affect the above rule. We take into account the fact that the whole number has no decimal places, and when counting the respective numbers of decimal places we count none for the whole number. For example:

$$
\begin{array}{r}
15.26 \\
12 \\
\hline
30\ 52 \\
152\ 6 \\
\hline
182.12
\end{array}
$$

The first factor has 2 decimal places, and the second factor has 0 decimal places. The product has $2 + 0 = 2$ decimal places.

PROBLEMS

255. Perform the following multiplications: (*a*) 3.6 · 1.7; (*b*) 6.89 · 2.34; (*c*) 10.89 · 3.015; (*d*) 8.89 · 12.756; (*e*) 15.46 · 10.034.

256. Perform the following multiplications:

0.0018 · 3.5 · 0.6

5 · 0.814 · 15

5.19 · 0.415 · 9.6

0.6 · 0.8 · 1.6 · 2.4

0.07 · 0.001 · 2.5 · 0.215

257. Obtain the following parts: (*a*) 0.4 of 200; (*b*) 0.75 of 59; (*c*) 0.86 of 150; (*d*) 0.015 of 1,246; (*e*) 0.33 of 814.

258. The side of a square is 1.5 inches. What is the area of the square?

259. What is the volume of a cube whose edge is 2.5 inches?

260. The circumference C of a circle is computed according to the formula

$$C = 6.28 \cdot r,$$

where r is the radius of the circle. Compute the circumferences of the following circles: (*a*) $r = 24$ inches; (*b*) $r = 2.5$ feet; (*c*) $r = 15.2$ inches; (*d*) $r = 6.4$ feet; (*e*) $r = 152$ inches.

261. The area A of a circle is computed according to the following formula:

$$A = 3.14 \cdot r^2,$$

where r is the radius of the circle. Compute the areas of the circles whose radii are given in Problem 260.

262. The formula for the area A of the side surface of a cylinder is

$$A = 6.28 \cdot r \cdot h,$$

where r is the radius of the base and h is the height of the cylinder. Compute the areas of the cylinders whose dimensions are given below:

	r	h
a	2.5 in.	1 ft.*
b	14.5 in.	3 ft.*
c	4.7 in.	14 in.
d	1.5 ft.	6.5 ft.
e	9.6 in.	42.8 in.

* *Hint:* Change feet into inches.

263. The formula for the volume V of a cylinder is

$$V = 3.14 \cdot r^2 \cdot h,$$

where r is the radius of the base and h is the height of the cylinder. Compute the volumes of the cylinders whose dimensions are given in Problem 262.

264. The surface A of a sphere is computed by means of the formula

$$A = 12.56 \cdot r^2,$$

where r is the radius of the sphere. Compute the areas of the surfaces of the spheres whose radii are: (a) 3.6 inches; (b) 12.5 inches; (c) 6.7 inches; (d) 3.2 feet; (e) 15.4 inches.

265. Round to tenths the products obtained in Problems 258 to 264.

Division of decimal fractions

The division of numbers containing decimal fractions is performed in the same manner as the division of whole numbers.

The only difference between the division of whole numbers and that of numbers containing decimal fractions is that we must take into consideration in the latter case the fact that some portion of either the dividend or the divisor, or of both, is fractional as indicated by the decimal points. Furthermore, when we performed division with whole numbers we often could not complete this operation exactly; that is, we obtained a remainder. Thus we have before us two questions:

> *i.* Where shall we locate the decimal point in the quotient?
> *ii.* What shall we do in the case of a remainder?

Here again we shall recall the observations made by us on page 111 when we examined the effect of the moving of the decimal point. Let us apply the results then obtained to the process of division. Furthermore, the reader should consult the section on the dependence of the quotient, page 70; the results obtained in that section will be applied below.

Let us first examine the division of a decimal fraction by a whole number, for example, $111.78 \div 9$. We shall proceed along the same lines as in the division of whole numbers, that is, in part:

$$
\begin{array}{r|l}
111.78 & \,9 \\
\underline{9} & 12 \\
21 & \\
\underline{18} & \\
3 & \\
\end{array}
$$

Note that the division of the whole part leaves a remainder 3, and that we have a fractional part, 0.78; that is, we are left with 3.78. From this point on we cannot expect anything else but some fraction in the quotient, if we continue the division. If now we bring down the next digit, that is, 7, we actually will have 3.7, or 37 tenths. If we divide 37 tenths by 9 we shall have a certain number of tenths in the quotient. We shall, therefore, place a decimal point after the 2 in the quotient obtained so far and continue our division as usually. We have, then:

$$
\begin{array}{r|l}
111.78 & \,9 \\
\underline{9} & 12.42 \\
21 & \\
18 & \\
\hline
3\,7 & \\
3\,6 & \\
\hline
18 & \\
18 & \\
\hline
\end{array}
$$

CHECK

$$
\begin{array}{r}
12.42 \\
\underline{9} \\
111.78 \\
\end{array}
$$

Thus we observe that the division of a decimal fraction by a whole number is performed in the same manner as the division of a whole number by a whole number. The whole part of the decimal fraction will give the whole part of the quotient. As soon as we bring down the first digit from the decimal part of the dividend we shall begin to obtain the decimal part (the fractional part) of the quotient. This procedure always serves for the division of decimal numbers by whole numbers.

Now we shall apply the results just obtained to the division of decimal fractions by decimal fractions. Let us perform the division $176.28 \div 2.6$.

We know (see page 73) that the multiplication of the dividend and of the divisor by the same number does not produce any change in the quotient. When we multiply the dividend by some number, the quotient is multiplied by the same number; but when we multiply the divisor by some number the quotient is divided by this number. If, therefore, we multiply the dividend and the divisor by the same number, the two multiplications nullify each other's effect on the quotient and leave it unchanged. This fact enables us to change the dividend 2.6 into a whole number. This change is accomplished by moving both decimal points one place to the right; thus both the divisor and dividend are multiplied by 10. The divisor 2.6 becomes 26, and the dividend 176.28 becomes 1,762.8.

```
          67.8
26 | 1,762.8        1,762.8 | 26         CHECK
    1 56            1 56      67.8         6 6.8
    ───             ───                      2.6
     202             202                   ─────
     182             182                   40 6 8
     ───             ───                   135 6
      20 8            20 8                 ───────
      20 8            20 8                 176.2 8
      ───             ───
```

Let us consider one more example, the division of a whole number by a decimal fraction, as 285 ÷ 2.5. Here, again we shall multiply the divisor by 10 so that it becomes a whole number. A corresponding increase of the dividend must be made so that the quotient to be obtained is unchanged. The division is then performed as follows:

```
          114
25 | 2,850         2,850 | 25          CHECK
    2 5             2 5     114         11 4
    ───             ───                   2.5
     35              35                 ─────
     25              25                 57 0
     ───             ───                228
     100             100                ───────
     100             100                285.0
     ───             ───
```

PROBLEMS

266. Perform the following divisions:

$168.7 \div 7$	$395.76 \div 68$
$237.6 \div 8$	$417.48 \div 84$
$268.2 \div 6$	$740.74 \div 77$
$445.9 \div 7$	$318.94 \div 37$
$673.2 \div 9$	$395.92 \div 49$

267. Perform the following divisions:

$14.832 \div 3.6$	$6.7977 \div 0.0091$
$3.4524 \div 8.4$	$67.745 \div 0.85$
$344.96 \div 0.49$	$8,611.2 \div 9.6$
$1.9952 \div 0.086$	$5.1156 \div 0.58$
$14.586 \div 0.78$	$4.2112 \div 0.00047$

268. Perform the following divisions. Then see the example worked out and explained below.

$6.2016 \div 6.8$	$7.1724 \div 83.4$
$5.6721 \div 7.3$	$17.794 \div 57.4$
$3.7912 \div 56$	$2.1771 \div 36.9$
$3.1772 \div 4.7$	$54.264 \div 646$
$6.6405 \div 75.3$	$2.5504 \div 7.97$

Explanatory note: In these problems the whole part of the dividend is smaller than the divisor. The divisor, then, is not contained as often as once in the dividend, and the quotient is less than 1, that is, a pure decimal fraction. This condition continues to exist after the dividend and divisor have been multiplied by whatever number is necessary to make the divisor a whole number:

$$2.5234 \div 68.2 = 25.234 \div 682 = ?$$

Let us rewrite this problem one further step:

$$25.234 \div 682 = 25,234 \text{ thousandths} \div 682 = ?$$

Now we can compute:

```
        37 thousandths
682 | 25,234 thousandths        25,234 thousandths | 682
      20 46                       20 46              _____
      ─────                       ─────              37   thousandths
       4 774                       4 774
       4 774                       4 774
```

But 37 thousandths is equal to 0.037, a pure decimal fraction. A check will show that it is the correct answer:

$$
\begin{array}{r}
68.2 \\
.03\ 7 \\
\hline
477\ 6 \\
2\ 046 \\
\hline
2.523\ 4
\end{array}
$$

Can we arrive at this correct answer 0.037 by a simpler procedure? Let us stop worrying about the dividend which is smaller than the divisor and compute:

$$
\begin{array}{cc}
0.03 & \\
682\ \overline{\left)\ 25.234\right.} & 25.234\ |\ 682 \\
20.46 & 20.46 \quad 0.03 \\
\hline
4.77 & 4.77
\end{array}
$$

Thus we find that by taking 0.03 as a trial quotient we seem to be off to a sound start, for $0.03 \cdot 682 = 20.46$ just as $3 \cdot 682 = 2,046$ in the division of 25,234 thousandths. We complete the computation

$$
\begin{array}{cc}
0.037 & \\
682\ \overline{\left)\ 25.234\right.} & 25.234\ |\ 682 \\
20.46 & 20.46 \quad 0.037 \\
\hline
4.774 & 4.774 \\
4.774 & 4.774 \\
\hline
\end{array}
$$

and find further that $0.007 \cdot 682 = 4.744$. If we try other divisions of the same sort, we find that our method is sound. We have placed the decimal point in the quotient so as to give us the same number of decimal places in the products that there are in the partial dividends. When the partial dividend was 25.23 we wrote our partial quotient with two decimal places, 0.03; when the partial dividend was 4.774 we wrote our partial quotient as 0.007, that is, we put the 7 at the right of 0.03 to make the quotient 0.037, as above. Mechanically, it may be noted that this practice will result, in the left-hand method of recording, in putting the quotient's decimal point immediately above the dividend's decimal point. Most computers, performing such operations every day, do not realize that the products are numbers with decimal fractions, since it is not the custom to write the decimal points in them.

$$
\begin{array}{r}
0.037 \\
682\ \overline{\left)\ 25.234\right.} \\
20\ 46 \\
\hline
4\ 774 \\
4\ 774 \\
\hline
\end{array}
$$

Quotients with repeated decimals

Very often the division of numbers, whether whole numbers or numbers with decimal fractions, cannot be completed to give an exact result. At some stage of the division we reach a situation wherein the quotient or a part of the quotient repeats itself, and thus the division may be carried on indefinitely. In all such cases, however, an exact quotient cannot be obtained. In such situations the process of division must be stopped at some place. Where it should stop must be decided by the computer. Oftentimes the point where the division should stop is determined in the statement of the problem.

The following example will illustrate the repeating:

$$
\begin{array}{r|l}
11 & 6 \\ \hline
6 & 1.83333\cdots \\ \hline
50 & \\
48 & \\ \hline
20 & \\
18 & \\ \hline
20 & \\
18 & \\ \hline
20 & \\
18 & \\ \hline
20 & \\
18 & \\ \hline
2 & \\
\end{array}
$$

Note that during the division above we brought down zeros whenever we wished to continue the process. All these zeros assumedly came from the places to the right of the decimal point.

We note that the quotient $11 \div 6 = 1.833 +$ can contain as many repeated 3's as we wish. However, if we decide to stop, we must employ the rule for rounding digits. Thus, since 3 is less than 5, we merely drop the digits that are beyond the place where we wish to stop. If we want to retain three decimal places, we write the quotient as $1.833 +$. The plus $(+)$ sign signifies that the actual quotient exceeds in magnitude the number we agreed to retain.

Another situation is shown below:

$$
\begin{array}{r|l}
17 & 9 \\
9 & \overline{1.88888\cdots} \\
\hline
80 & \\
72 & \\
\hline
80 & \\
72 & \\
\hline
80 & \\
72 & \\
\hline
80 & \\
72 & \\
\hline
80 & \\
72 & \\
\hline
8 & \\
\end{array}
$$

If in this quotient we wish to retain a certain number of places, say four decimal places, we write 1.8889 −, since 8 is greater than 5. The minus (−) sign signifies that the actual quotient is somewhat less than the number we retained.

In order to be able to round the quotient correctly, we must carry the division to one place farther than the place where we expect to stop. This extra place indicates the treatment for the last place in the retained quotient.

PROBLEMS

269. Perform the following computations:

$1.673 \cdot 12 + 0.567 \div 1.3$

$76.5 \div 0.18 - 256.2 \cdot (1.7 - 12.9)$

$3.7 \div [8.95 + (54.7 - 51.9) \cdot 0.37]$

$[12.35 + 5.678 \div (6.78 - 4.95)] \div (2.3 \cdot 3.9)$

$[(23.06 + 18.75) \div (4.785 + 1{,}756) - 11.87] \div [(0.756 + 5.457) \cdot 8]$

270. Perform the following computations:

$$\frac{5.67 \cdot 17.5}{225}$$

$$\frac{47 \cdot 18.3 \cdot 0.32}{2.44 \cdot 0.3 \cdot 1.88}$$

$$\frac{81.6 \cdot 1.2 \cdot 1.3}{22.1 \cdot 0.24}$$

$$\frac{5.2 \cdot 14.4 \cdot 11 \cdot 6.75}{1.2 \cdot 88 \cdot 19.5 \cdot 2.7}$$

$$\frac{(12.6 + 5.6) \cdot (8.6 - 5.6)}{(7.24 - 1.26) \div (9.22 + 14.54)} + \frac{8.976}{0.24}$$

$$\left[\frac{48.18 \cdot 2.75 - (3.27 + 4.26)}{6.07 \cdot 3.04 - 3.4528} + \frac{0.01334}{0.01}\right] \div \left(\frac{240.9}{5.5} - 3.85\right)$$

271. The length C of the circumference of a circle is given by the formula

$$C = 6.28r,$$

where r is the radius of the circle.   What is the length of the radius if $C = 56.87$ feet?

10

Units of Measurement

What is measurement?

Measurement is an activity that leads to the determination and to the statement of the magnitude of an object. This magnitude is stated in terms of a number that is obtained as the result of measurement. When we measure, we compare the magnitude of one object measured with some other object's magnitude.

In order to render the statements concerning the magnitudes of objects universally understood and simple, we generally agree to perform the comparisons with objects widely familiar. Furthermore, the easiest way to compare the magnitudes of two objects, especially when these two objects may be removed from our actual presence, is to compare their measures. For this purpose, it has been found, numerical statements of measures are most convenient. We may say that one man is taller than another, but we cannot be content with such a statement—we want to know by what amount taller. We may say that a distance from one city to another is very great, but such a statement is not conclusive enough. When we know the magnitude of this distance, and we can convey this fact to other people in terms easily understood, we tell a complete story, we convey information that may be used for many purposes.

For the purpose of measurement we use special instruments which, in many cases, are applied directly to the object we measure. In other cases, we do not measure the object by direct application of the instrument, but we measure indirectly—we may apply the instrument to some part of the object (as in the case of the circumference of the circle, when we may measure the radius and then use a special formula for computation), or we can measure distant objects by special means and instruments (astronomers can measure temperatures of stars millions of millions of miles away).

In order to state measurements and measures in universal language we ordinarily use certain units of measure generally agreed upon either by custom or legislation. The magnitude of an object is then stated in terms of the number of these units it contains. For various properties we have special units, and these will be examined in this chapter.

Units of length

In the United States the generally used units for measuring length are the *inch, foot, yard,* and *mile*. At present these units are standardized; that is, their sizes are prescribed by law, and samples known as *standards* are prepared and kept by the Bureau of Standards of the United States Government.

The units stated above are related to one another as follows:

> 1 foot = 12 inches,
> 1 yard = 3 feet = 36 inches,
> 1 mile = 5,280 feet = 1,760 yards.

The smallest unit is the inch.

In scientific laboratories, as well as in all Continental Europe, another unit is in universal use. The units derived from this fundamental unit, known as the *meter*, are all based on the decimal system of numeration. One thousandth of a meter is known as a *millimeter*. A thousand meters is used as a unit for measuring distances. The system of these units is (the abbreviations for their names are also shown):

> 1 micron = 0.001 millimeter = 0.001 mm. = 0.000001 m. = 1 μ,
> 1 millimeter = 0.001 meter = 0.001 m. = 1 mm.,
> 1 centimeter = 0.01 meter = 0.01 m. = 1 cm. = 10 mm.,
> 1 meter = 1 m. = 0.001 kilometer = 0.001 km.,
> 1 kilometer = 1,000 meters = 1,000 m. = 1 km.

The relations between the units of length used in this country (known as the English system) and the units used in Continental

Europe (known as the metric system) are as follows

$$1 \text{ in.} = 2.54 \text{ cm.,}$$
$$1 \text{ cm.} = 0.3937 \text{ in.,}$$
$$1 \text{ ft.} = 30.48 \text{ cm.} = 0.3048 \text{ m.,}$$
$$1 \text{ m.} = 39.37 \text{ in.} = 3.281 \text{ ft.} = 1.094 \text{ yd.}$$

A table of comparisons of these units is given in the Appendix.

PROBLEMS

Note: Consult the table of Units of Length in the Appendix.

272. Convert the following into meters: (*a*) 13.4 inches; (*b*) 45.67 feet; (*c*) 120 yards; (*d*) 14 feet 5 inches; (*e*) 0.75 mile.

273. Convert the following into inches: (*a*) 15 centimeters; (*b*) 1.6 meters; (*c*) 67.5 millimeters; (*d*) 1 meter 37.6 centimeters; (*e*) 1.75 meters.

274. Convert the following into feet: (*a*) 45 meters; (*b*) 0.15 kilometers; (*c*) 75 centimeters; (*d*) 37.5 meters; (*e*) 14.6 centimeters.

Units of area

On page 100 we found that for the purpose of measuring areas we must use special units that are derived from the units for measuring length (or linear units). Ordinarily, a unit for measuring areas is obtained by squaring (raising to the second power) a linear unit.

Thus in the English system we have the square inch, (in.^{2}) and the square foot (ft.^{2}). In the metric system we have the square centimeter (cm.^{2}). All other units in the respective systems are derived by following the same method: squaring the linear unit.

The following facts are derived by the method of obtaining square units:

$$1 \text{ ft.}^2 = (12 \text{ in.})^2 = 144 \text{ in.}^2 \text{ or } 144 \text{ square inches}$$
$$1 \text{ yd.}^2 = (3 \text{ ft.})^2 = 9 \text{ ft.}^2 \text{ or } 9 \text{ square feet}$$

For the metric system we obtain the following:

$$1 \text{ m.}^2 = (100 \text{ cm.})^2 = 10,000 \text{ cm.}^2 \text{ or } 10,000 \text{ square centimeters}$$
$$1 \text{ cm.}^2 = (10 \text{ mm.})^2 = 100 \text{ mm.}^2 \text{ or } 100 \text{ square millimeters}$$

The relations between the English and the metric square units are:

$$1 \text{ in.}^2 = 6.452 \text{ cm.}^2$$
$$1 \text{ cm.}^2 = 0.155 \text{ in.}^2$$
$$1 \text{ ft.}^2 = 0.093 \text{ m.}^2$$
$$1 \text{ m.}^2 = 10.764 \text{ ft.}^2 = 1.196 \text{ yd.}^2$$
$$1 \text{ yd.}^2 = 0.836 \text{ m.}^2$$

A table of comparisons of these units is given in the Appendix.

PROBLEMS

Note: Consult the table of Units of Area in the Appendix.

275. Convert the following into square meters: (*a*) 45.6 square centimeters; (*b*) 25.7 square feet; (*c*) 17.86 square yards; (*d*) 87.5 square inches; (*e*) 3.6 square feet.

276. Convert the following into square feet: (*a*) 1,824 square inches; (*b*) 1,575 square yards; (*c*) 67.65 square meters; (*d*) 292.4 square centimeters; (*e*) 0.75 square meters.

277. Convert the following into square inches: (*a*) 45.6 square centimeters; (*b*) 3.4 square feet; (*c*) 1.5 square meters; (*d*) 0.35 square yards; (*e*) 27 square millimeters.

Units of volume

The method for obtaining a unit for measuring volumes was examined and described on page 102. Volume units, like area units, are derived from units for measuring lengths (linear units). Most units for measuring volumes are obtained by cubing (raising to the third power) linear units.

In the English system, accordingly, we have the cubic inch (in.³) and the cubic foot (ft.³). In the metric system we have cubic centimeter (cm.³). All other units in the respective systems are derived by following the same method: cubing the linear unit.

The following facts are derived by the method of obtaining cubic units:

$$1 \text{ ft.}^3 = (12 \text{ in.})^3 = 1{,}728 \text{ in.}^3 \text{ or } 1{,}728 \text{ cubic inches}$$
$$1 \text{ yd.}^3 = (3 \text{ ft.})^3 = 27 \text{ ft.}^3 \text{ or } 27 \text{ cubic feet}$$

For the metric system we obtain the following:

1 m.³ = (100 cm.)³ = 1,000,000 cm.³ or 1,000,000 cubic centimeters
1 cm.³ = (10 mm.)³ = 1,000 mm.³ or 1,000 cubic millimeters

The relations between the English and the metric cubic units are:

1 in.³ = 16.387 cm.³
1 cm.³ = 0.061 in.³
1 ft.³ = 0.028 m.³
1 m.³ = 35.314 ft.³ = 1.308 yd.³
1 yd.³ = 0.765 m.³

A table of comparisons of these units is given in the Appendix.

PROBLEMS

Note: Consult the table of Units of Volumes in the Appendix.

278. Convert the following into cubic meters: (*a*) 167.5 cubic centimeters; (*b*) 92.3 cubic feet; (*c*) 35.6 cubic yards; (*d*) 384.5 cubic inches; (*e*) 565 cubic feet.

279. Convert the following into cubic feet: (*a*) 482.6 cubic inches; (*b*) **7.68** cubic yards; (*c*) 154.5 cubic meters; (*d*) 1564.5 cubic centimeters; (*e*) **2.78** cubic meters.

280. Convert the following into cubic inches: (*a*) 135 cubic centimeters; (*b*) 7.56 cubic feet; (*c*) 1.7 cubic meters; (*d*) 0.87 cubic yards; (*e*) 15 cubic meters.

Units of weight

For measuring weights two different systems of units are generally employed. The one used in daily life and in business in the United States is based on the ounce and pound. In science and in most of Continental Europe the weight units are based on the centimeter. Theoretically, the weight of 1 cubic centimeter of pure water under certain conditions (such as temperature, humidity, air pressure) is taken as the unit of weight, known as the *gram*. (In strict fact, the gram is a fraction of the standard kilogram, a platinum mass kept in the International Bureau of Weights and Measures.)

In our system of units of weight:

> 1 pound   = 1 lb. = 16 ounces = 16 oz.
> 1 short ton = 2,000 pounds *
> 1 long ton = 2,240 pounds

In the metric system we have:

> 1 kilogram   = 1 kg. = 1,000 grams = 1,000 g.
> 1 metric ton = 1,000 kilograms

The relations between our and the metric units of weight are:

> 1 oz. = 28.35 g. = 0.02835 kg.   1 g. = 0.0353 oz.
> 1 lb. = 454 g.   = 0.454 kg.   1 kg. = 2.205 lb.
> 1 short ton = 907.2 kg.
> 1 long ton = 1,006 kg.
> 1 metric ton = 1.102 short tons = 0.984 long tons

A table of comparisons of these units is given in the Appendix.

PROBLEMS

Note: Consult the table of Units of Weight in the Appendix.

281. Convert the following into pounds: (*a*) 125.6 grams; (*b*) 0.754 short tons; (*c*) 1.56 long tons; (*d*) 3.45 metric tons; (*e*) 56.7 kilograms.

282. Convert the following into kilograms: (*a*) 8 pounds 7 ounces; (*b*) 1.5 short tons; (*c*) 2.7 long tons; (*d*) 89.4 pounds; (*e*) 0.563 short tons.

283. If 1 cubic centimeter of water weighs 1 gram, what is the volume in cubic feet of 1 short ton of water?

Units of capacity †—liquid measure

For measuring liquids, as for weights, two distinct systems of units are in wide use. In the United States, in business and everyday life, we use the liquid pint, the liquid quart, and the

---

* The unspecified word "ton," in everyday usage, refers to this weight.

† Units of capacity, it may be noted, are likely to be of a magnitude convenient for everyday use, easy handling, and simple computing; units of volume, on the other hand, have their magnitude determined by linear measurement and are likely to be most useful for engineering and scientific expression and computing. Consider the quart, pint, and gallon, as against the cubic inch or cubic foot—the three measures are far more useful to the milkman

gallon. In most of Continental Europe the units for the liquid measure of capacity are based on the centimeter; that is, metric units are employed.

Our liquid units for the measure of capacity are:

```
1 fluid ounce  = 1 fl. oz.
1 gill         = 4 fl. oz.,
1 liquid pint  = 4 gills = 16 fl. oz.
1 liquid quart = 2 liquid pints = 8 gills = 32 fl. oz.
1 gallon       = 4 liquid quarts = 8 liquid pints
               = 32 gills = 128 fl. oz.
```

In the metric system the liquid unit for measure of capacity is the *liter;* its volume for practical purposes is 1,000 cubic centimeters. Thus 1 liter of water weighs 1 kilogram.

The relations between the United States units and the metric units for liquid measure of capacity are:

```
1 gill         = 0.118 liter
1 liquid pint  = 0.473 liter
1 liquid quart = 0.946 liter
1 gallon       = 3.785 liters
```

The volume occupied by 1 liquid pint is 28.875 cubic inches. A table of comparisons of these units is given in the Appendix.

PROBLEMS

Note: Consult the table of Units of Liquid Measure of Capacity in the Appendix.

284. Convert the following into liters: (*a*) 3 liquid quarts; (*b*) 1.5 liquid pints; (*c*) 32.5 gallons; (*d*) 3.75 gills; (*e*) 11.5 liquid quarts.

285. What are the volumes in cubic inches of the measures in Problem 284?

or the housewife than the cubic foot or cubic inch might be; the two latter units are convenient for measuring an object that cannot be cut up and transferred from one container into another. Moreover, units of capacity can be, and in all likelihood many have been, devised without reference to linear measure. Any random vessel, with a mark scratched at a certain level, can be taken as a measure; filling it to this level and pouring the contents into another vessel, then scratching a mark at the level of the contents, duplicates the measure.

286. What are the volumes in cubic centimeters of the measures in Problem 284?

287. Convert the following:

13.75 liters into gallons
0.56 liter into liquid quarts
1.235 liters into gills
0.034 liter into fluid ounces
0.75 liter into liquid pints

288. What are the volumes in cubic inches of the measures in Problem 287?

289. What are the volumes in cubic centimeters of the measures in Problem 287?

Units of capacity—dry measure

For measuring the capacity of certain dry objects, grain for example, we use units of dry measure. In the United States, in business and everyday life, we use the dry pint, the dry quart, and the bushel. In most of Continental Europe the units for dry measure of capacity are the same as the units for liquid measure of capacity, except that one more unit is used, namely:

1 dekaliter = 10 liters.

Our dry units for measure of capacity are:

1 dry pint = 1 dry pint
1 dry quart = 2 dry pints
1 peck   = 8 dry quarts = 16 dry pints
1 bushel   = 4 pecks = 32 dry quarts = 64 dry pints

The relations between our units and the metric units for measure of capacity are:

1 dry pint = 0.551 liter
1 dry quart = 1.101 liter
1 peck   = 8.81 liters
1 bushel   = 35.238 liters

The volume occupied by 1 dry pint is 33.6 cubic inches. A table of comparisons for these units is given in the Appendix.

PROBLEMS

Note: Consult the table of Units for Dry Measure of Capacity in the Appendix.

290. Convert the following into liters: (*a*) 15.6 dry pints; (*b*) 57.8 dry quarts; (*c*) 65.4 pecks; (*d*) 675 bushels; (*e*) 0.75 bushel.

291. What are the volumes in cubic inches of the measures in Problem 290?

292. What are the volumes in cubic centimeters of the measures in Problem 290?

293. Convert the following: (*a*) 5.75 liters into dry pints; (*b*) 23.45 liters into dry quarts; (*c*) 15.65 dekaliters into pecks; (*d*) 1,235 liters into bushels; (*d*) 654.3 dekaliters into bushels.

294. What are the volumes in cubic feet of the measures in Problem 293?

295. What are the volumes in cubic meters of the measures in Problem 293?

Some other measures

Below are some units of measure that are in common use.

Temperature is measured in degrees. The freezing point of water on a Fahrenheit thermometer is 32°, and the boiling point of water is denoted 212° (for normal conditions).

In Continental Europe, temperature is measured on the Centigrade scale. The freezing point of water is 0°, and the boiling point is 100°.

The relation between the Centigrade and Fahrenheit scales is expressed by means of a conversion formula which will be found in the Appendix, page 308.

Power is measured in terms of *horsepower*. 1 horsepower, or 1 hp., is equivalent to the power required to lift a weight of 550 pounds 1 foot in 1 second, or 33,000 pounds 1 foot in 1 minute. Power is also measured in *watts* and in thousands of watts or *kilowatts*. The relation of the two units is:

$$1 \text{ horsepower} = 746 \text{ watts}$$
$$1 \text{ kilowatt} = 1.34 \text{ horsepower}$$

This unit is used in measuring the power of motors, machines, and other instruments that are used in performing work.

Wood is measured in terms of *cords;* 1 cord of wood measures 128 cubic feet.   Boards are measured in terms of *board feet;* 1 board foot measure is 1 foot in length, 1 foot in width, and 1 inch in thickness.

Arithmetic operations

Arithmetic operations with numbers such as discussed in this chapter are performed in the same manner as the operations with all other numbers.   However, since these numbers represent measures, and these measures are based on units, we call them *denominate numbers.*

Denominate numbers can be operated upon, that is, added, subtracted, multiplied, or divided, provided they are all of the same denomination for a given operation.   If we add inches and feet we must either convert inches into feet or feet into inches. For example, if we wish to add 6 inches and 7.5 feet we must change into 0.5 foot + 7.5 feet = 8.0 feet, or 6 inches + 90 inches = 96 inches.   Note that 96 inches can be converted into 8 feet.

The multiplication of denominate numbers can only be performed if there is some sense in doing so.   If we multiply lengths (of the same denomination) we get areas; if we multiply lengths by areas we get volumes.   If we multiply weight by weight we don't obtain anything sensible.   However, in physics and mechanics we may multiply weight by length (see page 135 regarding horsepower).   Here we should understand that multiplications described here are actually performed on numbers.   These numbers, however, must represent quantities of objects of the same kind, or measurements of the same kind.   We may multiply dollars by the number of units of weight or length and obtain a certain amount of money as the product.

The division of denominate numbers is permissible provided they are of the same denomination.   This computation will be discussed in Chapter 14.

11

Common Fractions

What is a common fraction?

Of all arithmetic operations examined by us, division is the only one which under certain conditions cannot be performed exactly. We learned in Chapter 9 that the division of two numbers may lead to a quotient that is a decimal fraction, and often this decimal fraction may contain repeated digits. If the division cannot be performed exactly, and we are interested only in a quotient that is a whole number, we obtain a remainder; thus, the division of 9 by 5 results in a quotient 1 and a remainder 4.

However, very often in practice we may be confronted with a situation that requires an exact division of some quantity (whose magnitude is represented by a whole number) by a whole number, as for example, $8 \div 3$, say eight apples divided among three persons, and we give each person two apples, but we are left with 2 (which is the remainder of the division of 8 by 2). Nevertheless, we usually overcome this difficulty by cutting up (or dividing up) the object into three equal parts (in the case of the two apples we cut them up), and we hand each person two such parts. Each part represents one-third, and the two parts are then two-thirds. This procedure enables us to overcome our difficulty.

In order to indicate this kind of operation we introduce in arithmetic a new kind of numbers. The purpose of these numbers is to indicate that we are dealing with parts of whole numbers, and hence we call such numbers *fractions*. In order to distinguish them from decimal fractions we call them *common fractions*. However, since we always use the term decimal fractions, we shall call the common fractions just *fractions* and understand that we are talking about common fractions.

Since common fractions are so closely connected with division we shall use the method of writing them by utilizing the division signs. Thus two-thirds is written as $2 \div 3$ or as $\frac{2}{3}$. Some writers also write $\frac{2}{3}$. The last writing will not be used in this book, however; we shall write $\frac{2}{3}$.

The number in a fraction above the line is known as the *numerator of the fraction,* and the number below the line is known as the *denominator of the fraction.* The denominator indicates into how many parts a unit quantity was divided, and the numerator indicates how many of such parts are under consideration or taken. When we read a fraction we read the numerator first (as *two*) and then the denominator is read (as *thirds*). Thus $\frac{2}{3}$ is two-thirds, $\frac{5}{7}$ is five-sevenths.

The introduction of common fractions enables us to perform *all* divisions exactly. We do not need to have a remainder any longer. For example, the division $68 \div 13$ gives the quotient $\frac{68}{13}$.

PROBLEMS

296. Read the following fractions: (*a*) $\frac{3}{4}$; (*b*) $\frac{5}{11}$; (*c*) $\frac{17}{23}$; (*d*) $\frac{18}{137}$; (*e*) $\frac{15}{223}$.

297. Write the following fractions: (*a*) seven-thirteenths; (*b*) eight twenty-sevenths; (*c*) one-fiftieth; (*d*) five thirty-seconds; (*e*) seven sixty-fourths.

Proper and improper fractions

If we divide one (1) into a certain number of parts and we take all these parts, this fact may be represented as a fraction. Suppose we divide one into seven parts; we then have $\frac{7}{7}$, as can be seen from the fact that all the parts of one were taken. Thus

$$\frac{7}{7} = 1.$$

It is a general property of fractions that if the numerator of a fraction is equal to the denominator, then the fraction is equal to 1.

From this observation we may reach two important conclusions.

i. If the numerator of a fraction is less than the denominator, then the fraction is less than 1. For example, $\frac{3}{4}$ is less than 1.

ii. If the numerator of a fraction is greater than the denominator, then the fraction is greater than 1. For example, $\frac{9}{7}$ is greater than 1.

If a fraction is less than 1, as $\frac{7}{12}$, it is called a *proper fraction*.

If a fraction is equal to 1 or greater than 1, it is called an *improper fraction*. For example, $\frac{16}{16}$ and $\frac{34}{25}$ are improper fractions.

PROBLEMS

298. Which of the following fractions are proper and which are improper? (*a*) $\frac{4}{5}$; (*b*) $\frac{7}{6}$; (*c*) $\frac{18}{19}$; (*d*) $\frac{17}{16}$; (*e*) $\frac{116}{125}$; (*f*) $\frac{33}{33}$; (*g*) $\frac{49}{48}$; (*h*) $\frac{56}{58}$; (*i*) $\frac{83}{84}$; (*j*) $\frac{32}{32}$.

299. Using the following numerals, write all possible proper fractions: 3, 7, 9, 11.

300. Write the fraction twice as great as $\frac{13}{12}$. To what whole number is this fraction equal?

301. Write the following numbers as improper fractions: 3, 4, 5, and 6.

302. To what whole number is the improper fraction $\frac{65}{13}$ equal?

303. Under what conditions will the improper fraction $\dfrac{m}{n}$ be equal to 10?

Mixed common fractions

Let us examine the improper fraction $\frac{17}{4}$. It states that a certain quantity was divided into four parts, and then 17 such parts were taken. Now, the number 17 contains 4 four times and one over. Thus, the seventeen-fourths can be represented as 4 times four-fourths and another one-fourth, that is,

$$\frac{17}{4} = 4 \cdot \frac{4}{4} + \frac{1}{4}.$$

But $\frac{4}{4}$ is equal to 1. Therefore, since $4 \cdot 1 = 4$, we can write

$$\frac{17}{4} = 4 + \frac{1}{4}.$$

This sum is always written as a simpler form as $\frac{17}{4} = 4\frac{1}{4}$, that is, the plus sign ($+$) is omitted.

The form $4\frac{1}{4}$ contains the number of whole units in the improper fraction $\frac{17}{4}$ and as soon as this number is obtained the improper fraction ceases to exist. In its place we have a *mixed common fraction*. It is a mixed fraction in the same sense as 3.45 is a mixed decimal fraction. Some, instead of calling it a mixed common fraction, call it a *mixed number*.

Any improper fraction can be changed into a mixed fraction (or mixed number) as follows: Divide the numerator by the denominator. The quotient, given in whole numbers, is the whole part, while the remainder indicates the proper fraction that is to be added to the whole number. The addition sign ($+$) is omitted in writing the mixed fraction.

A mixed fraction can be converted into an improper fraction. Here we should remember the fact obtained on page 135, that a fraction whose numerator and denominator are equal, for example $\frac{5}{5}$, is equal to 1. Furthermore, if we take such an improper fraction and multiply the numerator by some number, say 15, then the new improper fraction is equal to 15 (see Problems 302 and 303). With these facts at our command we can proceed with the converting of a mixed fraction into an improper fraction.

Let us take, for example, the mixed fraction $35\frac{2}{3}$. Note that the whole part of this mixed fraction consists of the number 35, while the fractional part has a fraction whose denominator is 3; that is, we deal with thirds. Now, since $\frac{3}{3} = 1$, we can convert 35 into thirds by multiplying 35 by 3, and this product will give us the number of thirds in 35. We have, then, that in 35 there are $35 \cdot 3 = 105$ thirds. To this we must add the 2 thirds from the fractional part, and this gives us $105 + 2 = 107$. This sum 107 is the numerator of the improper fraction whose denominator is 3. Thus, we have

$$35\frac{2}{3} = \frac{107}{3}.$$

Thus we see that the conversion of a **mixed fraction** (or

mixed number) into an improper fraction is performed as follows: Multiply the whole part of the mixed fraction by the denominator of the fraction. To this product add the numerator of the fractional part of the mixed fraction. Write this sum as the numerator of the fraction whose denominator is the same as the denominator in the mixed fraction. The result is an improper fraction equal to the mixed fraction.

For example, according to this rule we have

$$6\frac{5}{16} = \frac{6 \cdot 16 + 5}{16} = \frac{101}{16}.$$

That this improper fraction is equal to the mixed fraction may be checked by converting it into the mixed fraction according to the rule stated on page 140.

PROBLEMS

304. Convert the following improper fractions into mixed fractions:

$$\frac{101}{7} \qquad \frac{235}{16} \qquad \frac{1,134}{13} \qquad \frac{185}{8} \qquad \frac{2,359}{32}$$

305. Convert the following mixed fractions into improper fractions: (a) $8\frac{7}{9}$; (b) $11\frac{11}{25}$; (c) $45\frac{35}{64}$; (d) $18\frac{17}{33}$; (e) $32\frac{19}{48}$.

306. How many sixteenths are there in the whole numbers 5, 8, 10, and 15? State your answers as improper fractions.

307. How many fifths are there in the whole numbers 5, 12, 81, 96, and 143? State your answers as improper fractions.

308. How many fourths are there in $\frac{1}{2}$, $\frac{3}{2}$?

309. How many sixths are there in $\frac{1}{3}$, $\frac{7}{3}$, $6\frac{2}{3}$?

310. Convert the following mixed fraction into an improper fraction:

$$a + \frac{b}{c}.$$

The letters a, b, and c represent whole numbers.

Comparisons of fractions

The comparison of the magnitudes of whole numbers is based on the process of counting. We have a fairly good notion from the process of counting which of two numbers, say 25 and 32, is greater.

The comparison of fractions is not so simple. We must take into account the fact that in a fraction we have a numerator and denominator, and these two together determine the magnitude of a fraction.

In order to arrive at some method for comparison of the magnitudes of two or more fractions we shall examine two cases first. These two cases are:

    i. Fractions whose denominators are the same.

    ii. Fractions whose numerators are the same.

Let us consider the first case, that is, fractions whose denominators are the same. Let us consider the following fractions:

$$\frac{7}{29}, \quad \frac{3}{29}, \quad \frac{15}{29}, \quad \frac{2}{29}, \quad \frac{21}{29}.$$

The fact that these fractions have the same denominators indicates that they are all composed of various numbers of the same equal portions of unity (1), that is, 7 portions, 3 portions, and so on. Thus, in order to judge their magnitudes and to determine which of them is the smallest and which is the greatest, we need only compare their numerators. If we arrange them according to the numbers of these portions, we have

$$\frac{2}{29}, \quad \frac{3}{29}, \quad \frac{7}{29}, \quad \frac{15}{29}, \quad \frac{21}{29}$$

and they are arranged in the order of their magnitude.

We see that of two fractions with the same denominator, that fraction whose numerator is greater is the greater fraction.

Now let us consider the second case, that is, fractions whose numerators are the same, but whose denominators are different. Let us examine the following fractions:

$$\frac{4}{5}, \quad \frac{4}{9}, \quad \frac{4}{13}, \quad \frac{4}{25}, \quad \frac{4}{49}.$$

In this case the denominators are not equal. The greater the denominator of a fraction, the greater the number of equal portions into which unity (1) is subdivided. The more equal portions there are in unity, the smaller these portions are. Any number of big equal portions is a greater quantity than the same number of smaller equal portions. From this reasoning it follows that, in this case, a fraction with a greater denominator will be smaller than a fraction with a smaller denominator. Thus the above fractions, arranged in order of their magnitude (beginning with the smallest fraction), are:

$$\frac{4}{49}, \quad \frac{4}{25}, \quad \frac{4}{13}, \quad \frac{4}{9}, \quad \frac{4}{5}.$$

We see that of two fractions with the same numerator, that fraction whose denominator is smaller is the greater fraction.

Until we can establish a general rule for comparing any two fractions, let us consider the case of fractions whose numerators and denominators, though all different, are such that for each fraction the following difference is present:

$$\text{denominator} - \text{numerator} = 1,$$

as, for example,

$$\frac{2}{3}, \quad \frac{13}{14}, \quad \frac{23}{24}, \quad \frac{49}{50}, \quad \frac{89}{90}.$$

In order to compare the magnitudes of fractions of this kind, let us examine two of them, say $\frac{23}{24}$ and $\frac{89}{90}$. Note that each of these two fractions differs from unity (1) by a fraction whose numerator is 1 and whose denominator is denominator of the fraction. Thus the first fraction differs from unity by $\frac{1}{24}$ and the second fraction differs from unity by $\frac{1}{90}$. Comparing the two differences, we find that $\frac{1}{24}$ is greater than $\frac{1}{90}$. Thus, the second fraction is closer to unity, and hence it is greater; that is, $\frac{89}{90}$ is greater than $\frac{23}{24}$.

PROBLEMS

311. Arrange the following fractions in the order of their magnitudes (begin with the smallest):

$$\frac{8}{97}, \quad \frac{19}{97}, \quad \frac{2}{97}, \quad \frac{31}{97}, \quad \frac{47}{97}, \quad \frac{3}{97}, \quad \frac{67}{97}, \quad \frac{91}{97}.$$

312. Arrange the following fractions in the order of their magnitudes (begin with the greatest):

$$\frac{13}{77}, \quad \frac{13}{28}, \quad \frac{13}{14}, \quad \frac{13}{17}, \quad \frac{13}{29}, \quad \frac{13}{93}, \quad \frac{13}{18}, \quad \frac{13}{85}.$$

313. Arrange the following fractions in the order of their magnitudes (begin with the greatest):

$$\frac{13}{137}, \quad \frac{27}{137}, \quad \frac{81}{137}, \quad \frac{5}{137}, \quad \frac{37}{137}, \quad \frac{49}{137}, \quad \frac{72}{137}, \quad \frac{115}{137}.$$

314. Arrange the following fractions in the order of their magnitudes (begin with the smallest):

$$\frac{57}{65}, \quad \frac{57}{59}, \quad \frac{57}{89}, \quad \frac{57}{112}, \quad \frac{57}{137}, \quad \frac{57}{91}, \quad \frac{57}{71}, \quad \frac{57}{239}.$$

315. Which of each pair of fractions is the greater: (a) $\frac{17}{18}$ or $\frac{5}{6}$; (b) $\frac{21}{22}$ or $\frac{38}{39}$; (c) $\frac{43}{44}$ or $\frac{57}{58}$; (d) $\frac{74}{75}$ or $\frac{89}{90}$; (e) $\frac{109}{110}$ or $\frac{99}{100}$?

316. Arrange the following fractions in the order of their magnitudes (begin with the smallest):

$$\frac{56}{57}, \quad \frac{34}{35}, \quad \frac{64}{65}, \quad \frac{17}{18}, \quad \frac{89}{90}, \quad \frac{32}{33}, \quad \frac{44}{45}, \quad \frac{71}{72}, \quad \frac{24}{25}.$$

317. Arrange the following fractions in the order of their magnitudes (begin with the greatest):

$$\frac{51}{52}, \quad \frac{15}{16}, \quad \frac{107}{108}, \quad \frac{137}{138}, \quad \frac{67}{68}, \quad \frac{91}{92}, \quad \frac{35}{36}, \quad \frac{63}{64}, \quad \frac{74}{75}.$$

318. What part of a sheet of paper will be obtained if the sheet is cut in two halves, then one half is cut again into two halves, then one of these new parts is in turn cut into two halves, and finally, one of these last parts is cut again into two halves?

319. How many centimeters are there in 0.5 meter, 0.25 meter, 0.75 meter?

320. How many minutes are there in half an hour, one-sixth of an hour, one-tenth of an hour?

321. A ream of paper contains 480 sheets, a quire contains 24 sheets. What part of a ream is a quire? What part of a ream are 5 quires? What part of a ream are 10 quires?

322. A certain length must be divided into the following number of equal parts: 6, 9, and 12. How should this partition be performed with the least number of operations and consecutively?

323. What part of unity is one-tenth of five?

324. What part of a metric ton are: 5 kilograms, 60 kilograms, 200 kilograms, 400 kilograms?

325. What part of a short ton are: 100 pounds, 500 pounds, 1,000 pounds?

326. How many times are the following fractions contained in unity (1)?

$$\frac{1}{2}, \quad \frac{1}{3}, \quad \frac{1}{4}, \quad \frac{1}{5}, \quad \frac{1}{10}, \quad \frac{1}{15}.$$

327. If we erase the denominators, what will happen to the fractions below (How will their magnitude change?):

$$\frac{3}{4}, \quad \frac{5}{9}, \quad \frac{4}{13}, \quad \frac{2}{7}, \quad \frac{8}{25}.$$

12

Properties of
Common Fractions

Dependence of fractions on the magnitudes of the numerators and denominators

When we compared several fractions whose denominators were all the same, we concluded that the fraction whose numerator was smallest was the smallest in magnitude, and conversely, the fraction whose numerator was greatest was the greatest in magnitude (see page 142). In a similar manner, when we compared several fractions whose numerators were all the same, we concluded that the fraction whose denominator was greatest was the smallest in magnitude. The magnitude of a fraction is apparently related in some manner to the magnitude of its numerator and to the magnitude of its denominator.

Suppose we have a fraction, for example $\frac{5}{11}$, and we wish to triple it in magnitude. In other words, we have before us the problem of securing another fraction such that it shall be three times as great as $\frac{5}{11}$. In order to solve this problem we shall recall the fact that a fraction may be considered as containing a number (indicated by its numerator) of parts into which unity or 1 was divided (as indicated by the denominator). Thus in our fraction there are five parts, each equal to one-eleventh. In order to obtain a fraction three times as great we may take three times as many parts as in the original fraction; that is, we may take $3 \cdot 5 = 15$ parts. Hence our new fraction (and the answer to our problem) is

$$\frac{3 \cdot 5}{11} = \frac{15}{11}.$$

However, we may approach the same problem from a different point of view. We know that two fractions having the same numerators may be compared as to their magnitudes by considering their denominators. The fraction whose denominator is smaller will be a greater quantity than the fraction whose denominator is greater. Now, suppose we have the fraction $\frac{5}{12}$ and it is required to multiply it by 4. In order to solve the problem from this point of view, let us recall the fact that a fraction may be considered as a quotient of two numbers. The numerator represents the dividend, and the denominator represents the divisor. Recall (page 71) that the quotient is multiplied (and by the same number) if the divisor is divided by any number. Hence, in order to multiply the fraction by 4, we must divide the denominator by 4 while leaving the numerator unchanged.

We have then

$$\frac{5}{12 \div 4} = \frac{5}{3},$$

which is 4 times the original fraction $\frac{5}{12}$.

Recapitulating, we have learned that:

i. A fraction is multiplied by a certain number if we multiply the numerator by this number and leave the denominator unchanged.

ii. A fraction is multiplied by a certain number if we divide the denominator by this number and leave the numerator unchanged.

In order to divide a fraction by a certain number, we shall employ the results obtained on page 71.

i. A fraction (which can be considered as a quotient) is divided by a certain number if we divide the numerator by this number and leave the denominator unchanged.

ii. A fraction (which can be considered as a quotient) is divided by a certain number

if we multiply the denominator by this number
and leave the numerator unchanged.

For example, the fraction $\frac{3}{4}$ is divided by 3 if we divide the numerator by 3; that is,

$$\frac{3 \div 3}{4} = \frac{1}{4}.$$

Also the fraction $\frac{5}{9}$ is divided by 4 if we multiply the denominator by 4; that is,

$$\frac{5}{9 \cdot 4} = \frac{5}{36}.$$

PROBLEMS

328. Perform the following operations: (a) multiply $\frac{7}{13}$ by 4; (b) multiply $\frac{8}{35}$ by 6; (c) multiply $\frac{21}{26}$ by 5; (d) multiply $\frac{51}{100}$ by 7; (e) multiply $\frac{11}{105}$ by 17.

329. Perform the following operations: (a) divide $\frac{5}{11}$ by 6; (b) divide $\frac{18}{25}$ by 5; (c) divide $\frac{18}{35}$ by 7; (d) divide $\frac{13}{107}$ by 15; (e) divide $\frac{29}{125}$ by 12.

330. Using both methods, perform the following operations: (a) multiply $\frac{5}{18}$ by 3; (b) divide $\frac{25}{64}$ by 5; (c) multiply $\frac{15}{32}$ by 3; (d) divide $\frac{21}{13}$ by 7; (e) multiply $\frac{17}{96}$ by 12.

331. Multiply the following mixed numbers by 6: (a) $4\frac{5}{12}$; (b) $7\frac{2}{25}$; (c) $15\frac{7}{16}$; (d) $5\frac{13}{32}$; (e) $8\frac{17}{64}$. (*Hint:* Change them first into improper fractions.)

332. Divide the following mixed numbers by 8: (a) $9\frac{3}{7}$; (b) $5\frac{14}{25}$; (c) $3\frac{17}{50}$ (d) $1\frac{25}{32}$; (e) $14\frac{19}{64}$. (*Hint:* Change them first into improper fractions.)

The fundamental property of fractions

So far we have considered single changes in fractions. Either a fraction was multiplied (by multiplying the numerator or dividing the denominator) or it was divided (by dividing the numerator or multiplying the denominator). Now we shall examine the effect on a fraction when both the numerator and denominator are subject to multiplication or division at the same time. Here it will be worth while to recall the results obtained on page 147.

Suppose the numerator of a fraction is multiplied by 5 and the denominator is divided by 7. Multiplying the numerator by 5 multiplies the fraction by 5, and dividing the denominator by 7 multiplies the fraction by 7. Thus the double effect is to multiply the fraction by $5 \cdot 7 = 35$.

Suppose the numerator of a fraction is divided by 8 and the denominator of the same fractions is multiplied by 6. Dividing the numerator by 8 divides the fraction by 8. Multiplying the denominator by 6 also divides the fraction by 6. Thus the double effect is to divide the fraction by $8 \cdot 6 = 48$.

For example, let us perform the above operations on the fraction $\frac{8}{35}$. Multiplying the numerator by 5 and dividing the denominator by 7, we have

$$\frac{8 \cdot 5}{35 \div 7} = \frac{40}{5} = 8 \cdot \frac{5}{5} = 8.$$

According to our analysis above, we would expect this operation to be equivalent to multiplying the fraction by $5 \cdot 7 = 35$. Note now that if we multiply the fraction $\frac{8}{35}$ by 35, we have

$$\frac{8 \cdot 35}{35} = 8 \cdot \frac{35}{35} = 8,$$

which substantiates the correctness of our result.

Now suppose that the numerator of a fraction is multiplied by 15 and the denominator of the same fraction is multiplied by 5. Multiplying the numerator by 15 multiplies the fraction by 15. But multiplying the denominator by 5 divides the fraction by 5. The double effect is, then, a multiplication by $15 \div 5 = 3$.

If the numerator is divided, say by 7, and the denominator is divided by 28, then the effect on the fraction is as follows: the division of the numerator results in a corresponding division of of the fraction (by 7), while the division of the denominator results in a multiplication of the fraction (by 28). The entire change is, then, a multiplication of the fraction by $28 \div 7 = 4$.

Let us examine a special case, namely, when the numerator and denominator of a fraction are both multiplied by the same number or when the numerator and denominator of a fraction are both divided by the same number.

Suppose that the denominator and numerator of a fraction are both multiplied, say by 8. The fraction is multiplied by 8 as the numerator is multiplied by 8. But when the denominator is multiplied by 8 the fraction is divided by 8. The effect of these two operations is $8 \div 8 = 1$; that is, the fraction is left unchanged.

Suppose that the denominator and numerator of a fraction are both divided by the same number, say 15. The fraction is divided by 15 as the numerator is divided by 15. But when the denominator is divided by 15, the fraction is multiplied by 15. The effects of these two operations cancel each other, and in the final result the fraction is left unchanged.

From this examination, we arrive at a fundamental property of fractions:

> *i.* Any fraction is unchanged in magnitude if both the numerator and denominator are multiplied by the same number.
>
> *ii.* Any fraction is unchanged in magnitude if both the numerator and denominator are divided by the same number.*

According to this property we may always write

$$\frac{3}{4} = \frac{3 \cdot 5}{4 \cdot 5} = \frac{3 \cdot 16}{4 \cdot 16} = \frac{3 \cdot 75}{4 \cdot 75},$$

$$\frac{3}{4} = \frac{15}{20} = \frac{48}{64} = \frac{225}{300}.$$

* Multiplication or division by zero (0) of both numerator and denominator is not permissible (see pages 37 and 52).

PROBLEMS

333. Complete the following:

Numerator	Denominator	Fraction
Multiplied by 16	Multiplied by 8	?
Multiplied by 8	Multiplied by 16	?
Multiplied by 27	Divided by 3	?
Multiplied by 3	Divided by 27	?
Divided by 4	Multiplied by 20	?
Divided by 20	Multiplied by 4	?
Multiplied by 7	Multiplied by 7	?
Divided by 7	Multiplied by 7	?
Multiplied by 7	Divided by 7	?
Divided by 7	Divided by 7	?
Multiplied by 5	?	Multiplied by 15
Multiplied by 6	?	Divided by 2
Multiplied by 7	?	Divided by 28
Multiplied by 10	?	Unchanged
Divided by 5	?	Divided by 10
Divided by 6	?	Multiplied by 12
Divided by 12	?	Divided by 4
Divided by 15	?	Multiplied by 30
Divided by 3	?	Unchanged
?	Multiplied by 4	Multiplied by 8
?	Multiplied by 5	Multiplied by 3
?	Multiplied by 6	Divided by 6
?	Multiplied by 8	Divided by 4
?	Multiplied by 9	Unchanged
?	Divided by 7	Multiplied by 2
?	Divided by 7	Multiplied by 21
?	Divided by 5	Divided by 5
?	Divided by 5	Multiplied by 5
?	Divided by 5	Unchanged

334. What change will take place if the numerator is multiplied by 5 and the denominator is divided by 27?

335. Write in compact form the fundamental property of a fraction developed on page 150, if its numerator is a and its denominator is b and the number by which they are multiplied is m. Do likewise for the same fraction when its numerator and denominator are divided by m.

336. Change the fraction ⁵⁄₇ into another and equal fraction whose denominator is 91.

337. Change the fraction ¹¹⁄₇ into another and equal fraction whose numerator is 154.

Prime and compound numbers

One of the most important applications of the fundamental property that we are studying is the possibility of converting fractions with different denominators (that is, fractions representing different divisions of unity into equal parts) into fractions with the same denominators. We can think of fractions with different denominators as *fractions of different kinds.* Very often, for example in addition and subtraction of fractions, we cannot perform the operations with fractions unless they are of the same kind. Here we are reminded of the restrictions that are placed on denominate numbers when addition and subtraction are to be performed (see page 136). In order to be able to convert fractions of different kinds readily into fractions of the same kind (that is, fractions with the same denominators), we must understand certain properties of numbers which have not thus far been mentioned. These properties will be examined now.

We know (see page 84) that a number can have several divisors. Numbers whose divisors are only 1 and the number itself are known as prime numbers. Thus 2, 3, 7, 11, 13, 17, 97, 101 are prime numbers. A list of prime numbers is given in the Appendix.

Each number not prime can be represented as a product of some other numbers. For example, 18 can be represented as

$$2 \cdot 9, \quad 2 \cdot 3 \cdot 3, \quad \text{and} \quad 3 \cdot 6.$$

(The factor 1 may be written or may be omitted, because the multiplication by 1 does not affect the product.) Prime numbers do not have any other factors except 1 and the numbers themselves. Thus, numbers that are not prime are known as *compound numbers,* and compound numbers can be represented as products of prime factors; in the case of 18 we have

$$18 = 2 \cdot 3 \cdot 3.$$

Another example will illustrate such a representation:

$$168 = 2 \cdot 2 \cdot 2 \cdot 3 \cdot 7.$$

This may also be written as

$$168 = 2^3 \cdot 3 \cdot 8.$$

How may we most quickly discover the prime factors of any compound number, that is, decompose it into its prime factors? This operation is usually performed as follows:

288	2
144	2
72	2
36	2
18	2
9	3
3	3
1	

Note that we start with the smallest prime number, 2, and divide the number and all the consecutive quotients by it until we obtain an odd quotient. Then we try 3 as a divisor of this quotient, now a dividend. In the above example it happens that the dividend is 9 and is divisible by 3. If it were not 9 and not divisible by 3, we should have had to try 5, 7, 11, 13, and all other prime numbers until we found a divisor. Naturally, if a dividend is prime we have to divide by this prime number, and this division completes the decomposition. For example:

357	3
119	7
17	17
1	

Thus the two numbers decomposed above can be represented as products of prime factors as follows:

$$288 = 2 \cdot 2 \cdot 2 \cdot 2 \cdot 2 \cdot 3 \cdot 3 = 2^5 \cdot 3^2,$$

and

$$357 = 5 \cdot 7 \cdot 17.$$

Information concerning the primeness or divisibility of numbers is very important in work with fractions. We are not interested in knowing whether or not a number is prime by itself as much as we are interested in knowing whether two or more numbers have a common divisor. Hence we shall extend our definition of prime numbers. Two numbers may be divided by some other number or they may not. For example, 27 and 45 are both divisible by 1, 3 and 9; 56 and 140 are both divisible by 1, 2, 4, 7, 14, and 28. But take the two numbers 18 and 35. They are both divisible by 1, but they are not both divisible by any other number. Such sets of numbers as 18 and 35 are called *prime to one another;* they do not have any common divisor except 1.

PROBLEMS

338. Which of these numbers are prime to one another: 28, 39, 72, 119, 599, 605, 215?

339. Find the prime divisors of the following numbers: 180, 400, 550, 1,712, 8,146, 2,864, 1,984, 4,608.

340. Decompose the following numbers into their prime factors: 100, 1,000, 10,000, 100,000, 300, 5,220, 15,360, 3,240, 10,368, 2,257, 1,902, 10,395, 41,472.

The greatest common divisor

When two numbers are considered with respect to their divisibility by some divisors, we are generally concerned with the question: Which of the divisors are common to the two numbers? Furthermore, from this arises another question which has direct application to the work with fractions: What is the greatest number by which these two numbers are divisible? This greatest number is known as the *greatest common divisor* of the two numbers.

In order to obtain the greatest common divisor of two numbers it is necessary first to decompose the two into their prime factors, for example:

$$144 = 2 \cdot 2 \cdot 2 \cdot 2 \cdot 3 \cdot 3 = 2^4 \cdot 3^2;$$
$$600 = 2 \cdot 2 \cdot 2 \cdot 3 \cdot 5 \cdot 5 = 2^3 \cdot 3 \cdot 5^2.$$

From these two decompositions we select those factors that are common to the two numbers. If we consider 2 we observe that in 144 this number occurs as a factor 4 times while in the number 600 it occurs as a factor 3 times. Thus 2 occurs as a common factor 3 times. The next number is 3. In 144 it occurs twice while in 600 it occurs only once. Thus 3 is a common factor only once. The next number is 5. It does not occur as a factor in 144 at all; for our purpose it must be discarded. There being no other prime factors left, we have $2^3 \cdot 3 = 24$ as the greatest common factor, which is the greatest common divisor of the two numbers.

Note that when the two numbers 144 and 600 are divided by their greatest common divisor, the two quotients obtained are prime to one another. Indeed,

$$144 \div 24 = 6, \quad \text{and} \quad 600 \div 24 = 25,$$

and 6 and 25 have no common divisor except 1.

The greatest common divisor of three or more numbers is obtained in the same manner as the greatest common divisor of two numbers. For example, consider the numbers 660, 1,080, 1,200, and 1,500. We have:

$$660 = 2 \cdot 2 \cdot 3 \cdot 5 \cdot 11 \qquad = 2^2 \cdot 3 \cdot 5 \cdot 11;$$
$$1,080 = 2 \cdot 2 \cdot 2 \cdot 3 \cdot 3 \cdot 3 \cdot 5 = 2^3 \cdot 3^3 \cdot 5;$$
$$1,200 = 2 \cdot 2 \cdot 2 \cdot 2 \cdot 3 \cdot 5 \cdot 5 = 2^4 \cdot 3 \cdot 5^2;$$
$$1,500 = 2 \cdot 2 \cdot 3 \cdot 5 \cdot 5 \cdot 5 \qquad = 2^2 \cdot 3 \cdot 5^3.$$

The greatest common divisor of the four numbers is $2^2 \cdot 3 \cdot 5 = 60$.

PROBLEMS

341. Find the greatest common divisors in each set of numbers:

360, 810, 3,240, and 4,608

15,360, 41,472, and 10,368

980, 1,176, and 1,225

475, 570, 741, and 757

1,008, 1,260, 882, and 1,134

342. Find the common divisors and the greatest common divisor in each set of numbers:

> 96, 84, and 246
>
> 105, 135, and 245
>
> 486, 729, and 1,152
>
> 360, 252, and 746
>
> 224, 168, 280, and 392

Using the greatest common divisor—reduction of fractions

The result obtained in the preceding section, together with the fundamental property of fractions (see page 148), is applied to an operation which reduces a fraction to a form such that its numerator and denominator are prime to one another, that is, the greatest common divisor of the numerator and denominator is eliminated as the result of dividing the two by it.

Performing this reduction brings a fraction to its simplest form. For example, consider the fraction $\frac{312}{390}$. Observe that both the numerator and denominator are even numbers; thus 2 must be a common divisor of the numerator and denominator. After dividing them by 2 we have $\frac{156}{195}$. This new fraction is simpler in form than the other. Now, we must try other prime numbers, such as 3, 5, 7, 11, 13, and so on. After an examination we find that 3 is a common factor of both the numerator and denominator. Performing the divisions, we obtain the fraction $\frac{52}{65}$. Examining the numerator and denominator once more, we find that 13 is a common factor of 52 and 65. After dividing them by 13, we obtain the fraction $\frac{4}{5}$. This last fraction is *in its lowest terms*. Its numerator and denominator are prime to one another; they have only one common divisor now; it is unity (1).

When the numerator and denominator of a fraction are prime to one another a fraction cannot be further reduced, and it is in its lowest terms.

PROBLEMS

343. Which fractions are in their lowest terms: $\frac{17}{68}$, $\frac{23}{93}$, $\frac{36}{144}$, $\frac{56}{336}$, $\frac{98}{21}$, $\frac{39}{104}$, $\frac{75}{525}$, $\frac{144}{363}$, $\frac{215}{634}$?

344. Reduce to their lowest terms the fractions $\frac{12}{18}$, $\frac{14}{35}$, $\frac{15}{35}$, $\frac{22}{140}$, $\frac{7}{140}$, $\frac{125}{355}$, $\frac{24}{66}$, $\frac{32}{72}$, $\frac{36}{92}$, $\frac{75}{90}$, $\frac{27}{63}$.

345. Reduce to their lowest terms the fractions:

$$\frac{840}{1{,}050}, \quad \frac{264}{312}, \quad \frac{255}{285}, \quad \frac{148}{185}, \quad \frac{750}{1{,}125},$$

$$\frac{1{,}000}{42{,}175}, \quad \frac{675}{975}, \quad \frac{1{,}008}{1{,}224}, \quad \frac{1{,}188}{1{,}485}.$$

346. Change the following fractions into mixed numbers with the fractions in their lowest terms: $\frac{12}{8}$, $\frac{6}{4}$, $\frac{30}{25}$, $\frac{48}{18}$, $\frac{95}{85}$, $\frac{300}{246}$, $\frac{660}{420}$, $\frac{145}{29}$, $\frac{430}{26}$.

347. What part of a yard are 9 inches, 12 inches, 16 inches, 24 inches, 30 inches?

348. What part of a long ton are 100 pounds, 56 pounds, 280 pounds?

349. What part of a pound are 4 ounces, 6 ounces, 8 ounces, 12 ounces?

350. What part of a day are 3 hours, 6 hours, 8 hours?

351. What part of a kilogram are 125 grams, 450 grams, 750 grams?

352. What part of a mile are 132 feet, 3,960 feet, 1,980 feet?

353. Change one-half into fourths, eighths, sixteenths, and thirty-seconds.

354. What part of a long ton is a short ton?

355. What part of a metric ton are 75 kilograms, 125 kilograms, 390 kilograms, 750 kilograms and 800 kilograms?

The least common multiple

When one number is exactly divisible by another, as, for example $56 \div 7 = 8$ or $56 \div 8 = 7$, the quotient is a whole number. However, we may consider this fact from another point of view. We may say that 56 is a *multiple* of 7 or of 8.

Numbers may be arranged in groups according to the prime numbers of which they are multiples. For example, any even numbers,

$$2, 4, 6, 8, 10, 12, 14, 16, 18, 20, 22, 24, \cdots,$$

are multiples of 2, because all even numbers are divisible by 2. All the numbers divisible by 3,

$$3, 6, 9, 12, 15, 18, 21, 24, 27, 30, 33, 36, \cdots,$$

are likewise all multiples of 3.

Note that the two groups above may be obtained in another manner. We may start with 2, add to it 2, and obtain 4. By adding 2 to 4 we obtain 6, and so on. By starting with 3 and adding 3 to it we obtain 6. By adding 3 to 6 we obtain 9, and so on. Using this scheme, we can obtain groups of numbers that are multiples of 5, 6, 7, 8, and all other numbers.

$$5, 10, 15, 20, 25, 30, 35, 40, 45, \cdots,$$
$$6, 12, 18, 24, 30, 36, 42, 48, 54, \cdots,$$
$$7, 14, 21, 28, 35, 42, 49, 56, 63, \cdots,$$
$$\cdots$$

Note that in the above groups of numbers we have certain numbers that repeat themselves; thus, 12, 18, and 24 appear in the lists of multiples of 2, of 3, and of 6. We call them *common* multiples of 2, 3, and 6. If the above groups of multiples were extended far enough we could observe many other numbers that are repeated. Note, however, that 18, for example is divisible by 9, while 12 and 24 are not. Furthermore, 24 is divisible by 8, while 12 and 18 are not. Again 24 is divisible by 12, while 18 is not. The three numbers 12, 18, and 24 are not common multiples of 8, 9, or 12.

What interests us at present is the *smallest number* that is a multiple of two or more given numbers. For example, what is the smallest number that is a multiple of both 9 and 12? We may take the product of these two numbers, that is, $9 \cdot 12 = 108$. But is it the smallest multiple? The examination of 108 shows that it can be represented as the products $2 \cdot 54$ and $3 \cdot 36$. The number 54 is a multiple of 9, but it is not a multiple of 12; 36, however, is a multiple of 9 and of 12, and 36 is less than 108. Thus, by experimenting, we found that the *least common multiple* (another name for the smallest common multiple) of 9 and of 12 is 36. Now we shall work out a general method for obtaining this least common multiple.

The factors of 9 and 12 are

$$9 = 3 \cdot 3, \quad \text{and} \quad 12 = 2 \cdot 2 \cdot 3.$$

From these factors we select those prime numbers which occur the most times in either of the numbers. Thus 3 occurs twice in 9, and 2 occurs twice in 12. Thus, the least common multiple must contain the following factors

$$2 \cdot 2 \cdot 3 \cdot 3 = 36.$$

Let us consider another example and find the least common multiple of the three numbers 48, 80, and 108. We have

$$48 = 2 \cdot 2 \cdot 2 \cdot 2 \cdot 3,$$
$$80 = 2 \cdot 2 \cdot 2 \cdot 2 \cdot 5,$$
$$108 = 2 \cdot 2 \cdot 3 \cdot 3 \cdot 3.$$

Selecting the factors, we take 2 four times, 3 three times, and 5 once. Thus, the least common multiple of the three numbers is:

$$2 \cdot 2 \cdot 2 \cdot 2 \cdot 3 \cdot 3 \cdot 3 \cdot 5 = 2,160.$$

PROBLEMS

356. Find the least common multiples of each of the following sets of numbers:

2, 5, and 25	224 and 288
12, 18, and 30	30, 45, 75, and 81
15, 16, and 18	27, 18, 60, and 90
11, 55, and 33	24, 108, 135, and 216
5, 9, and 16	462, 110, 210, and 231
5, 7, 10, and 28	1, 2, 3, 4, and 5
32, 36, and 48	6, 7, 8, and 9

1, 2, 3, 4, 5, 6, 7, 8, and 9

357. If three numbers are all prime to one another, what is their least common multiple?

358. The least common multiple of 126 and 336 is how many times their greatest common divisor?

Bringing fractions to a common denominator

By means of the procedure for finding the least common multiple we can change fractions of different kinds (that is, fractions with different denominators) into fractions of the same kind (that is, fractions all of whose denominators are the same). This procedure is important when fractions must be added or subtracted; it is known as bringing the fractions to a common denominator.

For example, let us consider the three fractions $\frac{1}{6}$, $\frac{7}{30}$, and $\frac{16}{75}$. Their denominators are all different. In order to compare the magnitudes of these fractions, or in order to add them (if addition is required), we must express them in the same parts of unity. In other words, their denominators must be made equal.

Here we shall recall the fundamental property of fractions (see page 148) which allows the multiplication of the numerator and denominator of a fraction by the same number, since this operation does not change the value of the fraction. In order to obtain a common denominator for the three fractions we shall apply this property, as will be explained below.

Let us obtain the least common multiple of the three denominators, 6, 30, and 75. We have

$$6 = 2 \cdot 3,$$
$$30 = 2 \cdot 3 \cdot 5,$$
$$75 = 3 \cdot 5 \cdot 5.$$

The least common multiple is then

$$2 \cdot 3 \cdot 5 \cdot 5 = 150.$$

In order to change the fraction $\frac{1}{6}$ into a fraction whose denominator is 150, we must multiply the denominator by $150 \div 6 = 25$. But if we multiply the denominator of the fraction by 25 we must, in order to keep the value of the fraction unchanged, multiply the numerator of the fraction by 25. Thus we have

$$\frac{1}{6} = \frac{1 \cdot 25}{6 \cdot 25} = \frac{25}{150}.$$

In a similar manner, if we wish to change the fraction $\frac{7}{30}$ into a fraction whose denominator is 150, we must multiply the denominator by $150 \div 30 = 5$. But if we multiply the denominator of the fraction by 5 we must also, in order to keep the value of the fraction unchanged, multiply the numerator of the fraction by 5. We then have

$$\frac{7}{30} = \frac{7 \cdot 5}{30 \cdot 5} = \frac{35}{150}.$$

Finally, if we wish to change the fraction $\frac{16}{75}$ into a fraction whose denominator is 150 we must multiply the denominator by $150 \div 75 = 2$. And if we multiply the denominator of the fraction by 2 we must also, in order to keep the value of the fraction unchanged, multiply the numerator of the fraction by 2. We then have

$$\frac{16}{75} = \frac{16 \cdot 2}{75 \cdot 2} = \frac{32}{150}.$$

Thus the three fractions, $\frac{1}{6}$, $\frac{7}{30}$, and $\frac{16}{75}$ are changed into $\frac{25}{150}$, $\frac{35}{150}$, and $\frac{32}{150}$ respectively.

The above procedure illustrates the method for bringing several fractions to a common denominator.

Note that the three changed fractions can now be arranged in the order of their magnitude, as

$$\frac{25}{150}, \quad \frac{32}{150}, \quad \text{and} \quad \frac{35}{150},$$

which corresponds to

$$\frac{1}{6}, \quad \frac{16}{75}, \quad \text{and} \quad \frac{7}{30}.$$

The reader will recall that on page 141 we touched upon the question of comparing the magnitudes of fractions, but then we could not give the complete and final answer to the question. The method for bringing fractions to a common denominator answers this question completely.

PROBLEMS

359. Change the fraction $\frac{3}{4}$ into fractions of the same value whose denominators are 8, 20, 24, 32, 36, 44, 48, 54, 64, 72, 80, 88, and 96.

360. Change the fraction $\frac{2}{5}$ into fractions of the same value whose denominators are 10, 15, 25, 35, 45, 55, 65, 70, 85, and 100.

361. Rewrite the following fractions as fractions of the same value with the denominators 100: $\frac{1}{2}$, $\frac{3}{4}$, $\frac{4}{5}$, $\frac{9}{20}$, $\frac{13}{25}$, $\frac{18}{25}$, $\frac{17}{20}$.

362. Arrange the fractions of each group in the order of their magnitudes: (a) $\frac{3}{4}$, $\frac{9}{15}$, $\frac{3}{5}$, $\frac{2}{3}$, and $\frac{5}{6}$; (b) $\frac{23}{36}$, $\frac{7}{8}$, $\frac{47}{60}$, $\frac{17}{20}$, and $\frac{11}{18}$; (c) $\frac{7}{12}$, $\frac{9}{14}$, $\frac{11}{21}$, and $\frac{23}{42}$; (d) $\frac{5}{14}$, $\frac{11}{21}$, $\frac{13}{32}$, and $\frac{20}{48}$.

363. Bring the fractions of each group to a common denominator: (a) $\frac{1}{12}$ and $\frac{1}{16}$; (b) $\frac{5}{16}$ and $\frac{9}{10}$; (c) $\frac{6}{7}$ and $\frac{17}{19}$; (d) $\frac{13}{18}$ and $\frac{64}{75}$; (e) $\frac{1}{2}$, $\frac{1}{3}$, $\frac{1}{4}$, and $\frac{1}{6}$; (f) $\frac{5}{24}$, $\frac{7}{18}$, $\frac{3}{40}$, and $\frac{13}{20}$; (g) $\frac{3}{20}$, $\frac{7}{8}$, $\frac{1}{5}$, and $\frac{7}{16}$; (h) $\frac{31}{80}$, $\frac{13}{36}$, $\frac{29}{45}$, and $\frac{11}{18}$; (i) $\frac{7}{34}$, $\frac{3}{51}$, $\frac{9}{16}$, and $\frac{7}{24}$; (j) $\frac{49}{100}$, $\frac{241}{250}$, $\frac{17}{40}$, and $\frac{37}{80}$.

364. One worker can complete a certain job in 16 hours, another can complete the same job in 20 hours, while a third can complete it in 24 hours. What part of the job can be completed by each worker in 1 hour? Express the answer in fractions of the same kind.

13

Arithmetic Operations

With Fractions

Addition of fractions

When two or more fractions are to be added, these fractions must represent parts of unity (1) that have the same magnitude, each fraction representing certain quantities of these equal parts respectively. Numerically speaking, this means that all of these fractions must have the same denominators. If they have not, the fractions must be brought to a common denominator.

After the fractions have been brought to a common denominator (whenever necessary), the addition of the fractions is a simple process. Since each fraction represents a certain number of equal parts of unity (1), and since for all the fractions the magnitude of these equal parts is the same, therefore the sum of the fractions should represent the sum of all these numbers of the parts of unity. For example:

$$\frac{3}{25} + \frac{17}{25} + \frac{18}{25} + \frac{21}{25} = \frac{59}{25}.$$

Actually this addition represents the addition of all the numerators of the fractions; the sum of these numerators is the numerator of the resultant fraction, and the denominator of the sum is the same as the common denominator of the addends. In other words, the above addition was performed as follows:

$$\frac{3 + 17 + 18 + 21}{25} = \frac{59}{25}.$$

If the sum of the added fractions is an improper fraction (that is, if the numerator is equal to or is greater than the denominator), then the improper fraction should be converted into a mixed number. Thus the above sum is written as $2\frac{9}{25}$.

If the fractions that are to be added do not have the same denominator, then, before they are added, they must be brought to the same denominator. Suppose the three fractions to be added are

$$\frac{6}{7} + \frac{41}{42} + \frac{5}{12}.$$

These fractions must first be brought to the common denominator. The least common multiple of the three numbers 7, 42, and 12 is 84. The changed fractions then are

$$\frac{6 \cdot 12}{84} + \frac{41 \cdot 2}{84} + \frac{5 \cdot 7}{84},$$

or

$$\frac{72}{84} + \frac{82}{84} + \frac{35}{84} = \frac{72 + 82 + 35}{84} = \frac{189}{84}.$$

This sum is an improper fraction. When it is changed into a mixed number, we have $2\frac{21}{84}$, and after reducing its fractional part we finally obtain the sum $2\frac{1}{4}$.

Very often the fractions that are to be added are mixed numbers. The addition of mixed numbers is performed in two steps. The whole parts are added separately, and the fractional parts are added separately. Then, after the two separate sums have been obtained, they are written together as a mixed number. Very often the sum of the fractional parts is an improper fraction. This improper fraction is changed into a mixed number, and its whole part is added to the sum of the whole parts of the mixed-number addends. The following examples illustrate the addition of mixed numbers.

EXAMPLE.   Obtain the sum of $1\frac{1}{6}$, $4\frac{1}{4}$, and $3\frac{1}{5}$.
The sum of the whole parts is

$$1 + 4 + 3 = 8.$$

The sum of the fractional parts is

$$\frac{1}{6} + \frac{1}{4} + \frac{1}{5}.$$

The common denominator of the fractions is $2 \cdot 2 \cdot 3 \cdot 5 = 60$. Then the new fractions are

$$\frac{10}{60} + \frac{15}{60} + \frac{12}{60} = \frac{37}{60},$$

and the sum of the three mixed number is also a mixed number, $8\frac{37}{60}$.

EXAMPLE. Add the following mixed numbers: $27\frac{13}{15}$, $11\frac{11}{12}$, and $19\frac{11}{20}$.

The sum of the whole parts is

$$27 + 11 + 19 = 57.$$

The sum of the fractional parts is

$$\frac{13}{15} + \frac{11}{12} + \frac{11}{20}.$$

The common denominator of the fractions is $2 \cdot 2 \cdot 3 \cdot 5 = 60$. Then the new fractions are

$$\frac{52}{60} + \frac{55}{60} + \frac{33}{60} = \frac{140}{60}.$$

This last sum is an improper fraction, and it should be changed into a mixed number. We then have $2\frac{20}{60}$. The whole part, 2, of this mixed number is added to 57, the sum of the whole parts of the mixed-number addends; $57 + 2 = 59$, and this sum is the whole part of the final sum. The fractional part $\frac{20}{60}$ can be reduced; the greatest common divisor of the numerator and denominator is 20, hence the fractional part of the sum becomes $\frac{1}{3}$. The sum of the three mixed numbers is therefore $59\frac{1}{3}$.

PROBLEMS

365. Perform the following additions: (a) $\frac{5}{16} + \frac{1}{4}$; (b) $\frac{9}{13} + \frac{1}{143}$; (c) $\frac{7}{10} + \frac{19}{25}$; (d) $\frac{7}{30} + \frac{11}{36}$; (e) $\frac{4}{9} + \frac{13}{15}$.

366. Perform the following additions: (a) $\frac{7}{30} + \frac{2}{15} + \frac{1}{6}$; (b) $\frac{7}{11} + \frac{4}{33} + \frac{3}{4}$; (c) $\frac{2}{9} + \frac{1}{4} + \frac{3}{8}$; (d) $\frac{7}{16} + \frac{19}{80} + \frac{29}{40}$; (e) $\frac{4}{9} + \frac{3}{10} + \frac{1}{2}$.

367. Perform the following additions: (a) $\frac{3}{4} + \frac{5}{8} + \frac{7}{8} + \frac{17}{24}$; (b) $\frac{2}{5} + \frac{8}{15} + \frac{7}{9} + \frac{2}{3}$; (c) $\frac{17}{72} + \frac{31}{63} + \frac{23}{35} + \frac{7}{16}$; (d) $\frac{9}{20} + \frac{59}{180} + \frac{14}{15} + \frac{8}{9} + \frac{23}{30}$; (e) $\frac{9}{10} + \frac{3}{5} + \frac{13}{20} + \frac{24}{25} + \frac{37}{50} + \frac{3}{16}$.

368. Perform the following additions: (a) $3\frac{1}{4} + 1\frac{2}{3}$; (b) $5\frac{1}{2} + \frac{7}{16}$; (c) $7\frac{7}{16} + 5\frac{2}{3}$; (d) $6\frac{7}{15} + 7\frac{5}{12}$; (e) $11\frac{5}{18} + 23\frac{7}{15}$.

369. Perform the following additions: (a) $5\frac{3}{16} + 8 + 17\frac{17}{28}$; (b) $11\frac{3}{4} + 9\frac{29}{30} + 3\frac{1}{8}$; (c) $3\frac{1}{4} + 7\frac{17}{18} + 15\frac{13}{18}$; (d) $13\frac{11}{24} + 15\frac{11}{18} + 19\frac{17}{12}$; (e) $37\frac{14}{15} + 31\frac{7}{12} + 43\frac{17}{20}$.

370. Perform the following additions: (a) $\frac{3}{4} + 17\frac{3}{8} + 31\frac{23}{33} + 39\frac{37}{60}$; (b) $10\frac{57}{80} + 5\frac{42}{48} + 6\frac{15}{32} + 17\frac{65}{88}$; (c) $14\frac{3}{8} + 24\frac{11}{18} + 17\frac{47}{60} + 35\frac{25}{88}$; (d) $4\frac{121}{180} + 3\frac{89}{120} + 5\frac{23}{40} + 7\frac{187}{300}$; (e) $11\frac{41}{150} + 18\frac{37}{120} + 34\frac{7}{8} + 51\frac{13}{40} + 82\frac{3}{5}$.

371. Perform the additions indicated in Problem 370 in some other order and check the commutative property of addition.

372. One worker can perform a certain job in 15 hours, another can complete the same job in 18 hours, while a third can complete it in 12 hours. If all three work together, what part of the job will they all complete in 1 hour?

373. An object dropped from a height falls a distance of $16\frac{1}{10}$ feet during the first second and its speed of falling increases by $32\frac{1}{5}$ feet during every succeeding second. How far will it fall in 5 seconds?

374. What is the weight of a loaded cartridge if the cartridge shell weighs $9\frac{2}{5}$ grams, the charge weighs $3\frac{1}{8}$ grams, and the bullet weighs $9\frac{5}{8}$ grams?

375. Gasoline is pumped into a tank. Three pumps are used. The first can fill the tank in 16 minutes, the second can fill the tank in 15 minutes, and the third can fill the tank in 18 minutes. What part of the tank is filled when the three pumps are operating at the same time for 2 minutes?

376. What will happen to the sum of two numbers if we add $15\frac{1}{3}$ to the first addend and $17\frac{3}{4}$ to the second addend?

377. Explosive powder (black powder) is prepared as a mixture of carbon, sulphur, and a nitrate. How much powder was made if $11\frac{1}{4}$ pounds of carbon, $11\frac{13}{16}$ pounds of sulphur, and $67\frac{1}{2}$ pounds of nitrate were mixed?

Subtraction of fractions

The subtraction of fractions can be performed only when the minuend and the subtrahend are both fractions of the same kind, that is, when their denominators are the same. If the denominators of the two fractions are different, the fractions must be brought to a common denominator before we can proceed with the subtraction.

After the fractions will have been brought to a common denominator (if such an operation is required) the subtraction is

performed.   The numerator of the subtrahend is subtracted from
the numerator of the minuend.   The difference so obtained is
the numerator of the difference of two fractions.   The denominator of the difference is the common denominator of the two frac-
tions.   For example, the difference of two fractions, $\frac{17}{21} - \frac{5}{24}$, is
obtained as follows.

The least common multiple of 21 and 24 is $2 \cdot 2 \cdot 2 \cdot 3 \cdot 7$
$= 168$.   Then the difference of the two fractions is

$$\frac{17 \cdot 8}{168} - \frac{5 \cdot 7}{168} = \frac{136}{168} - \frac{35}{168} = \frac{101}{168}.$$

Actually the subtraction is performed according to the above
description as follows:

$$\frac{136 - 35}{168} = \frac{101}{168}.$$

If the subtraction is to be performed on mixed numbers, the
operation is performed in two steps.   The whole parts of the
mixed numbers are subtracted separately, and the fractional parts
are subtracted separately. · The differences represent the whole
part and the fractional part of the difference respectively.   For
example, the difference of the two mixed numbers $15\frac{13}{18} - 7\frac{4}{21}$
may be obtained as follows:

The difference of the whole parts is

$$15 - 7 = 8.$$

The difference of the fractional parts is

$$\frac{13}{18} - \frac{4}{21}.$$

The common denominator of the fractions is $2 \cdot 3 \cdot 3 \cdot 7 = 126$.
The difference of the fractions is therefore

$$\frac{13 \cdot 7 - 4 \cdot 6}{126} = \frac{91 - 24}{126} = \frac{67}{126},$$

and the difference of the two mixed numbers is $8\frac{67}{126}$.

Very often it may happen that the immediate subtraction of the fractional parts cannot be performed because the subtrahend is greater than the minuend, as in the following example.

$$24\frac{5}{18} - 15\frac{13}{24} = ?$$

The difference of the whole parts is

$$24 - 15 = 9.$$

The common denominator of the two fractions is the product $2 \cdot 2 \cdot 2 \cdot 3 \cdot 3 = 72$. The difference of the two mixed numbers can then be written as

$$9\frac{5 \cdot 4 - 13 \cdot 3}{72} = 9\frac{20 - 39}{72}.$$

We cannot subtract $20 - 39$. However, this difficulty is overcome by borrowing 1 from the whole part, 9. This loan reduces the whole part by 1, and it becomes 8. Then we change the borrowed 1 into $\frac{72}{72}$ and add this fraction's numerator to the minuend, 20; the new minuend is 92. Then the difference of the two mixed numbers is

$$8\frac{92 - 39}{72} = 8\frac{53}{72}.$$

PROBLEMS

378. Perform the following subtractions: (a) $\frac{1}{4} - \frac{1}{9}$; (b) $\frac{4}{9} - \frac{3}{11}$; (c) $\frac{13}{15} - \frac{3}{7}$; (d) $\frac{8}{11} - \frac{5}{12}$; (e) $\frac{3}{4} - \frac{5}{24}$.

379. Perform the following subtractions: (a) $\frac{5}{18} - \frac{11}{90}$; (b) $\frac{5}{6} - \frac{3}{4}$; (c) $\frac{25}{42} - \frac{33}{56}$; (d) $\frac{21}{22} - \frac{31}{33}$; (e) $\frac{80}{91} - \frac{17}{78}$.

380. Perform the following subtractions: (a) $28\frac{3}{4} - 10\frac{2}{7}$; (b) $18\frac{5}{8} - 6\frac{5}{6}$; (c) $75\frac{8}{15} - 12\frac{7}{30}$; (d) $15\frac{19}{27} - 12\frac{11}{36}$; (e) $15\frac{59}{64} - 9\frac{27}{56}$.

381. Perform the following computations:

$(35\frac{41}{48} - 12\frac{53}{72}) - (27\frac{19}{36} - 23\frac{19}{24})$

$(7\frac{5}{9} - 2\frac{19}{21}) - (3\frac{27}{35} - 1\frac{39}{56})$

$25\frac{11}{23} - (18\frac{27}{46} - 6\frac{4}{5})$

$35\frac{11}{35} - [25\frac{7}{8} - (53\frac{1}{3} - 42\frac{5}{12})]$

$[35\frac{4}{45} - (5\frac{3}{8} - 1\frac{13}{15})] - [11\frac{2}{5} - (4\frac{1}{12} - \frac{29}{30})]$.

382. A container and the liquid in it weigh $4\frac{18}{25}$ kilograms. The container weighs $\frac{9}{10}$ kilograms. What is the weight of the liquid?

383. How much must be added to $\frac{1}{10}$ of a number in order to obtain $\frac{1}{2}$ of it?

384. How much must we subtract from $3\frac{2}{3}$ in order to obtain $1\frac{3}{7}$?

385. Perform the following computations:

$$(31\frac{2}{3} - 17\frac{3}{4}) + (18\frac{2}{3} - 15\frac{3}{10}) + (25\frac{1}{4} - 18\frac{13}{18})$$

$$24\frac{3}{4} - (12\frac{2}{3} - 4\frac{7}{8} + 1\frac{5}{12}) + (15\frac{13}{16} - 12\frac{7}{9}) - 5\frac{25}{48}$$

$$7\frac{2}{9} + [15\frac{1}{6} + 3\frac{5}{8} - 12\frac{1}{9} - (27\frac{17}{36} - 25\frac{7}{16})]$$

386. A board whose length is $6\frac{3}{4}$ feet was cut into three pieces. The length of the first piece was $2\frac{1}{2}$ feet. The length of the second piece was $3\frac{1}{4}$ feet. What was the length of the third piece?

387. From a spool of wire 75 yards long two wires, each $12\frac{3}{4}$ yards long, were cut off; then three wires, each $7\frac{2}{3}$ yards, long were cut off. How much wire was left on the spool?

388. A certain job was completed (partly) as follows: During the first week $\frac{4}{15}$ of the job was completed. During the second week $\frac{5}{12}$ of the job was completed. What portion of the job was not completed at the end of two weeks?

389. Three pipes are attached to a tank. Through the first pipe the tank can be filled in 10 hours. Through the second pipe the tank can be filled in 8 hours. The third pipe is used for drawing the water out of the tank, and a full tank can be emptied through it in 5 hours. What portion of the tank will be filled if at the start the tank was empty, and the three pipes were put in operation for 1 hour?

390. How will a sum change if the first addend is increased by $5\frac{3}{8}$, the second addend is increased by $6\frac{7}{9}$, and the third addend is decreased by $7\frac{5}{16}$?

391. How will a difference change if the minuend is increased by $15\frac{5}{8}$, and the subtrahend is decreased by $8\frac{7}{10}$?

392. How will a difference change if the minuend is decreased by $12\frac{3}{16}$, and the subtrahend is increased by $5\frac{7}{20}$?

Multiplication of fractions

The multiplication of fractions must be considered in three special cases:

i. The multiplication of a fraction by a whole number.

ii. The multiplication of a whole number by a fraction.

iii.   The multiplication of a fraction by a fraction.

The multiplication of a fraction by a whole number may be considered as a repeated addition.   The fraction is repeated as an addend as many times as is indicated by the whole number. Thus this kind of multiplication does not differ from the multiplication of whole numbers.   For example, the product $\frac{7}{9} \cdot 6$ is obtained as follows

$$\frac{7}{9} \cdot 6 = \frac{7}{9} + \frac{7}{9} + \frac{7}{9} + \frac{7}{9} + \frac{7}{9} + \frac{7}{9}$$

$$= \frac{7 + 7 + 7 + 7 + 7 + 7}{9} = \frac{7 \cdot 6}{9} = \frac{42}{9}$$

$$= 4\frac{6}{9} = 4\frac{2}{3}.$$

Here we can introduce a short-cut which will lead to multiplication by smaller numbers.   The fraction $\dfrac{7 \cdot 6}{9}$ has in its numerator the number 6 and in the denominator the number 9. These two numbers have a greatest common divisor 3.   Thus, before we proceed with the multiplication (in the numerator) we can reduce the fraction, as follows:

$$\frac{7 \cdot \overset{2}{\cancel{6}}}{\underset{3}{\cancel{9}}} = \frac{7 \cdot 2}{3} = \frac{14}{3}.$$

After the greatest common divisor of the numbers in the numerator and denominator is determined, these two numbers are divided by this divisor.   This division is indicated by a mark / drawn so as to indicate that the number is crossed out; then above the number (in the numerator) and below the number (in the denominator) the respective quotients are written.   Hereafter we shall employ this method of reduction.

The above example shows that *to multiply a fraction by a whole number we multiply the numerator of the fraction by this whole number.* If necessary, a reduction is performed before the product of the numbers in the numerator is obtained. When the multiplication in the numerator is completed, the product so obtained is the numerator of the final result. The denominator of the result is either the denominator of the original fraction or (when reduction has taken place), the quotient of this denominator.

The multiplication of a whole number by a fraction cannot be described as continued addition. It would make no sense to talk about repeating some number as an addend a fractional number of times, say five-sevenths times. We shall, therefore, need another approach to this problem.

Suppose that we wish to multiply 24 by $\frac{1}{6}$. Now the fraction $\frac{1}{6}$ has a definite meaning; it represents one-sixth of unity (1). In other words, one-sixth is obtained as a result of dividing 1 by 6 (see page 138). In a similar manner one-sixth of 2 is obtained by dividing 2 by 6, that is, we obtain $\frac{2}{6}$. Also one-sixth of 8 is obtained by dividing 8 by 6, and we obtain $\frac{8}{6}$. But note that $\frac{2}{6}$ can be obtained by multiplying $\frac{1}{6}$ by 2, and $\frac{8}{6}$ can be obtained by multiplying $\frac{1}{6}$ by 8.

The reader should recall that when we examined the properties of multiplication of whole numbers we arrived at the commutative property of multiplication (see page 35), that the product of two or more whole numbers is not changed if we change the order of the factors. This property should hold in the case of fractions also. That it does hold can be seen from the following. Note that a fraction represents a quotient resulting from division. Thus, the fraction $\frac{1}{6}$ represents the division of 1 by 6. We can write it as $(1 \div 6)$, as was mentioned on page 138. Then the product of 24 multiplied by $\frac{1}{6}$ can be written as $24 \cdot (1 \div 6)$, and we know how to perform this operation. The result is $\frac{24}{6}$. But this result is the same as if we had multiplied $\frac{1}{6}$ by 24.

Thus, in order *to multiply a whole number by a fraction we multiply the whole number by the numerator of the fraction and write the product as the numerator of a greater fraction having the same denominator.*

For example, the multiplication $15 \cdot \frac{17}{75}$ is performed as follows:

$$\frac{\overset{1}{\cancel{15}} \cdot 17}{\underset{5}{\cancel{75}}} = \frac{17}{5} = 3\frac{2}{5}.$$

Multiplication when the two factors are a mixed number and a whole number may be performed as above if the mixed number is converted into an improper fraction. For example, the product of 36 and $3\frac{7}{27}$ may be obtained as follows:

$$36 \cdot \frac{88}{27} = \frac{\overset{4}{\cancel{36}} \cdot 88}{\underset{3}{\cancel{27}}} = \frac{352}{3} = 117\frac{1}{3}.$$

The multiplication of a whole number by a fraction may also be explained as the obtaining of a portion of the number indicated by the denominator of the fraction, and then repeating this portion as an addend (multiplying it) as indicated by the numerator of the fraction. For example, multiply 72 by $\frac{5}{9}$. We obtain one-ninth of 72, by means of division, $72 \div 9 = 8$. Then we multiply 8 by 5: $8 \cdot 5 = 40$. Note that we obtain the same result when we perform the multiplication as follows:

$$72 \cdot \frac{5}{9} = \frac{\overset{8}{\cancel{72}} \cdot 5}{\underset{1}{\cancel{9}}} = \frac{8 \cdot 5}{1} = \frac{40}{1} = 40.$$

Here we also obtained a very important result: a whole number may be written as a fraction whose numerator is equal to the whole number and whose denominator is 1.

The multiplication of a fraction by a fraction may now be considered. In this case we shall make use of the results obtained in studying multiplication when one factor is a whole number and the other is a fraction.

Suppose that we wish to multiply $\frac{5}{6}$ and $\frac{7}{9}$. The multiplication by $\frac{7}{9}$ may be thought of as the combination of division by 9 (obtaining a ninth part) and then, after this is performed, multiplication by 7. Thus, we first must obtain a ninth part of $\frac{5}{6}$. This ninth part must be a fraction such that multiplying it by 9 yields $\frac{5}{6}$. We know (see page 143) that the denominator of such a fraction must be greater than 6; it is $6 \cdot 9 = 54$. Thus a ninth part of $\frac{5}{6}$ is $\frac{5}{54}$. Next, this fraction $\frac{5}{54}$ must be multiplied by 7. We then have

$$\frac{5 \cdot 7}{54} = \frac{35}{54}.$$

Thus we see that *in the multiplication of two fractions the numerators are multiplied separately and the denominators are also multiplied separately. The product of the numerators is the numerator of the fraction representing the product, and the product of the denominators is the denominator of the fraction representing the product.* For example:

$$\frac{5}{6} \cdot \frac{7}{9} = \frac{5 \cdot 7}{6 \cdot 9} = \frac{35}{54}.$$

All the possible reductions should be performed before the actual multiplication takes place. Doing so will simplify the numerical work in multiplication. For example, let us multiply the two fractions $\frac{18}{65}$ and $\frac{52}{81}$:

$$\frac{18}{65} \cdot \frac{52}{81} = \frac{18 \cdot 52}{65 \cdot 81}.$$

Here let us recall the fact that if a product of two or more numbers is divisible by some number then one of the factors is divisible (not necessarily one; there may be several) by this number (see page 90). This fact is important when we shall reduce the fraction before multiplication takes place. Note that in the present operation 18 and 81 have a greatest common divisor 9, and 52 and 65 have a greatest common divisor 13. The reduction is

$$\frac{\overset{2}{\cancel{18}} \cdot \overset{4}{\cancel{52}}}{\underset{5}{\cancel{65}} \cdot \underset{9}{\cancel{81}}} = \frac{2 \cdot 4}{5 \cdot 9} = \frac{8}{45}.$$

Mixed numbers may be multiplied in this way if they are changed into improper fractions before the multiplication is performed. For example:

$$3\frac{5}{9} \cdot 4\frac{7}{8} = \frac{32}{9} \cdot \frac{39}{8} = \frac{\overset{4}{\cancel{32}} \cdot \overset{13}{\cancel{39}}}{\underset{3}{\cancel{9}} \cdot \underset{1}{\cancel{8}}} = \frac{4 \cdot 13}{3} = \frac{52}{3} = 17\frac{1}{3}.$$

Note that 32 and 8 have a greatest common divisor 8, and 39 and 9 have a greatest common divisor 3. After the multiplication was performed we changed the improper fraction $\frac{52}{3}$ into a mixed number.

The three multiplication cases described on page 170 and studied above can be written down in compact form as follows:

$$\frac{a}{b} \cdot c = \frac{a \cdot c}{b}. \qquad (i)$$

$$a \cdot \frac{c}{b} = \frac{a \cdot c}{b}. \qquad (ii)$$

$$\frac{a}{b} \cdot \frac{c}{d} = \frac{a \cdot c}{b \cdot d}. \qquad (iii)$$

Here all the letters, a, b, c, and d represent whole numbers.

PROBLEMS

393. Perform the following multiplications: (a) $\frac{2}{5} \cdot 7$; (b) $\frac{15}{34} \cdot 17$; (c) $\frac{5}{6} \cdot 35$; (d) $\frac{9}{15} \cdot 3$; (e) $\frac{11}{15} \cdot 25$; (f) $\frac{15}{68} \cdot 17$; (g) $\frac{42}{95} \cdot 19$; (h) $\frac{55}{123} \cdot 82$; (i) $\frac{81}{91} \cdot 13$; (j) $\frac{9}{14} \cdot 35$.

394. Perform the following multiplications: (a) $4\frac{5}{12} \cdot 6$; (b) $3\frac{13}{15} \cdot 5$; (c) $5\frac{3}{22} \cdot 11$; (d) $6\frac{53}{84} \cdot 24$; (e) $2\frac{15}{34} \cdot 17$.

395. Perform the following multiplications: (a) $2 \cdot \frac{1}{32}$; (b) $15 \cdot \frac{17}{25}$; (c) $7 \cdot \frac{23}{49}$; (d) $85 \cdot \frac{19}{68}$; (e) $19 \cdot \frac{75}{114}$.

396. Perform the following multiplications: (a) $3 \cdot 5\frac{17}{18}$; (b) $17 \cdot 3\frac{16}{51}$; (c) $21 \cdot 15\frac{31}{86}$; (d) $4 \cdot 15\frac{4}{8}$; (e) $3 \cdot 1\frac{17}{51}$.

397. Perform the following multiplications: (a) $\frac{5}{27} \cdot \frac{18}{35}$; (b) $\frac{13}{63} \cdot \frac{42}{65}$; (c) $\frac{17}{18} \cdot \frac{21}{85}$; (d) $\frac{15}{91} \cdot \frac{84}{125}$; (e) $\frac{22}{25} \cdot \frac{16}{33}$.

398. Perform the following multiplications: (a) $1\frac{1}{3} \cdot 3\frac{1}{4}$; (b) $3\frac{3}{8} \cdot 4\frac{7}{8}$; (c) $18\frac{2}{3} \cdot 1\frac{2}{11}$; (d) $5\frac{1}{4} \cdot 8\frac{1}{11}$; (e) $17\frac{5}{6} \cdot 3\frac{3}{7}$; (f) $21\frac{7}{12} \cdot 11\frac{5}{7}$; (g) $15\frac{5}{16} \cdot 7\frac{9}{32}$.

399. Perform the following multiplications:

$\frac{3}{4} \cdot \frac{5}{6} \cdot \frac{8}{15}$

$\frac{4}{5} \cdot \frac{3}{8} \cdot \frac{3}{4} \cdot \frac{3}{4} \cdot \frac{2}{3}$

$2\frac{1}{2} \cdot 5\frac{2}{3} \cdot 2\frac{1}{11}$

$\frac{5}{14} \cdot 2\frac{2}{25} \cdot \frac{7}{12} \cdot 7\frac{1}{5} \cdot 2\frac{7}{10}$

$4\frac{2}{7} \cdot \frac{56}{135} \cdot 22\frac{10}{11} \cdot 3\frac{3}{8} \cdot \frac{25}{28}$

400. Perform the following computations:

$(\frac{3}{4} + \frac{5}{6}) \cdot 3 + (\frac{5}{6} - \frac{3}{4}) \cdot 4$

$(2\frac{3}{8} + 1\frac{5}{7}) \cdot 14 - (2\frac{1}{2} - \frac{3}{8}) \cdot 4$

$(1\frac{4}{9} + 2\frac{5}{8} - \frac{11}{12}) \cdot (2\frac{1}{2} - \frac{11}{14})$

$(\frac{4}{5} + \frac{1}{6}) \cdot (23\frac{2}{3} - 15\frac{5}{9}) \cdot \frac{45}{58}$

$[(3\frac{2}{5} + 1\frac{7}{10}) \cdot 1\frac{3}{17} - (2\frac{7}{23} - 1\frac{45}{46}) \cdot \frac{69}{80}] \cdot 1\frac{1}{3}$

Applications of the multiplication of fractions

By means of the multiplication of fractions certain problems in arithmetic may be solved. The nature of these problems is directly associated with the nature of fractions.

The meaning of a fraction, when considered numerically, is that it represents a certain number of equal parts of unity, and the total number of these parts into which unity was divided is indicated by the denominator of the fraction. Thus the fraction $\frac{3}{7}$ indicates that unity was divided into seven parts and three of these parts were taken, and thus we have three-sevenths of unity.

If we multiply a whole number, a mixed number, or a proper fraction by a fraction we obtain a portion of the whole number, or of the mixed number, or of the proper fraction. Thus, multiplication by a fraction is a process by means of which we may obtain a portion (indicated by the fraction) of some given quantity. For example $\frac{3}{4}$ of 16, or of $2\frac{2}{5}$, or of $\frac{16}{21}$ are:

$$\frac{\overset{4}{\cancel{16}} \cdot 3}{\underset{1}{\cancel{4}}} = 12, \qquad \frac{\overset{3}{\cancel{12}} \cdot 3}{5 \cdot \underset{1}{\cancel{4}}} = \frac{9}{5} = 1\frac{4}{5}, \qquad \text{and} \qquad \frac{\overset{4}{\cancel{16}} \cdot \overset{1}{\cancel{3}}}{\underset{7}{\cancel{21}} \cdot \underset{1}{\cancel{4}}} = \frac{4}{7}.$$

respectively.

PROBLEMS

401. The production of a dairy farm is 8,240 gallons of milk daily. Of this production, $\frac{5}{8}$ is shipped to a pasteurizing plant. How many gallons are shipped daily?

402. The sugar content of sugar beets is $\frac{4}{19}$ of the weight of the raw beets. How much sugar is contained in 6,890 short tons of sugar beets?

403. A Fahrenheit degree is equal to $\frac{5}{9}$ of a Centigrade degree. How many Fahrenheit degrees are equivalent to 65 Centigrade degrees?

404. The circumference of a circle is approximately equal to $3\frac{1}{7}$ times its diameter. What is the circumference of a circle whose diameter is 2 feet? $35\frac{1}{2}$ feet?

405. Walking at the rate of about $3\frac{1}{8}$ miles per hour, a man walked 2 hours and 12 minutes. How far did he walk? (*Hint:* Convert the minutes into a fraction of an hour.)

406. A wire 69 yards long was cut into three pieces as follows: The first piece was $\frac{1}{4}$ of the entire length. The second piece was $\frac{8}{9}$ of what was left after the first piece was cut off. What were the lengths of the three pieces of wire?

407. In 3 hours and 20 minutes a tank was emptied through two pipes opened at the same time. The flow of liquid through the first pipe was $\frac{4}{5}$ of a gallon per minute, while the flow through the second pipe was $\frac{3}{4}$ of that of the first pipe. What amount of liquid was in the tank?

408. Three workers were assigned at the same time to do a certain job. The first worker could complete the job alone in 8 days, the second could complete it in 10 days, and the third could complete it in 12 days. What part of the job remained to be completed after they worked 3 days together?

409. Two trains leave two stations at the same time and travel toward one another. One train can cover the distance between the two stations in 45 minutes, while the second train can cover this distance in 72 minutes. What part of the total distance will be covered by the two trains during the first 10 minutes after departure?

Division of fractions

The division of fractions must be considered in three special cases:

    i. The division of a fraction by a whole number.

    ii. The division of a whole number by a fraction.

    iii. The division of a fraction by a fraction.

Division of a fraction by a whole number. We have already learned two ways to accomplish this computation (page 147): *A fraction is divided by a certain number if we divide the numerator by this number and leave the denominator unchanged. A fraction is likewise divided by a certain number if we leave the numerator unchanged and multiply the denominator by the number given.* The division of $\frac{2}{3}$ by 7, then, can be performed in either of two ways:

$$\frac{2}{3} \div 7 = \frac{2 \div 7}{3} \qquad \text{or} \qquad \frac{2}{3} \div 7 = \frac{2}{3 \cdot 7} = \frac{2}{21}.$$

The choice between these two ways must be made by the computer according to convenience in the problem at hand. The method at the right is the simplest because it involves multiplication, which can always be performed upon whole numbers, while not all divisions can be performed exactly.

If the fraction that is to be divided by a whole number is part of a mixed number, the dividend may first be converted into an improper fraction before the division can take place. Thus, for example, the division of $7\frac{11}{15}$ by 8 is performed as follows:

$$7\frac{11}{15} \div 8 = \frac{116}{15} \div 8 = \frac{\overset{29}{\cancel{116}}}{15 \cdot \underset{2}{\cancel{8}}} = \frac{29}{30}.$$

Note that in this case, just as in the case of the multiplication of fractions, we first reduce the fraction, if possible.

We then see that the division of a fraction by a whole number is most simply performed as follows: We keep the numerator of the dividend unchanged, but we multiply the denominator of the dividend by the divisor.

Division of a fraction or whole number by a fraction. The reader will recall that in the preceding section we found that any whole number may be written as a fraction whose denominator is 1, and whose numerator is the whole number. If we keep this in mind we can combine the cases *(ii)* and *(iii)* and examine the division of a fraction by a fraction only.

In order to work out a method for dividing a fraction by a fraction, let us recall the language used in division. We learned in Chapter 5 that

$$\text{dividend} \div \text{divisor} = \text{quotient.}$$

Using these definitions, we also learned that

$$\text{quotient} \cdot \text{divisor} = \text{dividend.}$$

We shall use this fact to obtain a method for turning the operation of division into multiplication.

Suppose we wish to divide the dividend $\frac{2}{3}$ by the divisor $\frac{5}{7}$. We do not know the quotient, so we will represent it by the letter q. Then:

$$\frac{2}{3} \div \frac{5}{7} = q$$

and

$$q \cdot \frac{5}{7} = \frac{2}{3}.$$

If two quantities are equal to each other and we multiply them by the same number, then the two products are equal to each other. Let us multiply both of our two equal quantities by 7:

$$\frac{7 \cdot q \cdot 5}{7} = \frac{7 \cdot 2}{3}.$$

If two quantities are equal to each other and we divide them by the same number, then the two quotients are equal to each other. Let us divide both of our two equal quantities by 5, using the method we have just learned, that is, multiplying the divisors by 5. Thus:

$$\frac{7 \cdot q \cdot 5}{5 \cdot 7} = \frac{7 \cdot 2}{5 \cdot 3}.$$

Now let us reduce the fraction on the left:

$$\frac{7 \cdot q \cdot \overset{1}{\cancel{5}}}{\underset{1}{\cancel{5}} \cdot \underset{1}{\cancel{7}}} = \frac{7 \cdot 2}{5 \cdot 3}, \quad \text{or} \quad q = \frac{7 \cdot 2}{5 \cdot 3}.$$

Returning to the statement of the problem with which we began:

$$\frac{2}{3} \div \frac{5}{7} = q = \frac{7 \cdot 2}{5 \cdot 3} = \frac{14}{15}.$$

Note, however, that $\dfrac{2 \cdot 7}{3 \cdot 5}$ can be represented as the product of two fractions:

$$\frac{2}{3} \cdot \frac{7}{5}.$$

The first factor, $\frac{2}{3}$ is the dividend. But the second factor is the divisor $\frac{5}{7}$ written, so to speak, upside down—the numerator and denominator of the divisor have changed places. We call this way of writing the fraction *inverting* it.

Thus the division of a fraction by a fraction is performed as follows: *Multiply the dividend by the inverted (written upside down) divisor.* If there is a chance to perform reduction, it should be done before the final multiplication should take place. If the quotient is an improper fraction it should be changed into a mixed number.

The division of a whole number by a fraction is thus performed as a multiplication of the whole number by the inverted divisor. For example,

$$15 \div \frac{6}{7} = \frac{\overset{5}{\cancel{15}} \cdot 7}{\underset{2}{\cancel{6}}} = \frac{5 \cdot 7}{2} = \frac{35}{2} = 17\frac{1}{2}.$$

Should the dividend, or the divisor, or both the dividend and the divisor be mixed numbers, they may be first changed into improper fractions before the division is performed. After the mixed numbers have been changed into improper fractions we can proceed with the division. For example,

$$6\frac{2}{3} \div 3\frac{1}{5} = \frac{20}{3} \div \frac{16}{5} = \frac{\overset{5}{\cancel{20}} \cdot 5}{3 \cdot \underset{4}{\cancel{16}}} = \frac{5 \cdot 5}{3 \cdot 4} = \frac{25}{12} = 2\frac{1}{12}.$$

The three division cases can be written down in compact form as follows:

$$\frac{a}{b} \div c = \frac{a}{b \cdot c}. \tag{i}$$

$$a \div \frac{b}{c} = \frac{a \cdot c}{b}. \tag{ii}$$

$$\frac{a}{b} \div \frac{c}{d} = \frac{a}{b} \cdot \frac{d}{c} = \frac{a \cdot d}{b \cdot c}. \tag{iii}$$

PROBLEMS

Perform the following divisions:

410. (a) $\frac{8}{11} \div 4$; (b) $\frac{7}{9} \div 14$; (c) $\frac{27}{32} \div 63$; (d) $\frac{18}{25} \div 12$; (e) $\frac{8}{27} \div 16$.

411. (a) $4\frac{2}{3} \div 7$; (b) $7\frac{3}{5} \div 57$; (c) $4\frac{2}{3} \div 7$; (d) $10\frac{7}{8} \div 9$; (e) $4\frac{2}{3} \div 21$.

412. (a) $12 \div \frac{3}{4}$; (b) $18 \div \frac{54}{61}$; (c) $32 \div \frac{24}{25}$; (d) $8 \div \frac{5}{7}$; (e) $15 \div \frac{4}{15}$.

413. (a) $1 \div 2\frac{1}{2}$; (b) $18 \div 2\frac{1}{4}$; (c) $10 \div 1\frac{7}{8}$; (d) $35 \div 2\frac{4}{5}$; (e) $175 \div 8\frac{1}{8}$.

414. (a) $\frac{5}{8} \div \frac{4}{9}$; (b) $\frac{7}{6} \div \frac{11}{36}$; (c) $\frac{35}{48} \div \frac{21}{32}$; (d) $\frac{51}{64} \div \frac{68}{75}$; (e) $\frac{29}{30} \div \frac{7}{50}$.

415. (a) $1\frac{2}{3} \div 3\frac{1}{2}$; (b) $4\frac{2}{3} \div \frac{5}{23}$; (c) $\frac{2}{3} \div 1\frac{1}{4}$; (d) $15\frac{7}{24} \div 3\frac{7}{120}$; (e) $38\frac{19}{80} \div 231\frac{4}{5}$; (f) $6\frac{11}{25} \div \frac{15}{36}$; (g) $1\frac{5}{184} \div 31\frac{4}{11}$; (h) $68\frac{17}{18} \div 8\frac{1}{18}$; (i) $8\frac{2}{3} \div 11\frac{13}{19}$; (j) $12\frac{3}{5} \div 1\frac{1}{20}$.

416. Perform the following computations:

$$2\frac{3}{4} \div \left(1\frac{1}{2} - \frac{2}{3}\right) + \left(\frac{3}{4} + \frac{5}{6}\right) \div 3\frac{1}{6}$$

$$\left(\frac{2}{15} + 1\frac{7}{12}\right) \cdot \frac{30}{103} - \left(2 \div 2\frac{1}{4}\right) \cdot \frac{9}{32}$$

$$3\frac{1}{8} \div \left[\left(4\frac{5}{12} - 3\frac{1}{4}\right) \cdot \frac{4}{7} + \left(3\frac{1}{18} - 2\frac{7}{12}\right) \cdot 1\frac{10}{17}\right]$$

$$\left[\left(\frac{5}{6} - \frac{3}{8}\right) \div \frac{3}{4} - \left(\frac{3}{8} + \frac{7}{20}\right) \div 1\frac{9}{20}\right] \div \frac{1}{50}$$

$$\left\{\left[\left(\frac{17}{24} + \frac{9}{40}\right) - \left(\frac{11}{48} + \frac{31}{80}\right)\right] \div 3\frac{4}{5}\right\} \div 1\frac{5}{7}$$

Applications of the division of fractions

Since division is an operation that is opposite to multiplication the problems that require the application of the division of fractions or the division by fractions are opposite to the problems in multiplication of fractions. The multiplication of fractions leads to the solution of problems in which a part of a quantity is obtained according to a given fraction. Problems requiring division lead to the finding of the total quantity if a portion of it is given and the fraction describing this portion is stated. For example: If $\frac{3}{7}$ of a number is 15, what is the number? Let us solve this problem in detail. If $\frac{3}{7}$ of a number is 15, then $\frac{1}{7}$ is $\frac{15}{3}$, and $\frac{7}{7}$ is $\frac{15 \cdot 7}{3} = 35$. Note that here we divided 15 by $\frac{3}{7}$.

Such problems may be stated in many ways. A number of these are found in the problems below. These problems belong to the type wherein the total quantity is found from a given portion of it.

PROBLEMS

417. What number must be multiplied by $\frac{5}{9}$ in order to obtain $7\frac{1}{2}$?

418. By what must we multiply the difference of the numbers $4\frac{1}{6}$ and $3\frac{1}{5}$ in order to obtain their sum?

419. What number must be divided by $\frac{2}{3}$ in order to obtain $6\frac{3}{4}$?

420. A worker completed $\frac{4}{5}$ of his assignment, but had 32 pieces left to work on. How many pieces were in his assignment?

421. Two toolmakers worked on a certain job. One completed $\frac{3}{7}$ of the job, while the second completed the balance. The second received $42 more than the first for the work performed. What was the cost of the job?

422. When vegetables are dried they lose $\frac{5}{7}$ of their weight. What was the weight of the fresh vegetables if the weight of the dried vegetables was 2 short tons and 400 pounds. (Change the pounds into a fraction of a ton.)

423. The difference of two numbers is $7\frac{5}{8}$. One is $3\frac{1}{3}$ times the other. Find the numbers.

The conversion of common fractions into decimal fractions

Very often problems arise in which a part of the numerical information is given in terms of common fractions and a part is given in terms of decimal fractions. Arithmetic operations on these numbers can be performed only when all of the fractions are common fractions or when all are decimal fractions; if we have a combination of them, some common and some decimal fractions, one kind must be converted so that all fractions are of the same kind.

Now, if a common fraction has a denominator of the form 10, 100, 1,000, or the like, that is, a 1 with zeros on its right, it is easily converted into a decimal fraction. For example:

$$\frac{5}{10} = 0.5, \qquad \frac{17}{100} = 0.17, \qquad \frac{156}{1,000} = 0.156,$$
$$\frac{875}{1,000,000} = 0.000875.$$

Note that we have as many decimal places in the decimal fraction as there are zeros in the denominator.

Some fractions may not have denominators of the kind shown above.   However, it may be possible to obtain such denominators if we remember the fundamental property of a common fraction, that is, that the value of a fraction remains unchanged if the numerator and denominator of a fraction are both multiplied by the same number.   But, and this fact is important, the fraction that can be so changed must have a denominator of a special kind.

Note that the prime factors of 10 are 2 and 5.   The prime factors of all numbers whose first digit on the left is 1, and all others to the right are zeros are

$$10 = 2 \cdot 5,$$
$$100 = 2 \cdot 2 \cdot 5 \cdot 5,$$
$$1,000 = 2 \cdot 2 \cdot 2 \cdot 5 \cdot 5 \cdot 5,$$
$$10,000 = 2 \cdot 2 \cdot 2 \cdot 2 \cdot 5 \cdot 5 \cdot 5 \cdot 5,$$

and so on.   This factoring shows the important fact mentioned above.   If a common fraction has a denominator that can be decomposed into prime factors 2 and 5 (the number of them is immaterial) and no others except 1, then such a fraction can, as will be shown, be converted into an exact decimal fraction.

For example, the fraction $\frac{3}{4}$ is converted as follows.   Note that $4 = 2 \cdot 2$.   We multiply 4 by as many fives (5) as there are twos (2).   Thus if we multiply 4 by $5 \cdot 5 = 25$ we have $4 \cdot 5 \cdot 5 = 100$.   But in order to preserve the value of the fraction we must multiply the numerator 3 by 25 also.   We thus have

$$\frac{3}{4} = \frac{3 \cdot 25}{4 \cdot 25} = \frac{75}{100} = 0.75.$$

Let us convert the fraction $\frac{63}{960}$ into a decimal fraction.   Note that 63 and 960 have a greatest common divisor 3.   Reducing the fraction, we obtain $\frac{21}{320}$.   Disregarding the zero in the denominator we find that $32 = 2 \cdot 2 \cdot 2 \cdot 2 \cdot 2 = 2^5$.   According

to the above rule we must multiply the numerator and denominator by $5^5 = 3,125$. Thus, we have:

$$\frac{21}{320} = \frac{21 \cdot 3,125}{320 \cdot 3,125} = \frac{65,625}{1,000,000} = 0.065625.$$

If the denominator of the fraction contains prime factors other
than 2 and 5 (even if it also contains 2 and 5), such as 3, 7, 11,
13, 17, 19, and so on, such fractions cannot be converted into
decimal fractions exactly. Thus, such fractions as

$$\frac{2}{3}, \quad \frac{5}{6}, \quad \frac{3}{7}, \quad \frac{7}{9}, \quad \frac{13}{14}, \quad \frac{11}{18}, \quad \frac{7}{15},$$

and the like cannot be converted into decimal fractions exactly.

It is possible to convert a common fraction into a decimal by
means of long division. Thus, $\frac{3}{4}$ can be converted as follows:

```
        0.75
   4 | 3.           or        3. | 4
      2 8                     2 8   0.75
      ---                     ---
        20                      20
        20                      20
        --                      --
```

Also, $\frac{63}{960}$ is converted as follows:

```
          0.065625
   960 | 63.              or       63. | 960
       57 60                       57 60   0.065625
       ------                      ------
        5 400                       5 400
        4 800                       4 800
        -----                       -----
         6000                        6000
         5760                        5760
         ----                        ----
         2400                        2400
         1920                        1920
         ----                        ----
         4800                        4800
         4800                        4800
         ----                        ----
```

The use of the long division is permissible because we can consider a common fraction as an indication of a division that is to be performed.

The method of long division may be applied to the conversion of common fractions that cannot be expressed exactly as decimal fractions.

For example let us take $\frac{2}{3}$. Performing the long division, we have:

$$
\begin{array}{r}
0.6666 \\
\hline
3 \enclose{verticalstrike}{\,2.\,} \\
18 \\
\hline
20 \\
18 \\
\hline
20 \\
18 \\
\hline
20 \\
18 \\
\hline
2
\end{array}
\qquad \text{or} \qquad
\begin{array}{r}
2. \enclose{verticalstrike}{\,3\,} \\
18 \quad 0.6666 \\
\hline
20 \\
18 \\
\hline
20 \\
18 \\
\hline
20 \\
18 \\
\hline
2
\end{array}
$$

Thus we observe that we could go on indefinitely, but would never be able to complete the division. We may stop whenever we think we have carried the division far enough. But then we should follow the rule given on page 125, that is, carry on with the division so that we have one extra digit and then round the last place. Thus, if we wish to have three decimal places in the above decimal fraction, we write $0.667 -$. If we wish to indicate that the division can be carried on indefinitely we write $0.6666\cdots$; the dots indicate this fact.

At best we can only be satisfied with an approximate value of the decimal fraction, owing to the fact that the division cannot be completed.

In the above examples only one digit was repeated. We may have decimal fractions with more than one repeated digit. For example, $\frac{13}{27}$ repeats as below:

$$
\begin{array}{r}
0.481481 \\
\hline
27 \ | \ 13. \\
10\ 8 \\
\hline
2\ 20 \\
2\ 16 \\
\hline
40 \\
27 \\
\hline
130 \\
108 \\
\hline
220 \\
216 \\
\hline
40 \\
27 \\
\hline
13
\end{array}
\qquad \text{or} \qquad
\begin{array}{r}
13 \ \ | \underline{\ 2\ 7\ \ \ \ \ \ \ \ \ } \\
10\ 8 \quad 0.481481 \\
\hline
2\ 20 \\
2\ 16 \\
\hline
40 \\
27 \\
\hline
130 \\
108 \\
\hline
220 \\
216 \\
\hline
40 \\
27 \\
\hline
13
\end{array}
$$

Thus we note that in the decimal fraction $0.481481\cdots$ the sequence 481 repeats periodically. This periodicity gives rise to the special name for such decimal fractions; they are called *periodic fractions*, and the repeated sequence is called the *period of the fraction*.

In some periodic fractions the period begins immediately after the decimal point, or after one or more zeros, as, for example, $0.3333\cdots$, $0.00575757\cdots$. In other fractions, the period may begin after a certain number of digits that are not repeated, as $\frac{98}{225} = 0.43555\cdots$.

PROBLEMS

424. Use long division to convert the following common fractions into decimal fractions: $\frac{1}{8}, \frac{3}{25}, \frac{19}{25}, \frac{47}{50}, \frac{5}{8}, \frac{7}{8}, \frac{7}{16}, \frac{17}{20}, \frac{13}{32}, \frac{15}{64}, \frac{7}{40}, \frac{29}{250}, \frac{277}{400}$.

425. Which of the following common fractions can be converted into decimal fractions exactly: $\frac{12}{25}, \frac{19}{75}, \frac{15}{32}, \frac{17}{24}, \frac{27}{72}, \frac{16}{81}, \frac{99}{540}, \frac{36}{480}, \frac{115}{192}, \frac{118}{225}, \frac{91}{350}$?

426. Use long division to convert the following common fractions into decimal fractions: $\frac{1}{11}, \frac{3}{13}, \frac{1}{7}, \frac{5}{7}, \frac{5}{6}, \frac{7}{12}, \frac{5}{18}, \frac{4}{15}, \frac{17}{99}, \frac{235}{999}, \frac{61}{48}, \frac{97}{45}, \frac{101}{78}, \frac{125}{44}$.

The conversion of decimal fractions into common fractions

The conversion of decimal fractions into common fractions may often be required by the nature of the problem that is being solved.   This kind of problem will be discussed in Chapters 14 and 15.

If we have an exact decimal fraction, or any decimal fraction which is (so far as we are concerned) accepted as exact, then the conversion is very simple.   We rewrite this decimal fraction as a common one whose denominator is 1 with as many zeros as there are decimal places.   If possible, we reduce this fraction to its lowest terms, and the conversion is completed.   For example,

$$0.7 = \frac{7}{10}, \qquad 0.16 = \frac{16}{100} = \frac{4}{25},$$

$$3.125 = 3\frac{125}{1,000} = 3\frac{1}{8}, \qquad 6.73313 = 6\frac{73,313}{100,000}.$$

If we convert a periodic fraction into a common fraction, the procedure is different.   Here we must take into consideration the number of digits in the period.

Suppose that we wish to convert $0.47777\cdots$ into a common fraction.   Multiply this periodic fraction $0.47777\cdots$ by 10, that is, move the decimal point one place to the right.   We have then $4.7777\cdots$.   From this product subtract the original periodic fraction $0.47777\cdots$.   We then have:

$$
\begin{array}{r}
4.7777\cdots \\
0.4777\cdots \\
\hline
4.3000
\end{array}
$$

Note that all the digits which form the period have disappeared in the difference.   The difference is 9 times the original periodic fraction (with a small discrepancy in the last decimal place).   We multiplied it by 10 and subtracted once.   But in order to retain the original value of the periodic fraction we must divide the difference by 9.   We then have

$$0.47777\cdots = \frac{4.3}{9}.$$

Now, in order to remove the decimal point from the mixed decimal fraction in the numerator we shall multiply it by 10, and in order to retain the value of the fraction $\frac{4.3}{9}$ we must multiply the denominator by 10 also. Thus we have

$$0.47777\cdots = \frac{43}{90}.$$

Let us consider another example, the conversion of $17.634444\cdots$. Multiplying it by 10 and subtracting the original periodic fraction, we have:

$$
\begin{array}{l}
176.34444\cdots \\
\underline{17.63444\cdots} \\
158.71000
\end{array}
$$

Dividing this difference by 9, we have

$$17.634444\cdots = \frac{158.71}{9}.$$

Here, in order to eliminate the decimal places in the numerator we must multiply the numerator and denominator by 100. We have then that

$$17.634444\cdots = \frac{15{,}871}{900},$$

and after changing the improper fraction into a mixed number we obtain

$$17.634444\cdots = 17\frac{571}{900}.$$

We can, if we choose, convert only the pure decimal part of the number. Then we proceed:

$$
\begin{array}{l}
6.34444\cdots \\
\underline{0.63444\cdots} \\
5.71000
\end{array}
$$

$$0.634444\cdots = \frac{5.71}{9} = \frac{571}{900} \quad \text{and} \quad 17.634444\cdots = 17\frac{571}{900}.$$

If a periodic fraction has a period consisting of two digits we must multiply it by 100, and from there on the procedure is the

same as above. Thus, the conversion of the number 1.343434···
is as follows:

$$\begin{array}{r} 34.3434\cdots \\ 0.3434\cdots \\ \hline 34.0000 \end{array}$$

$$0.343434\cdots = \frac{34}{99} \quad \text{and} \quad 1.343434\cdots = 1\frac{34}{99}.$$

Note here that we divided the difference by 99 because we had
multiplied the periodic fraction by 100 and subtracted it once:
$100 - 1 = 99$.

Let us consider another example, the conversion of the periodic fraction in 2.7454545··· into a common fraction. After
multiplying it by 100 and subtracting the original periodic fraction, we have:

$$\begin{array}{r} 74.54545\cdots \\ 0.74545\cdots \\ \hline 73.80000 \end{array}$$

$$0.7454545\cdots = \frac{73.8}{99} = \frac{738}{990} = \frac{369}{495}$$

and

$$2.7454545\cdots = 2\frac{369}{495}.$$

Let us convert a periodic fraction whose period contains three
digits, as, for example, 0.4537537537···. Multiply this fraction
by 1,000 and subtract the original periodic fraction. We have:

$$\begin{array}{r} 453.7537\cdots \\ 0.4537\cdots \\ \hline 453.3000 \end{array}$$

Then

$$0.4537537\cdots = \frac{453.3}{999} = \frac{4{,}533}{9{,}990} = \frac{1{,}511}{3{,}330}.$$

Here we divided by 999 because the original periodic fraction was
multiplied by 1,000 and from this we subtracted the original
periodic fraction: $1{,}000 - 1 = 999$. To eliminate the decimal
point in the numerator, we multiplied both the numerator and

denominator of the fraction by 10. We then reduced the fraction to its lowest terms.

Converting the fraction in $18.481481\cdots$ to a common fraction is an especially interesting exercise at this point:

$$\begin{array}{r} 481.481\cdots \\ 0.481\cdots \\ \hline 481.000 \end{array}$$

$$0.481481\cdots = \frac{481}{999} = \frac{13}{27} \quad \text{and} \quad 18.481481\cdots = 18\frac{13}{27}.$$

This conversion should satisfy anyone who doubts that we have a reliable pair of processes for converting decimals into common fractions and common fractions into decimal fractions (see page 186).

We can now state a rule for the conversion of periodic fractions: *Multiply the periodic fraction by 10 if the period contains one digit, by 100 if the period contains two digits, by 1,000 if the period contains three digits, by 10,000 if the period contains four digits, and so on, by 100,000,000 if the period contains eight digits. From this product subtract the original periodic fraction, and the difference must be divided by a number containing the digit 9 repeated to make as many digits as there are in the period of the fraction. Then simplify the common fraction.*

PROBLEMS

427. Convert the following decimal fractions into common fractions: 0.34, 0.06, 0.075, 0.375, 0.456, 0.6738, 0.7575, 0.0085, 0.9215, 0.12567.

Convert the following periodic fractions into common fractions:

428. $0.4444\cdots$, $0.7777\cdots$, $0.15555\cdots$, $0.0456666\cdots$, $0.304444\cdots$, $23.5555\cdots$, $3.747777\cdots$.

429. $0.565656\cdots$, $0.3474747\cdots$, $0.045878787\cdots$, $1.34585858\cdots$, $34.0898989\cdots$, $15.34242424\cdots$, $92.078676767\cdots$.

430. $0.235235235\cdots$, $0.2563563563\cdots$, $0.3892892892\cdots$, $1.0478478478\cdots$, $45.23783783\cdots$, $210.12745745\cdots$, $15.479479\cdots$.

431. $1.45724572\cdots$, $16.68346834\cdots$, $982.63456345\cdots$, $0.8935489354\cdots$, $0.142857142857\cdots$, $0.384615384615\cdots$.

14

Ratio and Proportion

The comparison of two magnitudes

Two magnitudes can be compared in two ways. We can determine whether they are equal or unequal. If they are unequal then we may ask the following questions:

> *i.* By how much is one magnitude greater (or smaller) than another?
>
> *ii.* By how much must one magnitude be multiplied (or divided) to make it equal the other?

For example, two books can be compared as to the number of pages they contain. If one book has 267 pages, and the second contains 801 pages, then we may compare the sizes of the two books and find that the second book has 534 pages more than the first, or that the second has three times as many pages as the first.

To say that the second book has 534 pages more than the first is just the same as saying that the first book has 534 pages fewer than the second book. Also, to say that the second book has three times as many pages as the first is just the same as saying that the first book has one-third as many pages as the second book.

The first method of comparison, that is, determining by how much one quantity is greater (or smaller) than another, is known as the difference method, because we employ subtraction in order to obtain an answer to our question. However, this method of comparison is not as effective as the second method of comparing by multiplication or division. This second method allows us to use smaller numbers for comparison; it enables us to perform computations which could not be performed by means of the difference method; it is used in maps, in plans, in blueprints, in science, and in engineering.

By how much one quantity must be multiplied (or divided) to obtain another is discovered by means of division. We divide one quantity by another, and the quotient is the answer to our question. Thus, dividing the number of pages in the second book (see above) by the number of pages in the first book, we find that

$$801 \div 267 = 3.$$

If we divide the number of pages in the first book by the number of pages in the second book we obtain

$$267 \div 801 = \frac{1}{3}.$$

In the first case we obtain a whole number, and our answer is: multiply by 3.

In the second case we obtain a proper fraction, and the answer is: divide by 3.

This fact should be always remembered: If the quotient is a whole number or an improper fraction, then the quantity which is the dividend (801) is greater than the divisor (267). If the quotient is a proper fraction (that is, if it is less than 1), then the quantity which is the dividend (267) is smaller than the divisor (801). If the quotient is 1, then the dividend and the divisor are equal.

The ratio

When the relation between two quantities is expressed in terms of a quotient, such a relation is called the *ratio* of one quantity *to* another.

The quantities so compared must be of the same kind, that is, they must represent measures of the same kind and the same denomination. In other words, we cannot compare weight and volume. Nor can we compare a measure expressed in inches with a measure expressed in feet, or miles, or meters. However, whenever a conversion of one unit of measure into another is possible, we can obtain a ratio. Thus, we can compare 56 pounds with 120 kilograms, provided we convert pounds into kilograms or kilograms into pounds; we can compare 120 feet with 200 yards, provided we convert feet into yards or yards into feet; we can compare 45 meters with 60 feet, provided we convert meters into feet or feet into meters. But the comparison of 24 hours with 15 ounces is meaningless.

A ratio of two quantities is a number. After two quantities are compared and their relation is expressed in terms of a ratio, the denomination of these two quantities is of no consequence and of no importance. Thus, the ratio of 25 feet to 15 feet is

$$25 \div 15 = \frac{5}{3} = 1.666\cdots.$$

This form is one way of writing a ratio. In this method of writing we may consider division as a way of obtaining a ratio, and the ratio is the quotient of such a division.

Another way of writing a ratio is

$$\frac{25}{15} = \frac{5}{3} = 1.666\cdots.$$

This method of writing allows us to consider the ratio as a fraction whose numerator and denominator are the numbers representing the quantities that are compared.

The reader should note that such an expression as $\frac{25}{16}$ may represent a division, a fraction, or a ratio. The meaning of an expression of this kind, that is, $\frac{3}{4}$, $\frac{25}{14}$, $\frac{87}{100}$, or the like, depends on the statement of the problem, and until this statement is known and understood it is impossible to interpret it, as well as to proceed with any computation.

As a rule, whenever a ratio is given, it should be reduced (when this is possible) to its lowest terms. Doing so will simplify further computations. Thus the ratio $\frac{25}{15}$ should be reduced to $\frac{5}{3}$.

The simplification of ratios

In order to be able to perform computational work with ratios in the most efficient manner, ratios should be stated in the simplest form. For this reason a ratio should be reduced to its lowest terms.

The easiest method for the reduction of ratios is to write them as fractions. We know how to reduce fractions to their lowest terms.

The reduction of ratios to their lowest terms may reveal information concerning the relation between the magnitudes of the objects which is not easy to detect until it is reduced. For example, the ratio $\frac{282}{188}$ does not convey effectively the information concerning the relation between the two quantities whose magnitudes are 282 and 188 respectively. In a problem situation we may need to find two quantities related in the same ratio (usually one quantity is given and its magnitude is known, but the magnitude of the other must be determined). Now, if the ratio is $\frac{282}{188}$, that is, 282 to 188, the actual solution of the problem will then require the division of the known quantity into 282 parts; then 188 of such parts must be taken from the second quantity. Suppose that the two quantities 282 and 188 represent the weights in grams of two substances in some mixture, and we wish to obtain a similar mixture, but in considerably smaller amount. Thus in order to be able to perform operations of this kind as well as to apply ratios to practical situations it is preferable to work with ratios that are stated in terms of small numbers. By reducing the ratio $\frac{282}{188}$ to its lowest terms we obtain $\frac{3}{2}$.

Very often the reduction of a ratio to its lowest terms leads to a fraction whose denominator is 1. When we work with fractions, such a situation is always interpreted that the value of the fraction is a whole number. For example, the ratio $\frac{801}{267}$ given on page 191 is such a case. The value of the fraction $\frac{801}{267}$ after the fraction is reduced to its lowest terms in the whole number 3.   In the case of a ratio, the reduction should be written as

$$\frac{801}{267} = \frac{3}{1},$$

and this $\frac{3}{1}$ will signify that the ratio of 801 to 267 is 3 to 1.   The meaning of this ratio is that 801 is 3 times as great as 267.

If the quantities whose ratio must be determined are given as mixed numbers, as may happen very often, these mixed numbers must be changed into improper fractions, and then the ratio is computed by dividing these.   For example, the ratio of 12 feet 6 inches to 16 feet 8 inches is obtained by converting the two measures into feet, whence we have $12\frac{1}{2}$ feet and $16\frac{2}{3}$ feet.   Then the ratio is computed (after changing the mixed numbers into improper fractions):

$$\frac{25}{2} \div \frac{50}{3} = \frac{\overset{1}{\cancel{25}} \cdot 3}{2 \cdot \underset{2}{\cancel{50}}} = \frac{3}{4};$$

that is, the two measures are in the ratio of 3 to 4.

The same ratio could have been obtained if the two measures were changed into inches.   Thus 12 feet 6 inches = 150 inches, and 16 feet 8 inches = 200 inches, and

$$\frac{150}{200} = \frac{3}{4}.$$

If the two measures are given as proper fractions, then the ratio of these two measures is also obtained by dividing these two fractions.   For example, the ratio of $\frac{7}{10}$ kilogram to $\frac{21}{100}$ kilogram is computed as follows:

$$\frac{7}{10} \div \frac{21}{100} = \frac{\overset{1}{\cancel{7}} \cdot \overset{10}{\cancel{100}}}{\underset{1}{\cancel{10}} \cdot \underset{3}{\cancel{21}}} = \frac{10}{3}.$$

PROBLEMS

432. By how much is one number greater or smaller than the other: (a) 37 and 15; (b) 3.8 and 12.5; (c) 1.82 and 0.60; (d) 8.62 and 2.87; (e) 1,534 and 678; (f) $\frac{5}{6}$ and $\frac{7}{12}$; (g) $\frac{8}{15}$ and $1\frac{6}{25}$; (h) $4\frac{7}{16}$ and $\frac{9}{20}$; (i) $5\frac{2}{3}$ and $7\frac{3}{4}$; (j) $1\frac{5}{8}$ and 0.65?

433. Find the ratios of the following numbers: (a) 169 and 13; (b) 15 and 375; (c) 6.5 and 13; (d) 720 and 480; (e) 0.84 and 0.14; (f) $\frac{2}{3}$ and $\frac{3}{4}$; (g) $1\frac{1}{3}$ and $\frac{8}{9}$; (h) $\frac{2}{3}$ and $5\frac{2}{5}$; (i) $3\frac{1}{4}$ and $2\frac{1}{2}$; (j) 12 and $7\frac{3}{4}$.

434. Find the ratios of the following quantities: (a) 25 pounds and 12.5 pounds; (b) 18 feet and 10 feet 9 inches; (c) 32 yards and 45 meters; (d) 2 short tons and 4 metric tons; (e) 10 pounds and 5 kilograms.

Find the ratios of the following quantities:

435. (a) 2 ft.^{2} and 12 in.^{2}; (b) 3 ft.^{2} and 0.5 yd.^{2}; (c) 15 cm.^{2} and 10 in.^{2}; (d) 1.5 square miles and 2 km.^{2}; (e) 12 ft.^{2} and 5 m.^{2}

436. (a) 3 ft.^{3} and 0.1 yd.^{3}; (b) 15 in.^{3} and 5 cm.^{3}; (c) 1.5 yd.^{3} and 2 m.^{3}; (d) 25 ft.^{3} and 5 m.^{3}; (e) 750 cm.^{3} and 0.1 ft.^{3}

437. Write two ratios that are equivalent to each of the following ratios: (a) $\frac{5}{1}$; (b) $\frac{2}{3}$; (c) $\frac{7}{4}$; (d) $\frac{1}{6}$; (e) $\frac{11}{12}$.

Changes in ratios

Whether a ratio is written in division form (as, for example, $2 \div 3$) or in the fraction form (as, for example, $\frac{2}{3}$), the value of the ratio depends on the magnitudes of the numbers that go into the making of a ratio.

In division these two numbers have special names assigned to them, namely the dividend and the divisor. In the case of fractions we have corresponding names, that is, the numerator and the denominator of the fraction. In the case of a ratio we also have two names: the *antecedent* (occupying the place of the numerator) and the *consequent* (occupying the place of the denominator). We shall use, however, the following names: for the antecedent we shall use the *first term*, and for the consequent we shall use the *second term*.

Here, exactly as in the cases of division and of fractions (see pages 70 and 146), the value of a ratio depends on the values of the first and second terms. A change in the value of the first term, or of the second term, or of both necessarily produces a change in the value of the ratio (the changes may cancel each other).

Actually the effects of the changes in the first or second term (or both) of a ratio are exactly the same as in the case of division and fractions. We shall state them and illustrate them with examples.

If we multiply the first term of a ratio by a certain number, the ratio is also multiplied by the same number. For example, if we multiply the first term of the ratio $\frac{2}{3}$ by 5, we have $\frac{10}{3}$, and $\frac{10}{3} \div \frac{2}{3} = 5$.

If we divide the first term of a ratio by a certain number, the ratio is also divided by the same number. For example, if we divide the first term of the ratio $\frac{16}{5}$ by 4 we obtain $\frac{4}{5}$, and $\frac{4}{5} \div \frac{16}{5} = \frac{1}{4}$.

If we multiply the second term of a ratio by a certain number, the ratio is divided by the same number. For example, if we multiply the second term of the ratio $\frac{3}{4}$ by 7 we obtain $\frac{3}{28}$, and $\frac{3}{28} \div \frac{3}{4} = \frac{1}{7}$.

If we divide the second term of a ratio by a certain number, the ratio is multiplied by the same number. For example, if we divide the second term of the ratio $\frac{7}{25}$ by 5 we obtain $\frac{7}{5}$, and $\frac{7}{5} \div \frac{7}{25} = 5$.

If we multiply the first and the second terms of a ratio by the same number, then the ratio's value remains unchanged. For example, the multiplication of the two terms of the ratio $\frac{5}{7}$ by 8 gives $\frac{40}{56}$. The simplification of the ratio by reduction gives $\frac{5}{7}$.

Also, if we divide the first and second terms of a ratio by the same number, the ratio's value remains unchanged. For example, the division of the two terms of the ratio $\frac{7}{9}$ by 5 gives

$$\frac{\frac{7}{5}}{\frac{9}{5}} = \frac{7}{5} \div \frac{9}{5} = \frac{7 \cdot \overset{1}{\cancel{5}}}{\cancel{5} \cdot 9} = \frac{7}{9}.$$

PROBLEMS

438. Complete the following:

The first term	The second term	The ratio
Multiplied by 5	Unchanged	?
Multiplied by 3	Multiplied by 6	?
Multiplied by 6	Multiplied by 2	?
Multiplied by 5	Divided by 4	?
Multiplied by 3	Divided by 3	?
Divided by 3	Unchanged	?
Divided by 5	Multiplied by 2	?
Divided by 4	Multiplied by 8	?
Divided by 3	Divided by 9	?
Divided by 12	Divided by 4	?
Divided by 5	Divided by 5	?
?	Multiplied by 2	Unchanged
?	Multiplied by 3	Multiplied by 9
?	Multiplied by 4	Multiplied by 2
?	Multiplied by 6	Divided by 18
?	Multiplied by 8	Divided by 4
?	Divided by 2	Multiplied by 6
?	Divided by 6	Multiplied by 2
?	Divided by 5	Unchanged
?	Unchanged	Multiplied by 5
?	Unchanged	Divided by 10
Multiplied by 5	?	Multiplied by 10
Multiplied by 12	?	Multiplied by 6
Multiplied by 7	?	Unchanged
Multiplied by 3	?	Divided by 5
Multiplied by 15	?	Divided by 5
Divided by 6	?	Unchanged
Divided by 8	?	Multiplied by 4
Divided by 6	?	Multiplied by 24
Multiplied by 5	?	Multiplied by 20
Divided by 6	?	Divided by 6

439. A piece of brass contains 1.86 kilograms of copper and 1.26 kilograms of zinc. How much zinc should be in a piece of brass 6 times as heavy?

440. An ingot of alloy weighing 324 pounds contains 54 pounds of copper, 189 pounds of tin, and the balance is antimony. What is the ratio of the copper content to the total weight of the alloy? Obtain similar ratios for the tin and the antimony. What is the sum of the three ratios?

441. Compute ratio of the areas of two rectangles whose dimensions are:
First rectangle: Length 25 inches, width 20 inches.
Second rectangle: Length 24 inches, width 15 inches.

Solution of problems involving ratio

The practical applications of the notion of a ratio are numerous, and the listing of them would take up too much space.

The problems involving ratios may be subdivided into four groups:

i. Find the ratio of two magnitudes.

ii. Given the ratio of two magnitudes and the magnitude that corresponds to the first term, find the magnitude that corresponds to the second term.

iii. Given the ratio of two magnitudes and the magnitude that corresponds to the second term, find the magnitude that corresponds to the first term.

iv. Given the ratio of two magnitudes and sum (or difference) of the two magnitudes, find the magnitudes.

The problems in finding ratios were discussed and illustrated on pages 190–193.

Problems in which a ratio is given and one of the magnitudes is also given are solved in the following manner. Suppose the ratio of two quantities is $\frac{2}{3}$, the quantity that corresponds to the first term is 100, and it is required to find the quantity that corresponds to the second term. Note that the ratio indicates that the first term consists of 2 equal parts and the second term consists of 3 equal parts, all 5 parts being of the same magnitude. In order, then, to obtain the quantity that corresponds to the second term we must obtain one part of the first term (this is obtained by dividing 100 by 2, that is, $\frac{100}{2}$); after this part is obtained it is multiplied by 3, that is, $\dfrac{100 \cdot 3}{2}$. Performing the computations, we find that the quantity that corresponds to the second term is 150.

If we examine the fraction $\dfrac{100 \cdot 3}{2}$ we may note that 100 is multiplied by the denominator of the fraction $\frac{2}{3}$, and it is divided by the numerator of the same fraction. This double operation is exactly what is done when we divide 100 by the fraction $\frac{2}{3}$.

Thus the solution of our problem is obtained as the result of dividing the known number by the fraction that represents the ratio.

Now let us consider the case when the ratio and quantity that corresponds to the second term are given, and it is required to find the quantity that corresponds to the first term of the ratio. Suppose that the given ratio is $\frac{5}{7}$, and the quantity that corresponds to the second term is 28. It is required to find the quantity that corresponds to the first term.

Note that the ratio indicates by its second term that the quantity corresponding to it consists of 7 equal parts, while the quantity that corresponds to the first term consists of 5 such equal parts. Thus, if we divide 28 by 7 we shall obtain one such part. We have then $\frac{28}{7}$. Multiplying $\frac{28}{7}$ by 5, we obtain the quantity that corresponds to the first term of the ratio, that is, $\dfrac{28 \cdot 5}{7} = 20$.

If we examine the fraction $\dfrac{28 \cdot 5}{7}$ we may note that 28 is multiplied by the numerator of the fraction $\frac{5}{7}$ and it is divided by the denominator of the same fraction. This double operation is exactly what is done when we multiply 28 by the fraction $\frac{5}{7}$.

The rule for solving the problems with ratio when a quantity that corresponds to one term of the ratio is given is as follows: *In solving for the second term*, DIVIDE; *in solving for the first term* MULTIPLY the fraction that represents the ratio. Here the reader may find it worth while to remember a simple rule that will enable him to select the proper arithmetic operation. Solving for the first term (which is in the position of the numerator) we multiply. Solving for the second term (which is in the position of the denominator) we divide.

Case (*iv*) will be discussed in the section on Proportional Division.

Let us consider a few typical problems.

EXAMPLE. The scale on a map is $\frac{1}{100,000}$. What will be the length on the map representing a distance of 200 miles? Before we proceed with the computation we must recognize the term to which the number 200 corresponds. The scale on the map as given by the ratio indicates that every distance on the map is the real distance divided by 100,000. The second term, therefore, corresponds to the actual distances, and 200 miles is the actual distance. In order to solve our problem we must multiply 200 by the fraction representing the ratio, and the numerical result will give the distance on the map. This distance is, then,

$$\frac{200}{100,000} = \frac{2}{1,000}$$

mile. Translating this fraction into feet, we have

$$\frac{5,280 \cdot 2}{1,000} = 10.56 \text{ feet.}$$

EXAMPLE. The distance between two points on a map is 3 inches. What is the actual distance between these two points if the map scale is $\frac{1}{10,000,000}$? The 3 inches corresponds to the first term of the ratio. The solution of the problem is then

$$3 \cdot 10,000,000$$

inches. Converting this distance into miles, we have

$$\frac{3 \cdot 10,000,000}{12 \cdot 5,280} = 473.5 \text{ miles.}$$

When solving problems involving ratios, one must be extremely careful in examining the nature of the quantities whose ratio is given. If the ratio involves linear measures, that is, measures of length, and the question proposed concerns areas, then the ratio must be squared before computations can be performed. If the question concerns volumes, then the ratio must be cubed before computations can be performed. For example, on the plan of a floor the scale is indicated as $\frac{1}{100}$, and the area on the *plan* is 12 square inches. What is the actual size of the area? After squaring the ratio, we have the scale as to areas $\frac{1}{10,000}$, and the actual size of the area is

$$12 \cdot 10,000 = 120,000 \text{ square inches.}$$

We know that 1 square foot = 144 square inches. Then the actual size of the area in square feet is

$$\frac{120,000}{144} = \frac{10,000}{12} = 833.3 \text{ square feet.}$$

PROBLEMS

442. The length of a room is 17.5 feet. The ratio of the length to the width is $\frac{4}{3}$. What is the area of the floor of the room?

443. The ratio of the weight of copper to the weight of zinc in brass is $\frac{3}{2}$. What is the weight of copper in a piece of brass if the zinc content is 5.88 pounds?

444. The ratio of the length of the circumference of a circle to the diameter of the circle is $\frac{3.14}{1}$. What is the length of the circumference of the circle if the diameter is 15.6 inches long?

445. On the drawing of a plan, every 10 feet is represented by 1 inch. What is the scale?

446. What is the weight of a cast if its model weighs 2.7 kilograms and the ratio of the weight of the cast to the weight of the model is $\frac{12}{1}$?

447. A field is 850 feet long. Its width is 340 feet less. On the drawing of the plan the length of the field is 17 inches. What is the width of the field on the plan?

448. The scale of a map is $\dfrac{1}{10,000}$. What is the actual area of a field shown on the map as a rectangle 2 inches by 3 inches?

449. In order to obtain 18 ounces of water in a laboratory, 16 ounces of oxygen are required; the other substance needed is hydrogen. How much hydrogen is required for the production of 10 ounces of water?

450. The burning of 25 pounds of anthracite releases 178,000 calories of heat. How much heat will be released by 15 short tons of anthracite?

451. A vertical pole 5 feet high casts a shadow 7 feet 3 inches long. How tall is a tree that casts a shadow 25 feet 10 inches long?

Proportion

Two equal ratios are said to form a *proportion*, if these two ratios are joined by the equality sign. The following statements are proportions:

$$\frac{2}{3} = \frac{18}{27}, \qquad \frac{7}{13} = \frac{91}{169}.$$

A proportion may be also written as

$$2 \div 3 = 18 \div 27.$$

The proportions are read as follows: The ratio of 2 to 3 is the same as the ratio of 18 to 27. Generally, this reading is shortened: 2 is to 3 as 18 is to 27.

In every proportion there are four terms. The first and fourth are called the *extremes*, and the second and third are called the *means*. In the proportion

$$2 \div 3 = 18 \div 27, \qquad \text{or} \qquad \frac{2}{3} = \frac{18}{27},$$

2 and 27 are the extreme terms and 3 and 18 are the means.

The fundamental property of a proportion is that *the product of the means is equal to the product of the extremes*. In the above proportion,

$$2 \cdot 27 = 3 \cdot 18.$$

In the proportion

$$3 \div 8 = 75 \div 120, \qquad 3 \cdot 120 = 8 \cdot 75.$$

The fundamental property of a proportion is important in the solution of problems involving proportions. Generally, the solution of such problems requires the finding of one of the terms of a proportion when the other three are given. The missing term of the proportion is usually denoted by the letter x. Thus we may have the following proportions:

$$x \div 5 = 9 \div 15,$$
$$7 \div x = 28 \div 12,$$
$$7 \div 3 = x \div 12,$$
$$3 \div 5 = 9 \div x.$$

Applying the fundamental property of proportions we have the following statements:

$$15 \cdot x = 5 \cdot 9,$$
$$28 \cdot x = 7 \cdot 12,$$
$$3 \cdot x = 7 \cdot 12,$$
$$3 \cdot x = 5 \cdot 9.$$

Note that from these four statements the four values of x can be easily obtained. In each case, we divide the expressions on both sides of the equality sign by the multiplier of x. That this procedure is correct can be seen from observing that if $15 \cdot x = 5 \cdot 9$, then $1 \cdot x$ is $\frac{1}{15}$ of 45, or $\frac{5 \cdot 9}{15}$. Hence:

$$x = \frac{5 \cdot 9}{15},$$
$$x = \frac{7 \cdot 12}{28},$$
$$x = \frac{7 \cdot 12}{3},$$
$$x = \frac{5 \cdot 9}{3}.$$

From this set of results we conclude that:

i. In a proportion, a mean term is equal to the product of the extreme terms divided by the other mean term.

ii. In a proportion, an extreme term is equal to the product of the mean terms divided by the other extreme term.

For example, let us solve the following:

$$3.5 \div x = 0.8 \div 2.4.$$

We then have

$$x = \frac{3.5 \cdot 2.4}{0.8} = 10.5.$$

Another example:

$$\frac{2}{3}x \div \frac{1}{5} = 3\frac{1}{3} \div \frac{1}{6}.$$

We then have

$$\frac{2}{3}x = \left(\frac{1}{5} \cdot \frac{10}{3}\right) \div \frac{1}{6},$$

$$\frac{2}{3}x = \frac{2}{3} \div \frac{1}{6} = \frac{2 \cdot 6}{3 \cdot 1} = \frac{4}{1} = 4.$$

Now, in order to solve

$$\frac{2}{3}x = 4,$$

we reason as follows: two-thirds of some quantity is 4; one-third of it is $4 \div 2$; and three-thirds of it is $(4 \div 2) \cdot 3 = 2 \cdot 3 = 6$. Thus $x = 6$. Checking this value, by putting it into the original proportion, we have

$$4 \div \frac{1}{5} = 3\frac{1}{3} \div \frac{1}{6}.$$

Performing the computations will show that this statement is a proportion.

PROBLEMS

452. Check whether the following statements are proportions or not: (a) $14 \div 7 = 25 \div 12.5$; (b) $75 \div 15 = 120 \div 60$; (c) $4.2 \div 3 = 2.6 \div 2$; (d) $\frac{5}{6} \div \frac{1}{3} = 2.5 \div 1$; (e) $\frac{7}{15} \div \frac{1}{15} = \frac{6}{7} \div \frac{1}{7}$.

453. Check the fundamental property of a proportion on the following proportions: (a) $1 \div 3 = 6 \div 18$; (b) $2 \div 9 = 4 \div 18$; (c) $0.1 \div 0.5 = 2 \div 10$; (d) $8 \div 6 = \frac{1}{3} \div \frac{1}{4}$; (e) $45 \div 18 = 180 \div 72$.

454. Form proportions from the following statements: (a) $3 \cdot 24 = 8 \cdot 9$; (b) $2 \cdot 5 = 0.5 \cdot 20$; (c) $5 \cdot 12 = 3 \cdot 20$; (d) $3.8 \cdot 2 = 76 \cdot 0.1$; (e) $\frac{3}{4} \cdot \frac{1}{5} = \frac{5}{12} \cdot \frac{9}{25}$.

455. Will the proportion $75 \div 15 = 105 \div 21$ still hold if the members of the ratio on the left of the equality sign are both divided by 5, and the members on the right of the equality sign are both divided by 7?

456. Find the unknown members of the proportions: (a) $x \div 300 = 54 \div 40$; (b) $855 \div 720 = 570 \div x$; (c) $75 \div 9 = x \div 9$; (d) $608 \div 912 = x \div 768$; (e) $\frac{1}{8} \div \frac{1}{3} = \frac{3}{7} \div x$; (f) $0.25 \div 1.4 = 0.75 \div x$; (g) $3.1 \div 9.3 = x \div \frac{7}{9}$; (h) $\dfrac{3.5}{x} = \dfrac{8.4}{4.5}$; (i) $2\frac{1}{2} \div 1\frac{1}{4} = 2 \div x$; (j) $7 \div 1\frac{3}{4} = 3.6 \div x$.

Proportional quantities and problems in proportions

Many problems of practical nature as well as exercises involving proportions present cases of relationship between certain quantities. These relationships are often stated as of ratios.

There may be two kinds of proportional relationship between changing quantities:

Direct relation: As one quantity increases the other quantity associated with it increases also. As examples of such situations we may mention: the expenditure of gasoline increases with the distance traveled in a car; the time spent on traveling (at a constant speed) increases with the distance traveled; the cost of merchandise (at a given price) increases with the quantity of the merchandise; the output of work increases as the number of workers (working at a given rate) increases.

Inverse relation: On the other hand, there is a relationship in which one quantity increases as the other decreases, or conversely, one quantity decreases as the other increases. For example, if we increase the speed of a train it will take less time to cover a given distance; if the number of workers employed on a certain job is decreased the time it will take to complete the job increases; if the price of some object increases, a certain sum will buy less, or if the price of a certain object is lowered a certain sum will buy more; the farther we move away from a light, the less illumination we receive.

If we are to use these proportional relationships in computing, they must be systematic. If one end of a seesaw goes down a certain distance, the opposite end goes up a certain distance; the two changes are systematically related, and we can compute one if we know the other and the system according to which they are related. If Mr. Jones has a $2 lunch he may become drowsy and take a nap in the afternoon; but the price of Mr. Jones's lunch and the length of his nap are not systematically related and we cannot compute either when we know the other.

If two quantities are related to each other, and one becomes greater when the other also becomes greater (or smaller when the other becomes smaller), according to a system that enables us to compute (by adding or multiplying) the magnitude of one when the system and the magnitude of the other are known, we call their relation *direct proportionality*. We may have several kinds of direct proportionality.

If two quantities are related to each other, and one becomes smaller when the other becomes greater (or greater when the other becomes smaller), according to a system that enables us to compute (by subtracting or dividing) the magnitude of one when the system and the magnitude of the other are known, we call their relation *inverse proportionality*. We may have several kinds of inverse proportionality.

Of the various kinds of direct and inverse proportionality, we are for the moment interested in the simplest. We will study the *direct proportionality* in which, as one of two related quantities is multiplied, the other one is multiplied by the same number: if a car goes 60 miles on 4 gallons of gasoline, it will go 600 miles on 40 gallons. We will study the *inverse proportionality* in which, as one of two related quantities is multiplied, the other is divided by the same number: if a car goes 30 miles an hour and finishes a certain trip in 4 hours, it will finish the same trip in 2 hours if it goes 60 miles an hour. It might help to see the two proportions written. The direct proportion is:

$$4 \div 40 = 60 \div 600.$$

Gallons	Gallons times 10	Miles	Miles times 10

The inverse proportion is:

$$4 \div 2 = 60 \div 30.$$

Hours Hours Speed Speed
divided multi-
by 2 plied
by 2

These two types of relationships must be sought for whenever problems involving proportions are solved. The determination of the particular type of relationship, that is, whether we are confronted with a direct proportionality or an inverse proportionality, is important because this will help us to set up the correct proportion by means of which a problem is solved. The actual determination of the nature of proportionality follows from the statement of the problem. The following examples will illustrate the procedure in solving problems that involve proportions.

EXAMPLE. 100 pounds of grain yield 90 pounds of flour. How many pounds of grain are required in order to obtain 675 pounds of flour?

Let us denote the quantity of grain by x. Then we set up the following scheme:

90 pounds of flour are obtained from 100 pounds of grain;
675 pounds of flour are obtained from x pounds of grain.

Note that the relationship in this case is direct proportionality, because the more grain we use the more flour will be obtained. We then set up the proportion

$$90 \div 675 = 100 \div x.$$

From this proportion we obtain the value of x (which is an extreme member of the proportion):

$$x = \frac{675 \cdot 100}{90} = 750 \text{ pounds.}$$

EXAMPLE. 16 men can pave a highway in 21 days. How many men would be required in order to complete the job in 14 days?

Let us denote the number of men by x.   Then we set up the following scheme:

16 men complete the paving in 21 days;
x men complete the paving in 14 days.

Note that the relationship in this case is inverse proportionality, because in order to complete the work in a *fewer* number of days we need *more* men.   Also note that as we set up the proportion we reason as follows: As the number of the days is decreased from 21 to 14, the number of the men increases from 16 to x.   This increase is in the same ratio as 21 is to 14, because the division of one quantity by a certain number leads to a multiplication of the other quantity by the same number.   Thus the proportion is

$$21 \div 14 = x \div 16.$$

Thus in the case of inverse proportionality the proportion is set up as follows: the direct ratio of one set of quantities (read downward) is made equal to the inverse ratio (read upward) of the second set of quantities.   Thus

$21 \div 14$ is read downward and $x \div 16$ is read upward.

Solving the above proportion for x, we obtain

$$x = \frac{21 \cdot 16}{14} = 24 \text{ men.}$$

PROBLEMS

457. Indicate which of the following relationships represent direct proportionality and which represent inverse proportionality: (*a*) the weight of some goods and their cost; (*b*) the speed of a train and the time it takes to cover some distance; (*c*) the number of workers and the time it takes to complete a certain job; (*d*) the weight of an object and its volume; (*e*) the length and width of a rectangle whose area is unchanged; (*f*) the size of a ration apportioned from a given constant supply as the number of people changes.

458. How will the area of a square change as its side is doubled? tripled? quadrupled?

459. How will the volume of a cube change as its edge is doubled? tripled? quadrupled?

460. A clock loses $1\frac{1}{2}$ seconds in 3 hours and 45 minutes. How long does it take to lose $1\frac{1}{3}$ seconds? How much will it lose in a day? in a week?

461. A pump sends up 2,545 cubic feet of water in 4 hours and 12 minutes. How long will it take to pump up 74,300 cubic feet of water?

462. In order to heat a house, it was planned to order 90 short tons of coal for 60 days. For how long will this supply last if the expenditure of coal is cut to 1,155 pounds per day?

463. Two flywheels are joined by a belt. The circumference of one flywheel is 168 feet and it makes 60 revolutions per minute. How many revolutions per minute does the second flywheel make if its circumference is 64 feet?

464. The diameter of a flywheel is 72 inches and it makes 143 revolutions per minute. It is connected by a belt with another flywheel which makes 396 revolutions per minute. What is the length of the diameter of the second flywheel?

465. An airplane flew from one airport to another in 3 hours at the rate of 180 miles per hour. On the way back, due to a head wind, its speed was cut down to 160 miles per hour. How long did the return trip last?

466. A 4.5-pound weight balances a lever at the other end of which a 3.5-pound weight is attached. What is the length of the shorter part of the lever, if the longer is 1 foot long? (The weight is inversely proportional to the distance from the fulcrum.)

Proportional division

So far we examined and developed the methods for the solution of problems in ratio of the first three groups stated on page 198. Now we shall examine the last (fourth) group of problems, namely: Given the ratio of two magnitudes and the sum (or difference) of the two magnitudes, find the magnitudes.

Before we proceed with the solution of such problems let us examine any ratio, say $\frac{3}{4}$. This ratio indicates that the relation between the two quantities for which it was obtained is this: If the quantity corresponding to the first term is divided into 3 equal parts, then the quantity that corresponds to the second term can be divided into 4 equal parts, and each of these 4 parts is equal to each of the 3 parts of the first quantity.

From the above property we can obtain two very important facts:

i. The sum of the two quantities will contain 7 such equal parts, because $3 + 4 = 7$.

ii. The difference of the two quantities will contain 1 of these parts.

With the three facts just stated we can proceed with the solution of problems in proportional division. Let us consider the following examples.

EXAMPLE. Pure water is made up of hydrogen and oxygen, and the ratio of hydrogen to oxygen is $2 \div 16$. How much hydrogen and oxygen are there in 7.2 kilograms of water?

Since for every two parts of hydrogen there are 16 parts of oxygen, the total number of parts is $2 + 16 = 18$. Thus, in order to determine the amount of hydrogen and oxygen we must determine the magnitude of one part. We find that one part is equal to

$$\frac{7.2}{18} = 0.4 \text{ kilogram.}$$

Then, the amount of hydrogen is $0.4 \cdot 2 = 0.8$ kilogram, and the amount of oxygen is $0.4 \cdot 16 = 6.4$ kilograms. That our solution is correct is checked by the proportion

$$0.8 \div 6.4 = 2 \div 16.$$

EXAMPLE. On a farm the area of arable land exceeds the grazing land by 135 acres. How many acres of arable land and how many acres of grazing land are there on the farm if the area of arable land is $3\frac{1}{2}$ times as great as the area of grazing land?

The ratio of the arable land to the grazing land is $3\frac{1}{2} \div 1$, and by simplifying this ratio we obtain $\frac{7}{2} \div 1$ or $7 \div 2$. In this problem we have a case in which the difference is involved. Thus the 135 acres correspond to $7 - 2 = 5$ parts. Then 1 part is equal to $135 \div 5 = 27$ acres. From this computation we find that the arable land consists of $27 \cdot 7 = 189$ acres, and the grazing land consisted of $27 \cdot 2 = 54$ acres. The correctness of the solution is checked by the proportion

$$189 \div 54 = 7 \div 2.$$

We often have three quantities (or more than three quantities) whose sum is given. The ratio of three quantities is stated as follows, say, $2 \div 3 \div 4$. This latter statement means that the first quantity can be divided into 2 equal parts, and that the second quantity will contain 3 such equal parts and the third will contain 4 such equal parts. The total number of such parts in the sum of these three quantities is 9. If we have, for example, five such quantities, the procedure is exactly the same. For example, we may have the following ratio: $3 \div 5 \div 1 \div 7 \div 2$. The sum of these parts is then $3 + 5 + 1 + 7 + 3 = 18$. If the sum of the quantities is given, the division of the sum by the total number of parts will give the magnitude of one part, and when this part has been multiplied by each number given in the ratio we have found the magnitude of each quantity.

EXAMPLE. Four workers worked the following number of days: 5, 7, 10, and 12. Their total pay was $272. How much did each of them receive?

The total number of days for which payment was made was

$$5 + 7 + 10 + 12 = 34.$$

Then the pay for one day was $272 \div 34 = 8. The distribution of the money was as follows:

$$
\begin{aligned}
&\text{the first worker received } \$8 \cdot 5 \ \ = \$40, \\
&\text{the second worker received } \$8 \cdot 7 \ \ = \$56, \\
&\text{the third worker received } \$8 \cdot 10 = \$80, \\
&\text{the fourth worker received } \$8 \cdot 12 = \$96.
\end{aligned}
$$

The check is $40 + 56 + 80 + 96 = 272$, and

$$40 \div 56 \div 80 \div 96 = 5 \div 7 \div 10 \div 12.$$

Very often such problems are given in terms of the differences.

EXAMPLE. Three numbers are in the following ratio: $1 \div 5 \div 9$. The second exceeds the first by 36. Find the numbers.

The second contains $5 - 1 = 4$ parts more than the first. Then one such part is $36 \div 4 = 9$. The three numbers are: $9 \cdot 1 = 9, 9 \cdot 5 = 45$, and $9 \cdot 9 = 81$.

The check is $45 - 9 = 36$, and

$$9 \div 45 \div 81 = 1 \div 5 \div 9.$$

PROBLEMS

467. Soft solder is composed of two parts of tin and one part of lead. How much tin and how much lead should go into the making of 24 pounds of solder?

469. Divide the number 7,200 into two parts which will be in the ratio of $7 \div 5$.

469. Divide the number 480 into two parts which will be in the ratio $\frac{5}{3} \div \frac{5}{6}$.

470. Divide the number 750 into two parts which will be in the ratio of the two numbers 1.3 and 1.2.

471. The difference of two numbers is 75, and their ratio is $18 \div 3$. Find the numbers.

472. Divide 1,815 into three parts proportional to the numbers 9, 11, and 13.

473. Divide 100 into three parts proportional to the three fractions $\frac{1}{2}$, $\frac{3}{4}$, $\frac{5}{6}$. (*Hint:* Bring the three fractions to a common denominator.)

474. Divide 810 into three parts such that the first is 3 times the second and 6 times the third.

475. Three numbers are in the ratio $3 \div 5 \div 8$, and the third number is 112. Find the other two.

476. Divide 632.7 into parts proportional to 0.1, 0.01, and 0.001.

477. Five numbers are in the ratio $1 \div 2 \div 3 \div 4 \div 5$. Find the numbers if the difference of the fifth and the second is 51.

478. Three groups collected money for the purchase of an ambulance. The amounts collected were in the ratio $0.75 \div \frac{2}{3} \div 1\frac{1}{15}$. How much was collected by each group if the first collected $250 more than the second?

479. Black powder consists of 6 parts of sulphur, 39 parts of nitrate, and 5 parts of carbon. How much of each substance must be taken in order to obtain 75 pounds of black powder?

480. Three men worked as follows: the first 2 days of 6 hours each; the second 3 days of 5 hours each, and the third only one day of 8 hours. They received $70 together. How much was each paid?

481. A wire 124 feet long was divided into three parts. The ratio of the first to the second was $3 \div 5$, and the ratio of the second to the third was $2 \div 3$. Find the lengths of each part.

15

Percents

What are percents?

In everyday life we often use numbers which carry with them
the description *percent*. Numerically, percents do not represent
anything new. Furthermore, percents are not used numerically
for computation purposes, as it will be shown presently. Percents are used only as descriptive aids whenever fractions or
ratios are replaced by them.

The word *percent*, in everyday English, means *a hundredth*,
or a hundredth part of a quantity or of a number.

In writing numbers denoting percents we use a special symbol %.

Thus, one percent is written as 1%. One percent means one
one-hundredth part. Five percent is written as 5%. Five
percent means five one-hundredths.

The expression 0.25% is read twenty-five one-hundredths
of a percent, and it means 0.25 of one one-hundredth, that is
$0.25 \cdot 0.01 = 0.0025$.

The expression 100% means one hundred percent or 100
one-hundredths, that is, $100 \cdot 0.01 = 1$. Thus 100% represents
the entire quantity under discussion. The expression 200%
means two hundred percent or 200 one-hundredths, that is,
$200 \cdot 0.01 = 2$. Thus 200% represents the quantity doubled.

PROBLEMS

482. Read the following: (*a*) 15%; (*b*) 75%; (*c*) 0.1%; (*d*) 1.25%; (*e*)
0.01%; (*f*) $\frac{1}{2}$%; (*g*) $\frac{3}{4}$%; (*h*) $12\frac{1}{2}$%; (*i*) $33\frac{1}{3}$%; (*j*) $66\frac{2}{3}$%.

483. Write the following: (*a*) twenty percent; (*b*) fifty-one percent; (*c*)
forty-nine percent; (*d*) five and one-third percent; (*e*) six one-hundredths of a
percent; (*f*) one one-thousandth of a percent; (*g*) ninety-nine percent.

484. What percent of a given number is represented by the number itself?

213

485. What percent of a given number is a number twice as large? four times as large?

486. What percent of a given number is a number twelve times as large? twenty-five times as large?

Changing percents into decimal fractions

For the purpose of computation, statements of percent must be changed into fractions, decimal or common.

The conversion of statements of percent into decimal fractions is accomplished by multiplying the number of percents by 0.01. Remember that 1% of a quantity represents 0.01 of a quantity. Thus 25% is changed into $25 \cdot 0.01 = 0.25$; 12.67% is changed into $12.67 \cdot 0.01 = 0.1267$.

PROBLEMS

Change the following into decimal fractions:

487. 1%; 7%; 10%; 32%; 57%; 136%; 362%; 100%; 200%; 1,000%.

488. 2.5%; 5.7%; 7.5%; 8.6%; 17.5%; 28.9%; 0.4%; 0.14%; 0.28%; 1.6%; 532.5%; 106.5%; 2,450.5%.

489. $1\frac{1}{2}$%; $\frac{3}{4}$%; $7\frac{5}{6}$%; $33\frac{1}{3}$%; $66\frac{2}{3}$%; $127\frac{1}{6}$%.

Changing percents into common fractions

The conversion of statements of percent into common fractions is accomplished by multiplying the number of percents by $\frac{1}{100}$. Again, here we must remember that 1% represents $\frac{1}{100}$ of a quantity. Thus 8% is changed into $8 \cdot \frac{1}{100} = \frac{8}{100} = \frac{2}{25}$; $33\frac{1}{3}$% is changed into $\frac{100}{3} \cdot \frac{1}{100} = \frac{1}{3}$.

PROBLEMS

Change the following into common fractions:

490. 2%; 9%; 12%; 27%; 35%; 55%; 75%; 25%; 50%; 125%; 150%; 175%; 250%; 475%.

491. 2.5%; 0.25%; 1.75%; 0.175%; 0.55%; 0.75%; 0.025%; 17.5%; 27.2%; 0.15%; 525.75%; 106.5%.

492. $1\frac{2}{3}$%; $2\frac{3}{4}$%; $15\frac{1}{6}$%; $66\frac{2}{3}$%; $7\frac{1}{6}$%; $155\frac{1}{6}$%; $106\frac{1}{8}$%.

Changing decimal fractions into percents

From the fact that 1% represents 0.01, and from the procedure of changing a number of percents into decimal fractions by multiplying this number by 0.01, we can obtain the rule for the changing of decimal fractions into percents.

The change of percents into decimal fractions requires the multiplication of the percent by 0.01, which is equivalent to the division by 100. *The changing of a decimal fraction into percents is actually a reversal of the procedure for changing a percent into a decimal fraction. Thus, in order to reverse the division by 100 we must multiply by 100.* For example, 0.25 when changed into percents becomes $0.25 \cdot 100 = 25\%$; 1.5 when changed into percents becomes $1.5 \cdot 100 = 150\%$.

PROBLEMS

Change the following into percents:

493. 0.1; 0.7; 0.12; 0.27; 0.45; 0.51; 0.75; 0.99; 0.01; 0.05; 0.001; 0.007; 0.015; 0.075; 0.089; 0.125; 0.355; 0.499; 0.501; 0.755; 0.999.

494. 1.1; 1.5; 1.9; 1.25; 1.75; 2.55; 1.06; 4.75; 5.01; 7.25; 7.66; 8.33; 9.57; 9.99; 10.125; 25.075.

Changing common fractions into percents

From the fact that 1% represents $\frac{1}{100}$, and from the procedure of changing a number of percents into common fractions by multiplying this number by the common fraction $\frac{1}{100}$, we can obtain the rule for changing common fractions into percents.

The change of percents into common fractions requires the multiplication by $\frac{1}{100}$, which is equivalent to the division by 100. *The changing of a common fraction into percents is then actually a reversal of the procedure for changing a percent into a common fraction. Thus, in order to reverse the division by 100 we must multiply by 100.* For example, $\frac{1}{4}$, when changed into percents, becomes $\frac{1}{4} \cdot 100 = 25\%$; $1\frac{1}{5}$, when changed into percents, becomes $\frac{6}{5} \cdot 100 = 120\%$.

Very often the denominator of the common fraction that must be changed into percents contains factors other than 2 and 5.

In such a case the percents can be expressed in mixed numbers; for example, $1\frac{1}{3}$, when changed into percents, becomes

$$\frac{4}{3} \cdot 100 = \frac{400}{3}\% = 133\frac{1}{3}\%.$$

If we wish to use decimal fractions in the expression of percents we obtain in this case a periodic fraction, and the number of decimal places that are retained is determined by the computer or by the statement of the problem that is to be solved. Thus, $1\frac{1}{3}$, when changed into percents, becomes $\frac{400}{3}\% = 133.33\cdots\%$, if two decimal places are retained.

PROBLEMS

495. Change the following into percents: $\frac{1}{100}$; $\frac{1}{2}$; $\frac{1}{4}$; $\frac{1}{5}$; $\frac{1}{10}$; $\frac{1}{20}$; $\frac{1}{25}$; $\frac{1}{40}$; $\frac{1}{50}$; $\frac{1}{8}$; $\frac{1}{16}$; $\frac{1}{32}$; $\frac{1}{64}$; $\frac{3}{4}$; $\frac{5}{8}$; $\frac{8}{25}$; $\frac{17}{125}$; $\frac{51}{100}$; $\frac{49}{250}$; $\frac{89}{500}$; $\frac{99}{1000}$; $\frac{29}{80}$; $\frac{17}{160}$; $\frac{57}{320}$.

496. Change the following into percents: $15\frac{1}{2}$; $7\frac{7}{8}$; $9\frac{4}{5}$; $17\frac{7}{25}$; $5\frac{3}{4}$; $6\frac{15}{32}$; $16\frac{17}{50}$; $35\frac{15}{64}$; $10\frac{37}{125}$.

497. Change the following into percents; represent them by means of mixed numbers: $\frac{2}{3}$; $\frac{4}{7}$; $\frac{5}{9}$; $\frac{7}{11}$; $\frac{19}{35}$; $\frac{27}{49}$; $\frac{75}{82}$; $\frac{135}{112}$; $\frac{245}{275}$; $\frac{321}{360}$; $\frac{477}{700}$.

498. Change the following into percents; represent them by means of mixed numbers: $1\frac{2}{7}$; $3\frac{4}{9}$; $7\frac{5}{11}$; $6\frac{7}{15}$; $9\frac{8}{21}$; $15\frac{4}{27}$; $5\frac{6}{35}$; $7\frac{5}{18}$.

499. Change the following into percents; represent them by means of decimal fractions having two decimal places: $\frac{2}{7}$; $\frac{5}{9}$; $\frac{8}{9}$; $\frac{9}{17}$; $\frac{15}{23}$; $\frac{23}{27}$; $\frac{18}{35}$; $\frac{36}{49}$; $\frac{13}{45}$; $\frac{37}{75}$; $\frac{49}{82}$; $\frac{73}{98}$.

500. Change the following into percents; represent them by means of decimal fractions having two decimal places: $2\frac{5}{6}$; $1\frac{7}{9}$; $3\frac{8}{11}$; $4\frac{3}{13}$; $5\frac{2}{15}$; $7\frac{5}{18}$; $6\frac{5}{21}$; $1\frac{4}{35}$; $4\frac{5}{42}$.

Finding the percent of a number

Since 1% is equivalent to 0.01 of a given quantity, the finding of 1% is performed by multiplying the numerical value of the quantity by 0.01. The finding a certain number of percents, say 25%, of a given quantity is performed by multiplying the numerical value of the given quantity by 0.25.

Thus, for example, 35% of $250 is obtained as follows:

$$\$250 \cdot 0.35 = \$87.50,$$

that is, 87 dollars and 50 cents.

If we wish to use common fractions in place of decimal fractions, the same problem is solved as follows:

$$250 \cdot \frac{35}{100} = \frac{250 \cdot 35}{100} = 87\frac{50}{100},$$

or $87.50.

The procedure for solving problems in finding a percent of a number can be stated in compact form as follows:

$$A = N \cdot \frac{p}{100}, \quad \text{or} \quad A = N \cdot p \cdot 0.01,$$

where N is the numerical value of the given magnitude, p is the number of percents, and A is the percent of N that is to be found. Translated into words, this rule is as follows: *Multiply the given numerical value of the magnitude by the number of percents, and divide the product by 100 (or multiply the product by 0.01).*

There are numerous problems that require finding the percent of a number. We shall examine the most common of them.

Finding a part of a number

Under this group fall all those problems in which percents are used either in place of fractions, or as ratios (including proportional division).

EXAMPLE. A factory employed 6,000 workers; 45% of them were women. How many women and how many men were employed?

We have, then, that the number of women employed in the factory was

$$6,000 \cdot 0.45 = 2,700.$$

The number of men was then

$$6,000 - 2,700 = 3,300.$$

EXAMPLE. An alloy consists of 64.8% copper, 32.8% zinc, and 2.4% lead. How many pounds of copper, zinc, and lead must be taken in order to obtain 1.5 short tons of alloy?

In this problem percents are used as ratios. We could state that the ratios of copper, zinc, and lead are $0.648 \div 0.328 \div 0.024$. We have then, after converting 1.5 short tons into pounds (1.5 short tons = 3,000 pounds), the following amounts:

$$\begin{array}{llll}
\text{Copper} & \dots\dots\dots & 3{,}000 \cdot 0.648 = & 1{,}944 \text{ pounds,} \\
\text{Zinc} & \dots\dots\dots & 3{,}000 \cdot 0.328 = & 984 \text{ pounds,} \\
\text{Lead} & \dots\dots\dots & 3{,}000 \cdot 0.024 = & 72 \text{ pounds.}
\end{array}$$

Note that $64.8\% + 32.8\% + 2.4\% = 100\%$. This addition indicates that the total amount is represented by 100%, and that no other substances were used.

PROBLEMS

501. The amount of sugar that can dissolve in cold water is equal to 66.1% of the weight of the water in which it is placed. How much sugar will dissolve in a glass of water (250 grams)?

502. A certain steel contains 1.05% carbon, 1.1% manganese, and 0.2% silicon, and the remainder pure iron. How much of each substance is there in 10,000 short tons of this steel?

503. A lot of pig iron contains 3.5% carbon, 1.5% silicon, 1% manganese, 0.4% phosphorus, and 0.01% sulphur. The remainder is pure iron. How much of each substance is there in this lot of pig iron if it weighs 25,000 short tons?

504. A corporation pays 2.5% of an employee's salary into his pension retirement fund. The employee contributes an equal amount. How much is paid into this fund yearly if the employee's monthly salary is $275?

505. A fire insurance company charges $\frac{7}{8}\%$ of the valuation for insuring a building. What was the insurance premium on a $35,000 fire insurance policy?

Profit and loss

If a merchant buys some article at one price and sells it at another he may sell it for a sum of money greater than he has paid (the excess is called a *margin*), or he may sell for less than he has paid (thus he incurs a *loss*).

There are two basic ways of computing margin. There are also two basic ways of computing loss. We may compute them from the cost, and we may compute them from the selling price.

There is no hard and fast rule as to which method should be employed. The correct procedure then is to state explicitly and beforehand the method that is used, and thus to avoid confusion.

In the illustrative examples below the two methods will be employed.

EXAMPLE. A radio dealer bought a radio set for $45 and sold it at a 35% margin. What was the selling price?

If we compute the margin from the cost, then the selling price was

$$\$45 + \$45 \cdot 0.35 = \$45 + \$15.75 = \$60.75.$$

If we compute the margin from the selling price, then the cost was $100\% - 35\% = 65\%$ of the selling price. This procedure requires the finding of a number from a given percent of it, which will be taken up on pages 225–226.

EXAMPLE. A used-car dealer bought a used car for $550 and sold it at a 20% loss. What was the selling price?

If we compute the loss from the cost, then the selling price was

$$\$550 - \$550 \cdot 0.20 = \$550 - \$110 = \$440.$$

If we compute the loss from the selling price, then the cost was $100\% + 20\% = 120\%$ of the selling price. The selling price is taken as 100%. This procedure requires the finding of a number from a given percent of it, which will be taken up on pages 225–226.

PROBLEMS

Compute the following from cost.

506. An article that cost $75 sold at a margin of 15%. How much margin was added?

507. An article was bought for $90. To this cost 15% was added for handling and repair. Then it was sold at a margin of 30%. What was the margin?

508. An article was bought for $2.50 and was sold at a margin of 40%. What was the selling price?

509. An article cost $15 and it was sold at a loss of 18%. What was the loss?

510. An article was bought for $3.75, and it was sold at a loss of 40%. What was the selling price?

Discount and chain discount

Very often the selling price carries with itself a deduction (or reduction). This deduction may be for paying cash, or for paying the bill before a certain date. Such a deduction is known as a discount.

For example, an article may be billed $200, 10% off for cash. The cash price is then $100\% - 10\% = 90\%$ of the billed price, that is,

$$\$200 \cdot 0.90 = \$180.$$

Some wholesale merchants offer several discounts which are applied in succession. For example, a bill may carry the following discounts: 10%, 8%, and 2%. *Each must be computed separately.* Let us assume that the bill was $500. Then the first discount, 10%, reduces the price to

$$\$500 \cdot 0.90 = \$450.$$

Applying the second discount, 8%, we find that the balance is $100\% - 8\% = 92\%$ of $450, and this amount is

$$\$450 \cdot 0.92 = \$414.$$

Finally, applying the third discount, 2%, we find that the balance is $100\% - 2\% = 98\%$ of $414, and this amount is

$$\$414 \cdot 0.98 = \$405.72.$$

It is sometimes convenient to compute the discount and subtract it from the billed price. Thus 2% of $414 is

$$\$414 \cdot 0.02 = \$8.28,$$
and

$$\$414 - \$8.28 = \$405.72.$$

PROBLEMS

511. An article was billed at $175 less 8% for cash. What was the cash price?

512. An article was billed at $35 less 2% if paid before the first of the month following the date of the bill. The payment was made in time to earn this discount. Then this article was sold at 20% profit. What was its selling price?

513. An article was billed at $300 with the following discounts: 12%, 5%, 3%. How much was paid on this bill?

514. An article was billed at $1,500, less 8%, 5%, and 1%; but to the bill was also added the following item: Federal tax on price billed, 7.5%. What was the amount paid on the bill?

515. An article was billed at $750, discount for cash 8%; but to the bill were added the following items: Federal tax on price billed 8%, and State tax on price billed 5%. The article was sold at a profit of 25%. What was the profit?

Note on chain discount. Chain discount can be computed by means of a short-cut introduced in the computation. Instead of computing every discount separately we may work on the percents. Suppose that the following discounts have been offered: 15%, 10%, 8%, and 2%. We proceed as follows:

$$100\% - 15\% = 85\%.$$

Subtract 10% of 85%:

$$85\% - 8.5\% = 76.5\%.$$

Subtract 8% of 76.5%

$$76.5\% - 6.12\% = 70.38\%.$$

Subtract 2% of 70.38%

$$70.38\% - 1.4076\% = 68.9724\%.$$

The total discount is then

$$100\% - 68.9724\% = 31.0276\%.$$

Thus, if the billed price is $1,000, then the discount is $310.276, or $310.28, and the amount paid is

$$\$1,000 - \$310.28 = \$689.72.$$

Problems 513 and 514 may be solved using this method, and the results checked with those already obtained.

Simple interest

Money is a commodity, and for its use we must pay a price. The money paid for the privilege of using money is known as interest or discount. If the charge is paid at the beginning of a loan it is called discount. If it is paid after the borrower has had the use of the money, it is called interest. Discount and interest are computed in terms of so many dollars per $100 per year. This rate is expressed in terms of percents, because actually it means so many units per hundred. Interest may be stated for other periods of time, often per month, but generally it is stated on the yearly basis, frequently (in business language) *per annum.*

When interest is stated for a definite period (per annum, or per month), and the money was used the entire period the calculation of the interest is simple. For example, if $500 was borrowed for one year, and the rate of interest charged was 6%, then the interest was $500 · 0.06 = $30. At the end of the year, if the loan was paid back, it was computed as follows:

Principal (the amount borrowed)........ $500
Interest at 6%.......................   30
Total amount paid back............... $530

The same problem may be solved in another manner. We start with $1. At the end of one year the total amount that must be paid back is $1 + $0.06 = 1.06. Multiplying this result by 500, we obtain 500 · $1.06 = $530.

In order to simplify the computations, banks and almost all business institutions consider the year equal to 360 days, and each month equal to 30 days. Thus the year is subdivided into 12 periods (months), each of 30 days' duration.

If the money that was borrowed was used less than a year or more than a year, the division of the 360-day year into 12 periods enables us to compute the interest easily. For example, suppose that the \$500 was repaid in 5 months. Then the interest that was due on the loan was $\frac{5}{12}$ of the 6%, or

$$\$500 \cdot 0.06 \cdot \frac{5}{12} = \$500 \cdot \frac{0.01 \cdot 5}{2} = \$12.50.$$

If the \$500 was kept 1 year and 4 months, then the interest was

$$\$500 \cdot 0.06 \cdot \frac{16}{12} = \$500 \cdot 0.01 \cdot 8 = \$40.$$

PROBLEMS

516. \$1,500 was borrowed at 8% per annum and was repaid in $5\frac{1}{2}$ months. How much was paid?

517. \$2,000 was borrowed at $5\frac{1}{2}$% per annum. It was repaid in installments of \$1,000 each, one in 3 months and the second 2 months later. How much was repaid?

518. \$60,000 was borrowed and was repaid in twelve equal monthly installments (with the interest due on each), beginning one year after the loan was made. The interest was at 4% per annum. How much was paid back altogether?

519. \$300 was borrowed at the rate of 2% per month, and it was repaid in 12 equal monthly installments beginning a month after the loan was made. How much was paid back?

520. \$5,000 was borrowed at the rate of 5% per annum, and it was repaid 185 days later. How much was paid back?

Compound interest

Very often, money that was borrowed draws interest, and the interest is added to the principal. Then the principal and interest continue to accumulate more interest. In other words, not only the principal, but the interest also draws interest.

This kind of interest is known as *compound interest* because the principal and interest are compounded.

For example, suppose that $100 is deposited in a bank which pays 3% interest annually.

At the end of the first year the interest is
  computed and added to the amount on
  deposit, and the total is............. $100 · 1.03 = $103.00
At the end of the second year it becomes $103 · 1.03 = $106.09
At the end of the third year it becomes $106.09 · 1.03 = $109.27
At the end of the fourth year it becomes $109.27 · 1.03 = $112.55*
At the end of the fifth year it becomes $112.55 · 1.03 = $115.93*

Some banks pay interest (although considered at a yearly rate) at shorter intervals, as semiannually, or quarterly. The yearly rate of interest is divided by the number of intervals in the year (semiannually computed interest is paid twice, every six months; quarterly computed interest is paid four times a year, every three months). For example, if the $100 above were drawing 3% per annum interest paid quarterly, then every three months the interest rate would be 0.75%, and we would have the following:

At the end of the first period (3 months)
  the total amount becomes.......... $100.75
At the end of the second period the total
  amount becomes................. $100.75 · 1.0075 = $101.51*
At the end of the third period the total
  amount becomes................. $101.51 · 1.0075 = $102.27*
At the end of the fourth period the total
  amount becomes................. $102.27 · 1.0075 = $103.04*

Compare these results with the first line of the computations of interest on the yearly basis above. Note that the quarterly interest earns an extra 4 cents.

In Chapter 17 we shall state a formula which will enable us to compute the amount of capital drawing compound interest.

---

* Some institutions adopt the practice of computing interest on dollar amounts only, ignoring cents. These amounts would be less if this practice were in effect.

PROBLEMS

521. $300 is deposited in a savings bank that pays 2% per annum compounded quarterly. This deposit is withdrawn after interest has been credited at the end of 3 years. How much was there on deposit on the day of withdrawal?

522. $5,000 is borrowed for 1 year. The interest to be paid was 5.6% to be compounded every 45 days. How much was paid back?

523. A man deposits $100 every three months with a bank that pays 3% per annum compounded quarterly. How much will he have at the end of two years?

524. A man borrowed $1,000 for a period of 4 years at 6% per annum compounded semiannually. The terms of the loan call for payment of accumulated interest each year and also for a payment of $250 at the end of each year to reduce the principal. How much interest did the borrower pay after the $1,000 was paid off?

525. $300 is borrowed for six years at 2% per year. The interest is compounded annually until the loan is paid back. How much was repaid?

Finding a number from a given percent of it

The reader should recall the problems in fractions where a certain number was given and described as a certain fraction of some other number, and it was required to find the latter number (see page 180).

EXAMPLE. Suppose we have the number 85, and we are told that this is 17% of some other number. It is required to compute that number. We proceed as follows:

It is given that 85 is 17% of some number, that is, 0.17 of that number. Then 0.01 of that number is $\frac{85}{17}$, and the unknown number is 100 times as large as this fraction; that is,

$$\frac{85 \cdot 100}{17} = 500.$$

Thus we have the method for the solution of the problems requiring the finding of a number from a given percent of it. We divide the given percent of a number by the number of percents and multiply the quotient by 100.

The procedure for solving problems in finding a number from a given percentage can be stated in compact form as follows

$$N = \frac{A \cdot 100}{p},$$

where N is the number that is sought, p is the number of percents, and A is the percent of N that is given. Translated into English, this rule reads as follows: Multiply the given percent of a number by 100 and divide the product by the given number of percents.

Computation of profit and loss from the selling price

On page 219 we illustrated the computation of profit and loss from the cost price of an article, and we stated that the computation of profit and loss from the selling price will be illustrated in this section.

Let us take up the examples given on page 219. A radio dealer bought a radio set for \$45 and sold it at a margin of 35% figured from the selling price. What was the selling price?

We found on page 219 that, considering the selling price at 100%, the cost of the radio set was $100\% - 35\% = 65\%$ of the selling price. Hence we have that \$45 was 65% of the selling price, and the selling price was

$$\frac{45 \cdot 100}{65} = \$69.23.$$

Again, if the used car was bought for \$550 and was sold at 20% loss, then, considering the selling price as 100%, the cost of the car was $100\% + 20\% = 120\%$ of the selling price. Thus we have that \$550 was 120% of the selling price, and the selling price was

$$\frac{550 \cdot 100}{120} = \$458.33.$$

Note that computing the margin from the selling price we subtract the percent of margin from the 100% that is assigned to the selling price. The difference gives us the percent that corresponds to the cost, which becomes a percent of the selling price.

In computing the loss from the selling price we add the percent of loss to the 100% that is assigned to the selling price, and this sum of the percents corresponds to the cost which is now a percent of the selling price.

PROBLEMS

526. Solve Problem 506 figuring the margin from the selling price.

527. Solve Problem 507 figuring the margin from the selling price.

528. Solve Problem 508 figuring the margin from the selling price.

529. Solve Problem 509 figuring the loss from the selling price.

530. Solve Problem 510 figuring the loss from the selling price.

Problems in finding a number from a given percent of it

In the following problems the rule for finding the number from a given percent of it is, as stated on page 226,

$$N = \frac{A \cdot 100}{p}.$$

Read each problem carefully. In some cases the statement of the percent that corresponds to the given percent of a number is the sum of 100% and some stated percent given in the problem directly. As an example of this type of procedure see the second illustrative example on page 219.

PROBLEMS

531. Of what numbers is 54 equal to the following percents: (a) 3%; (b) 5%; (c) 8%; (d) 12%; (e) 20%; (f) 33⅓%; (g) 66⅔%; (h) 125%; (i) 175%; (j) 250%?

532. Find the number to which the following statements refer: (a) 3% is 36; (b) 14% is 7; (c) 4.5% is 9; (d) 3.75% is 75; (e) 12.5% is 7.5; (f) 5.6% is 4.2; (g) 5% is 22.5; (h) 112.5% is 81; (i) 225% is 154; (j) 375% is 225.

533. By adding to a number 12% of it, we obtain 420. What is the number?

534. By subtracting from a number 16% of it, we obtain 434. What is the number?

535. A shop produced 256 parts in 6 hours, and this output represented 32% of its daily quota. If the same rate of production were continued for 24 hours, how many parts beyond quota would this shop deliver? What was the daily quota?

536. A wooden model of a machine part weighs 6% of the weight of the part itself. What is the weight of the part if the model weighs 15 pounds?

537. The cost of a certain article plus the cost of its shipping is $788.40. The shipping cost is 8% of the billed price. What is the cost of the article?

538. A lathe, after a few years of service, is valued at $357, which is 68% of its original cost. What was the original cost?

539. A worker received a 15% raise in his wages. What were his wages before the raise if after the raise his monthly wages were $276?

540. Coffee loses 12½% of its weight in roasting. How much coffee must be roasted in order to obtain 180 pounds of coffee?

541. The yield of cream is 21% of the weight of the milk from which it is obtained. The yield of butter is 23% of the weight of the cream from which it is obtained. How many pounds of milk are required to yield 350 pounds of butter?

The percent ratio of two numbers

In problems that require finding the relation between two numbers in terms of percents the solution consists of two steps:

> *i.* We divide the two numbers, and the divisor is that number with which we compare the second.
>
> *ii.* The quotient is multiplied by 100. The product is the number of percents required.

EXAMPLE. A worker's monthly wage of $180 was raised to $225. What percent increase has he received?

This problem may be solved in two ways. We divide $225 by $180. Note that $180 is the divisor because the increase is judged by the previous wages. Then we multiply the quotient by 100. We have then

$$\frac{225 \cdot 100}{180} = 125\%.$$

Subtract from 125% the percent that corresponds to $180, that is 100%. We have then

$$125\% - 100\% = 25\%.$$

We may solve the same problem by subtracting $180 from $225. We obtain the difference $225 − $180 = $45. This amount is the increase in the wages. By dividing $45 by $180 and multiplying the quotient by 100, we obtain

$$\frac{45 \cdot 100}{180} = 25\%.$$

In a similar manner we solve the following problem.

EXAMPLE. A tank of water, when filled, contained 2,500 gallons; 650 gallons were withdrawn. What percent of loss does this withdrawal represent? The solution is

$$\frac{650 \cdot 100}{2,500} = 26\%.$$

The procedure for solving problems in finding the percent from two given numbers can be stated in compact form as follows

$$p = \frac{A \cdot 100}{N},$$

where p is the number of percents that is being sought, N is the number with which the number A is being compared, and A is the number that is being compared.

PROBLEMS

542. What percent of $325 are the following: (a) $5; (b) $18; (c) $2.75; (d) $15.20; (e) $22.25?

543. What percent of 4.5 tons (1 ton = 2,000 pounds) are the following: (a) 255 pounds; (b) 1.5 tons; (c) 1,525 pounds; (d) 3.5 tons; (e) 1,895 pounds?

544. When 50 shots were fired from a rifle, 3 misses occurred. What was the percent of hits on the target?

545. Out of 300 tons of ore, 45.5 tons of copper were obtained. What was the percent of the yield?

546. An average yield of iron from iron ore is 112 parts of iron from 160 parts of ore. What is the percent of yield?

547. The yield from 1,200 pounds of sugar beets is 250 pounds of sugar. What percent of the sugar beets is sugar?

548. A factory bought a machine and paid $6,500 for it. It was figured that the life of the machine would be 10 years, and its scrap value $500. What is the percent of yearly depreciation in the value of the machine?

549. A factory changed the working time of a shift from 8 hours to 7 hours, but the wages of the workers were left unchanged. What was the percent of change in the hourly wages of the workers?

550. A factory changed the working time of a shift from 8 hours to 10 hours, but the wages of the workers were left unchanged. What was the percent of change in the hourly wages of the workers?

551. A factory produced 1,894 vehicles instead of the planned 1,800. What was the percent of overproduction?

552. In precision measurement, a ruler 1 yard long is allowed 0.01 inch margin of error. What is this error in percent?

553. The number 1.657 is rounded to hundredths. What is the percent error effected by this rounding?

554. When being copied, the number 5,078 was written as 578. What percent of the old number is the copied one? What percent error was incurred by the mistake in copying?

555. A warehouse received 49 tons of potatoes. After a lapse of time its found that this shipment weighed only 47.6 tons. What was the percent lost by drying?

556. A wage earner earns $180 a month. The cost of living rises 10%. What is the percent of his loss in real income?

Installment buying, mortgages, and small loans

Loans are very often repaid in installments. Installment selling is a major business in this country, and though many think the installment plan is a convenient method of buying, few realize the enormous rates of interest per annum that are being charged by those who sell "on time." The average purchaser thinks of 1% or 2% per month, or of 8% per year that he is supposedly paying. A few simple computations will convince him that not everything is as he thinks it is.

Let us consider an example that is typical. A clothing firm offers suits on a plan whereby the credit purchaser pays $1.00 down and the retail list price of the suit in 3 monthly installments. His suits are priced at $24.75. Let us tabulate the payments:

Payment	Amount	Balance unpaid
Down......................	$ 1.00	$24.75
End of first month...........	8.25	16.50
End of second month........	8.25	8.25
End of third month..........	8.25	—
Total....................	$25.75	$49.50

We may reason that the purchaser owed $8.25 for the entire period of three months, that in addition he owed a further $8.25 for two months, and that in addition during the interval between the down payment and the end of the first month he owed still an additional $8.25 for one month. Accordingly he owed the seller, during the life of this sales contract, the equivalent of $8.25 for six months. For the use of this amount he pay $1.00. Let us disregard the fact that he paid this $1.00 in advance and consider it as interest. On this plan, he would then have paid $2.00 interest for the use of $8.25 for 1 year. The rate of interest would then be

$$\frac{\$2.00 \cdot 100}{\$8.25} = 24.24\%.$$

By way of check, we can interpret the interest rate as $1.00 per $49.50 per month, or $12.00 per $49.50 per year, which is also 24.24% per year.

A further typical example is in the deferred-payment terms of a large mail-order house. This firm bases its deferred-payment charges entirely on the unpaid balance. If the unpaid balance is $55, an additional $5 is charged for the use of the money, and the payments are made at $5.00 per month:

Payment	Amount	Unpaid balance
Beginning of contract........	$00.00	$ 60.00
End of first month...........	5.00	55.00
End of second month........	5.00	50.00
End of third month..........	5.00	45.00
End of fourth month.........	5.00	40.00
End of fifth month...........	5.00	35.00
End of sixth month..........	5.00	30.00
End of seventh month........	5.00	25.00
End of eighth month.........	5.00	20.00
End of ninth month..........	5.00	15.00
End of tenth month..........	5.00	10.00
End of eleventh month.......	5.00	5.00
End of twelfth month........	5.00	—
Total...................	$60.00	$390.00

This tabulation shows us that the buyer's debt can be reckoned as equivalent to $390 for one month. The interest of $5.00 on $390 for one month is equivalent to $60 on $390 for one year, or

$$\frac{\$60 \cdot 100}{\$390} = 15.38\%.$$

Another typical plan is to calculate the charge for using the money, add it to the first of a series of equal payments for the merchandise, and collect as an initial payment the sum of the use charge and the first payment. Applied to the purchase of a vacuum cleaner, $39.50 list cash price, this contract results as follows:

List cash price..........................	$39.50
Deferral charge @ 10%.................	3.95
Monthly payment @ 10%..............	3.95
Initial payment.......................	$ 7.90

Payment	Amount	Balance unpaid
Initial.....................	$ 7.90	$ 35.55
End of 1 month.............	3.95	31.60
End of 2 months............	3.95	27.65
End of 3 months............	3.95	23.70
End of 4 months............	3.95	19.75
End of 5 months............	3.95	15.80
End of 6 months............	3.95	11.85
End of 7 months............	3.95	7.90
End of 8 months............	3.95	3.95
End of 9 months............	3.95	—
Total..................	$43.45	$177.75

The charge has been $3.95 for the use of $177.75 for one month, which is equivalent to paying $47.40 for the use of $177.75 for one year. The rate percent is therefore

$$\frac{\$47.40 \cdot 100}{\$177.75} = 26.67\%.$$

The same method of computation applies to mortgage loans. Let us consider the following example. A mortgage loan of $5,000 on a house is to be paid off in 5 years at $5\frac{1}{2}\%$ interest per annum, which is to be calculated on the unpaid balance. The payments are then as follows:

	Payment on principal	Interest	Total	Unpaid balance
				$ 5,000
End of 1 year.........	$1,000	$275	$1,275	4,000
End of 2 years........	1,000	220	1,220	3,000
End of 3 years........	1,000	165	1,165	2,000
End of 4 years........	1,000	110	1,110	1,000
End of 5 years........	1,000	55	1,055	—
Total.............	$5,000	$825	$5,825	$15,000

Thus we may consider as if $15,000 was kept for one year and the interest paid on it was $825.

$$\frac{\$825 \cdot 100}{\$15,000} = 5.5\%,$$

which is exactly the same rate as called for in the terms of the mortgage loan.

When money is borrowed or when goods are bought on the installment plan, it is not unusual to require the borrower or purchaser to pay various charges in addition to the interest. These may be title-search costs, insurance, investigation fees, recording fees, handling charges, and the like. Many of these, however titled, are a part of the cost for the money borrowed, so far as the borrower is concerned. Others, such as insurance, are not a part of such cost. Consider the insurance charge on automobile financing, for example—it may relieve the insured borrower of a liability he would otherwise have to assume; if he gets something for his insurance premium other than the use of borrowed money, the insurance charge is not a part of the charge for use of money. On the other hand, if the purchaser of an automobile has the choice of buying or not buying, then the costs other than net purchase price, so far as his personal finances are concerned, are all in a sense part of the interest; nevertheless, the finance company will not put the insurance fee on its books as money earned on the loaned principal.

PROBLEMS

557. An automobile was purchased from a dealer with the financing arranged by a finance company. The price of the automobile was $895. The cash payment was $350. The balance was to be paid in 12 months in equal installments. The interest rate was figured at 6% per annum (or 0.5% per month) on the unpaid balance. The finance company charged an additional $25 for insurance, and $10 for handling fees. What was the actual interest rate per annum?

558. A man borrows $300 from a loan company which is to be repaid in 6 months. The rate of interest is 1.75% per month on the unpaid balance.

He is charged a $10 handling fee which is deducted from the money he received. What was the actual yearly rate of interest?

559. A man borrows $250 from a loan company for one year. The rate of interest is 6% per annum, which is deducted in advance (from the money he is to receive from the company). He is to repay the $250 in 12 equal payments. He is also charged an insurance fee of $15, which is likewise deducted from the money he is to receive. What was the yearly rate of interest?

560. A radio set selling for $75 cash is purchased in an installment plan. The down payment is $15. The balance is to be paid off in 12 months in equal payments of $6.50 each. What is the yearly rate of interest charged?

561. A man borrows $150 from a loan company which is to be paid back in three monthly installments $53.98 each. What is the yearly rate of interest charged?

562. A mortgage loan of $3,000 was placed on a house, to be paid in 6 years. The rate of interest was 5.7% per annum. The title search and the lawyer's fees amounted to $125. The mortgage was paid off in 6 years. What was the actual yearly rate of interest?

563. A man borrows $500 on his car to be paid back in 10 equal monthly installments. The rate of interest is 1.85% per month on the unpaid balance. He is also charged $50 for insurance on the car and other fees. What was the actual yearly rate of interest?

564. A man borrows $200 from a loan company. The loan is to be repaid in 12 months on the following terms: The rate of interest is 2% per month (that is, 24% per annum) which is computed in advance and added to the loan. Also a $10 insurance and handling fee is added to the amount owed. The sum is divided by 12, and this quotient represents the monthly payment. What is the actual yearly and monthly rate of interest?

16

Simplified Computation

Exact and approximate numbers

When we count a few objects and we do not make a mistake we are certain of the number of these objects. Anyone else who wishes to check us will, if he does not make a mistake in the counting, obtain the same number. Counting change or money represents such a situation.

However, when we measure the distance between two cities, the length of a river, the height of mountain, or even such smaller distances as the length, width, or height of a room, or the length or width of a piece of ground, we cannot obtain numbers of which we can be as certain as when we count a few objects.

In order to realize the possibilities and impossibilities of this situation let us consider the following. Let us suppose that we wish to measure the width of a table. We use a yardstick marked to inches and eighths of inches. Let us try to be very careful and place the end of the yardstick so that it coincides with the edge of the table. Here we strike a snag. Regardless of how careful we are or may be, regardless of how many times we may try, we can never be certain that we attained exact coincidence. However, since we cannot offer any practical solution which would completely eliminate our inability to make a perfect coincidence, we shall take this uncertainty into account. Next, we can never be certain that our yardstick is perfectly constructed, that the markings on it are perfectly (evenly) spaced. Furthermore, we cannot be certain that the markings on the yardstick are exactly the same as on a standard measuring instrument; that is, we cannot be certain that an inch on the yardstick is equal exactly to the standard inch. We must also consider that the yardstick, if it is made of wood, may have warped because of humidity; that if it is made of metal it may have expanded (or contracted)

236

because of temperature changes. All these facts add up and act against the possibility of obtaining an *exact* measure of the width of the table. An exact number is that which was obtained from counting, if no mistake was made.

To the above facts (and there may be more which were not accounted for), we must add another important one. This consideration has to do with the human element. No two persons have eyesight of the same quality. No two persons read measures on any measuring instrument in the same manner and with the same care. When a measure is read we must depend on the judgment of him who does the measuring. However, some definite methods of procedure have been set up, and these enable us to obtain fairly satisfactory statements of measure.

Here the reader is advised to recall the method of rounding digits. If the first digit on the left of that portion of the number which has to be dropped is 0, 1, 2, 3, or 4, then that digit on the extreme right, which is to be retained, must be left unchanged. For example, 62.45346 is rounded to 62.45. If the first digit to be dropped is 5, 6, 7, 8, or 9, then the digit immediately on its left, that is to be retained, must be increased by 1. For example, 62.45346 is rounded 62.4535, or 62.453, or 62.45, or 62.5.

Now, since we cannot expect that the other side of the table that we measure will fall exactly on some division of the yardstick, we take that division line which is *nearest* to the edge of the table, and that reading is the best we can ever expect. This situation is illustrated in Figure 5 below. Note that in this drawing the edge of the table is closer to the line indicating $30\frac{7}{8}$ inches than to that indicating $30\frac{3}{4}$ inches. Therefore, we take this nearest graduation as the best measure we can obtain.

Some prefer to estimate the distance between the nearest division and the end of the object and add the estimate (or subtract it, if the nearest division is such that the statement is somewhat beyond the actual boundary of the object). This estimate depends on the judgment of the person who measures and it cannot be accepted as reliable.

Thus, we have before us a new kind of numbers, numbers that are not exact. We call them *approximate numbers*. They are as good and as reliable as the instrument of measurement that was

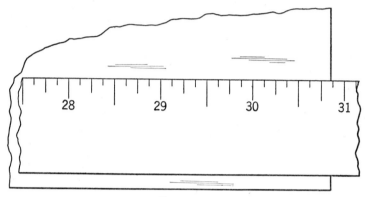

FIGURE 5

used in obtaining them. Unless we can get a better instrument than we have on hand, we cannot improve a number that has been obtained. Once an approximate number has been obtained from measurement, its limitations are final for a given situation, and no computation or numerical manipulation can ever improve it.

Error in measurement

Note that in the illustration of the measure of the width of the table in the preceding section we took as the best measure $30\frac{7}{8}$ inches, although the actual length of the table was *somewhat* less. This *somewhat* is not arbitrary, however. If the edge of the table were closer to the $30\frac{3}{4}$-inch division we would have taken it instead of the $30\frac{7}{8}$-inch division. The selection of the correct division line depends on the side of the mid-point between two neighboring division marks on which the object lies. Thus, the amount by which we may err is never greater than one-half of the smallest unit on the measuring instrument. In the case of the measure of the width of the table the difference between the actual width of the table and its measure cannot exceed one-half of $\frac{1}{8}$ inch, or $\frac{1}{16}$ inch.

Similarly, if we were measuring with a yardstick graduated to tenths of an inch, the difference between the actual width of the table and its stated measure could not exceed one-half of one-tenth of an inch, or 0.05 inch.

This fact is very important. If we have an approximate number, it cannot contain a greater error (we call the difference between the actual measure and its numerical statement the *error*) than one-half or 0.5 of the smallest unit in which it is expressed. Thus a report that a dimension is 12.34 feet implies that the measurement was made to 0.01 foot and the error is not greater than 0.5 of 0.01 foot, that is, 0.005 foot.

Note that here we have a justification for writing a zero in a decimal fraction in order to indicate that a measurement was performed. Thus, saying that a dimension is 15.00 feet indicates that the measurement was performed to hundredths of a foot. If we were confronted with an exact number these zeros would not have been necessary, and the number could be written as 15. In approximate numbers these zeros are very important.

PROBLEMS

565. State to what unit the following measurements were performed: (a) 12.7 inch; (b) 35.678 meters; (c) 2.75 kilometers; (d) 16 pounds 5 ounces; (e) 12.5 millimeters; (f) 55.670 feet; (g) 78.450 kilograms; (h) 42.6 miles; (i) 13.40 meters.

566. Convert the following common fractions into decimal fractions and state them correct to 0.001. Indicate the errors effected by rounding. (a) $\frac{1}{3}$; (b) $\frac{5}{6}$; (c) $3\frac{7}{9}$; (d) $5\frac{11}{13}$; (e) $6\frac{4}{15}$.

567. Indicate the errors in measurement in the measures in Problem 565.

Percent of error

The method of indicating the error in measurement enables us to judge the type of measuring instrument we use. The smaller the error, the finer is the measuring instrument, or, as we say, the more *precise* it is. A measure to 0.1 inch is not as precise as a measure to 0.01 inch. A measure to 0.01 meter is not as precise as a measure to 0.001 meter or to 0.0001 meter.   Thus, we have before us a method of judging the precision of a measurement.

However, how should we judge the following measurements, performed with the same precision: 12.5 inches and 125.6 inches? They are of the same precision.   The greatest possible error in either of them is 0.05 inch.

Note that in the case of 12.5 inches we can distribute the error 0.05 inch throughout the entire measure, and we have the quotient

$$\frac{0.05}{12.5}.$$

In the case of the 125.6 inches we have a similar quotient,

$$\frac{0.05}{125.6}.$$

We know how to judge and compare the magnitudes of two fractions.   The second fraction is smaller than the first because the denominator 125.6 is greater than the denominator 12.5.   Thus the amount of error per unit of measure in 125.6 inches is smaller than in the measure 12.5 inches.

We say that the second measure is more *accurate* than the first.

Of any two measurements, in general that measurement whose error, when divided by the measurement, gives the smaller quotient is the most accurate.

This quotient is called the *relative error*.

If we multiply this relative-error quotient by 100, we obtain a statement of the error as a percent of the measurement.   Thus, this percent error in a measurement of 12.5 inches is

$$\frac{0.05 \cdot 100}{12.5}\% = 0.4\%,$$

and the percent error in a measurement of 125.6 inches is

$$\frac{0.05 \cdot 100}{125.6}\% = 0.04\%.$$

PROBLEMS

568. Compute the percent errors of the measures given in Problem 565.

569. Arrange these percent errors in the order of their magnitude and indicate which of the measures is the most accurate and which is the least accurate.

Significant digits

If we know that a measurement has been performed correct to, say 0.1 inch, there is no sense in giving information concerning the hundredths and thousandths of an inch. Such information would be entirely unreliable. At no time could we substantiate any statement concerning it. This fact is indicated by the magnitude of the greatest possible error, which is 0.05 inch. Thus we have a definite limitation on the number that states the magnitude of the measure; any digit to the right of the tenths' place has no significance.

Now consider the following table of values:

Measure	Percent error
5	10%
5.0	1%
5.00	0.1%
5.000	0.01%

Note that as the number of digits in the measure increases the percent error becomes smaller. Thus we may infer that the accuracy of the measure has something to do with the number of the important, or *significant digits* in the statement of the measure or the approximate number.

The important fact is that all the digits in an approximate number to the left of the place where the error is are significant, because they tell about the magnitude of the measure.

There is one exception only. The zero in a pure decimal fraction which is to the left of the decimal point is not significant. For example, the zero in 0.654 is not significant. But the zero on the right of 0.730 is significant. If it were not significant we would have omitted it. Also zeros such as those in the number

0.0073 are not significant. Zeros between the digits 1, 2, 3, 4, 5, 6, 7, 8, and 9 are always significant.

PROBLEMS

570. How many significant digits are there in the following approximate numbers: (a) 45.673, error 0.05; (b) 6.003, error 0.0005; (c) 0.0125, error 0.00005; (d) 0.501078, error 0.00005; (e) 10.200, error 0.0005?

571. Convert the following common fractions into decimals, and write them with four significant digits: (a) $\frac{2}{3}$; (b) $\frac{5}{9}$; (c) $\frac{7}{11}$; (d) $\frac{1}{12}$; (e) $\frac{1}{24}$.

Addition of approximate numbers

The addition of approximate numbers is performed in the same manner as the addition of exact numbers. There are several limitations, however, which arise from the fact that the numbers are not exact.

The precision of the several measurements that are represented by the numbers to be added must be the same. This is a limitation that follows from the fact that if several numbers represent measurements, say to 0.01 foot, any additional information given by numbers correct to 0.001 foot or 0.0001 foot would be of no consequence because those numbers that are correct only to 0.01 would introduce errors in all the places to the right of the hundredths' place.

This limitation should make us recall that we had a similar rule, and should explain it, when we stated the procedure for adding decimal fractions. Thus, here we have the same rule as in the case of the addition of decimal fractions. The numbers should be rounded if they contain more information than the least precise number. For example, the sum of 34.56, 4.783, and 13.4098 should be added as follows:

$$
\begin{array}{r}
34.56 \\
4.78 \\
13.41 \\
\hline
52.75
\end{array}
$$

Generally, we cannot be certain of the last digit on the right of this sum because the errors in measurement always accumulate.

In the case of three addends the accumulated sum may be equal to 0.015 (for each error is assumed to be not greater than 0.015). However, for all practical purposes, if we have not more than 9 addends, we may retain the last digit on the extreme right. But, if there are some further computations to be performed we should keep in mind the fact that this digit may not be wholly reliable and take this uncertainty into account.

PROBLEMS

572. Add the following approximate numbers: (a) 34.567, 15.029, and 6.98034; (b) 1.369, 0.6605, and 0.9981; (c) 426.57, 89.4078, 601.3529, and 110.634; (d) 0.156, 0.01274, 1.1245, and 2.6607; (e) 8.9563, 5.62892, 3.005, 4.1372, and 2.563.

Subtraction of approximate numbers

The subtraction of approximate numbers is performed in the same manner as the subtraction of exact numbers.

The restrictions stated for the addition of approximate numbers likewise apply to the subtraction. Thus, if we subtract 34.892 from 156.34 we round the first number to 34.89, and the difference is:

$$\begin{array}{r} 156.34 \\ 34.89 \\ \hline 121.45 \end{array}$$

Also, if we subtract 48.93 from 138.787, we round the second number to 138.79, and the difference is:

$$\begin{array}{r} 138.79 \\ 48.93 \\ \hline 89.86 \end{array}$$

PROBLEMS

573. Perform the following subtractions: (a) 457.8093 − 226.77; (b) 1.02635 − 0.348; (c) 9.203 − 6.4467; (d) 10.25 − 8.7756; (e) 12.753 − 8.01457.

Multiplication of approximate numbers

When we multiply two exact numbers we obtain an exact product. Such is not the case, however, when two approximate numbers are multiplied, or when an exact number is multiplied by an approximate number.

The product of two approximate numbers cannot be exact. This fact can be seen from the following example. Let us multiply the two approximate numbers: 62.4 and 37.6. Note that the two numbers are both correct to three significant digits. Their fourth digits are unknown. Let us denote these unknown digits by x, and let us write the two numbers as $62.4x$ and $37.6x$. The product is then:

$$
\begin{array}{r}
62.4x \\
37.6x \\
\hline
.xxxx \\
37.44x \\
436.8x \\
1\ 872.x \\
\hline
2{,}345.xxxx
\end{array}
$$

Note that whenever any one of the partial products was affected by the unknown digit x we so stated in the product. Thus the first partial product is all affected by the unknown digit.

The sum has four digits that have not seemingly been affected by the unknown digit x. But this statement is not correct. The last digit on the right, that is, 5, was affected because the sum of the column on the place of the tenths, that is,

$$x = 4 + 8 + x$$

is greater than 10, and this fact necessitated the carrying over of one or some larger number into the place on the left. Thus, the place on the left of the decimal place is not reliable. In other words, the product contains three significant digits only. Correctly stated, the product is 2,350. The zero is not significant.

If one of the factors had four significant digits while the second factor had three significant digits we would have the following products, for example,

$$
\begin{array}{r}
62.46 \\
37.6 \\
\hline
37.476 \\
437.22 \\
1\ 873.8 \\
\hline
2{,}348.496
\end{array}
\qquad
\begin{array}{r}
62.4 \\
37.63 \\
\hline
1.872 \\
37.44 \\
436.8 \\
1\ 872. \\
\hline
2{,}348.112
\end{array}
$$

Here again the correctly stated products are **2,350** and **2,350**, the zeros not being significant.

Thus we have the rule concerning the multiplication of approximate numbers.

> *i.* The factors must contain the same number of significant digits, or one of them may have an extra significant digit.
>
> *ii.* The product contains the same number of significant digits as the factor with the least number of significant digits.

For example, if the two factors have four significant digits each, the product will also have four significant digits. If one factor has three significant digits, and the other factor has two significant digits, then the product will have two significant digits.

If we have a product of three approximate numbers, the same rule applies to them also. For example, the volume of a box whose dimensions are length 5.6 inches, width 2.8 inches, and height 1.5 inches is

(5.6 inches · 2.8 inches · 1.5 inches) = 23.520 cubic inches.

Rounding this result to two significant digits, we have **24** cubic inches.

PROBLEMS

574. What is the area of the rectangle whose length is 27.5 inches and width is 314.6 inches?

575. What is the volume of a box whose dimensions are: length 45.8 inches, width 21.5 inches, and height 18.4 inches?

576. Find the products of the following approximate numbers: (*a*) 6.7 and 8.92; (*b*) 15.25 and 62.4; (*c*) 8.92, 76.3, and 25.42; (*d*) 89.25, 75.42, and 24.3; (*e*) 2 · 3.14 · 4.75 (2 is an exact number).

Simplified multiplication

Note that in the multiplications performed in the preceding section we threw away about half of the digits in every product obtained because these digits were not significant. In other words, we wasted about half of the effort in every multiplication.

If we could determine in advance the number of significant digits in the product, and we now know how to do this according to the rule stated on page 245, we might find a way to simplify the multiplication and conserve our effort and energy while we obtain the correct product.

Let us consider the following product of the two approximate numbers 6.73 and 2.45. We shall perform the multiplication omitting the decimal points. We shall insert the decimal in the product after it is obtained. The product should contain four decimal places. The correct number of significant digits, after rounding, should be three. We have then:

$$
\begin{array}{r}
673 \\
245 \\
\hline
3365 \\
2692 \\
1346 \\
\hline
164885
\end{array}
$$

Inserting the decimal point we have 16.4885. Rounding to three significant digits, we have 16.5.

Note that we obtained six digits in the product, but we retained only three. In order to be able to round we should have at the most four digits in the product. Now let us perform the multiplication as follows:

$$
\begin{array}{r}
673 \\
542 \\
\hline
\end{array}
$$

In other words, we reverse the multiplier.

Let us begin the multiplication from the right. The first partial product is 673 · 2 = 1346. For the second partial product we do not multiply the entire factor 673 but only the digits 67, which give 67 · 4 = 268. But note that 3 · 4 = 12. We add the 1 to 268, and we have 268 + 1 = 269. Finally, for the third partial product we do not multiply 673 but only the digit 6, which gives us 6 · 5 = 30. But 7 · 5 = 35. We add the 3 to

30, and we obtain 33.   The multiplication as usually written is:

$$
\begin{array}{r}
673 \\
542 \\
\hline
1346 \\
269 \\
33 \\
\hline
1648
\end{array}
$$

Finally, inserting the decimal point, we have 16.48, and rounding, we obtain 16.5.

Let us consider another example, the product $8.34 \cdot 26.9$. Note that the whole parts indicate that there should be three places in the whole part of the product.   Let us keep this fact in mind for the correct insertion of the decimal point.   The multiplication is

$$
\begin{array}{rl}
834 & \\
962 & \\
\hline
1668 & \\
500 & (4 \cdot 6 = 24, \text{ and we must add 2}) \\
75 & (9 \cdot 3 = 27, \text{ and we must add 3, rounding 27}) \\
\hline
2243 &
\end{array}
$$

The product is 224.3.   Rounding to three significant digits, we obtain 224.   The reader may check this result by performing the multiplication the long way.

PROBLEMS

577. Perform the multiplications in Problems 574, 575, and 576, using the short method.

Division of approximate numbers

Since division is an operation that is the reverse of multiplication, it is reasonable to expect that the rules for the multiplication of approximate numbers apply to division of approximate numbers also.   That this expectation is so can be inferred from the following.

If we check division by multiplication (and bear in mind that we work with approximate numbers) we are controlled in multiplication by the rules for this operation.   Now let us suppose that we have the following:

> Dividend: has 4 significant digits,
> Divisor: has 4 significant digits,
> Quotient: to be determined.

Now, as a check of the division we have:

quotient · divisor = dividend.

The dividend is now a product. It has four significant digits, and so does the divisor, which is now one of the factors. Thus, in order to retain four significant digits in the product the second factor must have at least four significant digits (it may have five). Now, since the quotient is, in this form, the second factor, it should have four significant digits. We cannot accept a quotient with five significant digits in this situation because the fifth digit would not be reliable, as will be seen from the following example.

Let us obtain the quotient of the division

```
                3.635
   2652 | 9642|            9642|  | 2652
          7956             7956    3.635
          1686|0           1686|0
          1591|2           1591|2
            94|80            94|80
            79|56            79|56
            15|240           15|240
            13|260           13|260
             1|980            1|980
```

Note that if we continue the division we shall have to rely on digits that would be brought down from places to the right of the approximate dividend (as indicated by the vertical line). Thus these digits are not reliable. The quotient is correct to four significant digits. Note also that we have stopped the division. But the examination shows that the remainder is 1980. We must carry the division to the next digit in the quotient (which should be done for the purpose of rounding the quotient), 19800 would produce a digit that would necessitate the increase of the last digit on the right of the quotient.

PROBLEMS

578. Perform the following divisions: (a) 65.7 ÷ 3.56; (b) 1567.5 ÷ 4562.4; (c) 89.345 ÷ 24.36; (d) 2.56 ÷ 14.62; (e) 11.25 ÷ 0.925.

579. In order to judge the weight of substances in physics we have a measure which is given as a ratio in terms of the weight of 1 cubic foot of water. A cubic foot of water weighs approximately 62.5 pounds. This measure is known as

$$\text{specific gravity} = \frac{\text{weight of 1 cubic foot of substance}}{\text{weight of 1 cubic foot of water}}.$$

Find the specific gravities of the following substances, the weights of 1 cubic foot of which are: (a) anthracite, 112 pounds; (b) asbestos, 175 pounds; (c) butter 53.5 pounds; (d) oak charcoal, 35.5 pounds; (e) emery, 251.4 pounds; (f) flint, 164 pounds; (g) glass, 167.5 pounds; (h) ice, 57.2 pounds; (i) malachite, 256 pounds; (j) pyrite, 318 pounds; (k) quartz, 165 pounds; (l) topaz, 223.5 pounds.

Table of squares of numbers

The raising of a number to a power is actually a multiplication of a number by itself. In the case of squaring of an approximate number the rule for the multiplication of approximate numbers holds.

In order to simplify computations in which the squaring of a number enters as one of the processes, we may use tables of squares in which the squared numbers are listed so that they may be located whenever needed. However, such tables cannot contain all the numbers, nor can they contain approximate numbers. Such tables are prepared so that they contain only squares of exact numbers. Such a table of squares of all numbers from 0 to 99 is shown on page 250.

In order to locate the square of any two-place exact number in the table we note the following. The first digit (on the left) of the number is located in the column of the extreme left of the table. The second digit (the one on the right) of the number is located in the upper line in the table. Where the horizontal line drawn through the digit in the column on the right intersects with the vertical line through the digit on the top of the table there is the cell in which the square is located. Thus the square of 64

TABLE OF SQUARES

	0	1	2	3	4	5	6	7	8	9
0	0	1	4	9	16	25	36	49	64	81
1	100	121	144	169	196	225	256	289	324	361
2	400	441	484	529	576	625	676	729	784	841
3	900	961	1,024	1,089	1,156	1,225	1,296	1,369	1,444	1,521
4	1,600	1,681	1,764	1,849	1,936	2,025	2,116	2,209	2,304	2,401
5	2,500	2,601	2,704	2,809	2,916	3,025	3,136	3,249	3,364	3,481
6	3,600	3,721	3,844	3,969	4,096	4,225	4,356	4,489	4,624	4,761
7	4,900	5,041	5,184	5,329	5,476	5,625	5,776	5,929	6,084	6,241
8	6,400	6,561	6,724	6,889	7,056	7,225	7,396	7,569	7,744	7,921
9	8,100	8,281	8,464	8,649	8,836	9,025	9,216	9,409	9,604	9,801

is located where the line through the 6 in the vertical column intersects the line through the 4 on the top of the table, and we find in that cell the number $4,096 = 64^2$. Similarly we find that $83^2 = 6,889$.

Now, in order to find the square of an approximate number we must use a procedure which is known as *interpolation;* it is actually a method for reading between two numbers found in the table.

For example, let us find 64.3^2. In the table we find that

$$64^2 = 4,096,$$

and

$$65^2 = 4,225.$$

Thus 64.3^2 must be located somewhere between 64^2 and 65^2.

We take the difference between 65^2 and 64^2. It is equal to

$$4,225 - 4,096 = 129.$$

Then take 0.3 of this difference, that is,

$$129 \cdot 0.3 = 38.7.$$

Add this difference to $64^2 = 4{,}096$. We have then

$$64.3^2 = 4{,}096 + 38.7 = 4{,}134.7.$$

Since 64.3 is an approximate number, its square must contain three significant digits. Thus

$$64.3^2 = 4{,}130,$$

the zero not being significant.

If we move the decimal point in a number one place to the right, then the decimal point in its square should be moved two places to the right. For example,

$$643^2 = 413{,}000.$$

If we move the decimal place in a number one place to the left, then the decimal point in its square should be moved two places to the left. For example,

$$6.43^2 = 41.3.$$

If we move the decimal point in a number two places to the left, then the decimal point in its square should be moved four places to the left. For example,

$$0.643^2 = 0.413.$$

The general rule is, then, to move the decimal point in the square of the number twice as many places as it is moved in the number itself and in the same direction.

Note. The method just illustrated is good only for three-place approximate numbers.

PROBLEMS

580. Using the table of squares of numbers, find the squares of the following approximate numbers: 53.7; 26.8; 78.4; 45.3; 17.5; 22.6; 36.9; 71.6; 37.8; 92.4.

581. Find the squares of the following approximate numbers: 1.56; 7.89; 0.0653; 9.34; 8.21; 0.00108; 0.562; 6.34; 1.74; 0.0458.

The extraction of square roots

Very often we are confronted with the problem of finding a number whose square is given. For example, we are given 4,096, and we are asked to find that number which, when multiplied by itself, will give 4,096 as the product. Such an operation reverses the squaring, and it is known as the extraction of the square root of the number.

The symbol for this operation is $\sqrt{}$, and it is called the radical. We write

$$\sqrt{4,096} = 64,$$

and 64 is known as the square root of 4,096.

The extraction of square roots is a long operation which requires the calculation of every digit of the square root.

The following example illustrates the method of procedure used in the extraction of square roots of whole numbers.

EXAMPLE. Let us calculate $\sqrt{232,324}$, that is, extract the square root of 232,324.

We proceed as follows: Group the digits of 232,324 by pairs, beginning from the extreme right, thus:

$$23\ 23\ 24.$$

Obtain the nearest whole square root of the two-place number 23 that is on the extreme left. This root is 4, because $4^2 = 16$. Write the square of 4, that is 16, under the 23, thus:

$$
\begin{array}{l}
23\ 23\ 24 \\
16
\end{array}
$$

Subtract 16 from 23:

$$
\begin{array}{l}
23\ 23\ 24 \\
16 \\
\hline
7
\end{array}
$$

Write the 4, which is the first digit of the square root to be found, on the right of 232,324:

$$
\begin{array}{ll}
23\ 23\ 24 & \quad 4 \\
16 \\
\hline
7
\end{array}
$$

Bring down the next pair of digits and write them alongside

the 7:

$$23 \ 23 \ 24 \qquad 4$$
$$16$$
$$\overline{7 \ 23}$$

Double the 4 and write it on the left of the 723:

$$23 \ 23 \ 24 \qquad 4$$
$$16$$
$$8 \quad \overline{| \ 7 \ 23}$$

To the right of 8 we must write a digit such that the two-place number so formed, when multiplied by this digit, will give either 723, or a smaller number close to it. Now $72 \div 8 = 9$. But inspection shows that $89 \cdot 9$ is greater than 723. We therefore select 8.

$$23 \ 23 \ 24 \qquad 4$$
$$16$$
$$88 \quad \overline{| \ 7 \ 23}$$

Multiply 88 by 8 and write the product underneath 723 and subtract. Also write the 8, which is the second digit of the root to be found, at the right of the 4:

$$23 \ 23 \ 24 \qquad 48$$
$$16$$
$$88 \quad \overline{| \ 7 \ 23}$$
$$8 \quad | \ 7 \ 04$$

Subtract 704 from 723, then bring down the last pair, and write it at the right of the difference:

$$23 \ 23 \ 24 \qquad 48$$
$$16$$
$$88 \quad \overline{| \ 7 \ 23}$$
$$8 \quad | \ 7 \ 04$$
$$| \ \overline{19 \ 24}$$

Double 48 (or obtain the sum $88 + 8$) and write it to the left of 1924:

$$23 \ 23 \ 24 \qquad 48$$
$$16$$
$$88 \quad \overline{| \ 7 \ 23}$$
$$8 \quad | \ 7 \ 04$$
$$\overline{96} \quad | \ \overline{19 \ 24}$$

To the right of 96 write a digit such that the three-place number so obtained, when multiplied by this digit, will either give 1924, or a number close to it. We observe that $192 \div 88 = 2$.

Then:

```
                  23 23 24      482
                  16
         88  |  7 23
          8  |  7 04
        ─────
        962  |     19 24
          2  |     19 24
```

This digit, **2**, is written on the right of 48, and 482 is the square root or 232,324.

Not all numbers whose square root is to be extracted are perfect squares. If we have a number not a perfect square, we go on extracting the square root until we exhaust the whole number. This operation will give us the whole-number part of the square root. Then we may continue the extraction by bringing down two zeros at a time, and this further operation will give us the decimal part of the square root. We can continue this process until we decide to stop. As soon as we stop we may round the number so obtained (the approximate square root) in the same manner as we round quotients in division.

The following example will illustrate the procedure just explained.

EXAMPLE. $\sqrt{59,257}$

is to be computed with two decimal places. We group the digits by pairs, starting from the right. Then we follow the same procedure as described above.

```
          √5 92 57              = 243.427
           4
   44  |  1 92
    4  |  1 76
  ─────
  483  |    16 57
    3  |    14 49
  ─────
 4864  |     2 08 00
    4  |     1 94 56
  ─────
48682  |       13 44 00
    2  |        9 73 64
  ──────
486847 |        3 70 36 00
     7 |        3 40 79 29
       |          29 56 71
```

The square root correct to two decimal places is 243.43.

If the number whose square root is to be extracted is a mixed decimal, then the digits should be grouped by pairs to the left and right of the decimal point. Thus:

$$\sqrt{6\ 72.88\ 36} = 25.94$$

	4
45	2 72
5	2 25
509	47 88
9	45 81
5184	2 07 36
4	2 07 36

PROBLEMS

582. Obtain the square roots of the following numbers: 467,856; 118,336; 150,544; 62,001; 779,689; 2,085,136; 4,879,681; 34,012,224; 594,823,321; 244,140,625.

583. Obtain the square roots of the following numbers; extract to two decimal places: 438,976; 74,088; 830,584; 8,998,912; 12,649,337; 15,438,249; 143,877,824; 174,676,879; 814,780,504; 893,871,739.

584. Obtain the square roots of the following numbers; extract to five decimal places: 6.16441; 96.9536; 1.84119; 231.0844; 2791.057; 30.4795; 99.0959; 8.80627; 0.96332; 0.098991.

Square roots of approximate numbers and table of square roots

Square roots of approximate numbers are also approximate. Moreover, an approximate number is one that represents a magnitude that cannot be measured exactly. We cannot start with an approximate number and suddenly obtain an exact one from it.

Since the extraction of a root is an operation that reverses the raising to a power, it is reasonable to expect that the rules that hold for the number of significant digits in the square of an approximate number also hold for the number of significant digits in the square root of an approximate number. If we want to check the extraction of a square root we raise the obtained number to the second power. Doing this is multiplication, and thus we

TABLE OF SQUARE ROOTS OF NUMBERS
Part 1—Odd Number of Digits in the Whole Part

	0	1	2	3	4	5	6	7	8	9
1.	1.000	1.049	1.095	1.140	1.183	1.225	1.265	1.304	1.342	1.378
2.	1.414	1.449	1.483	1.517	1.549	1.581	1.612	1.643	1.673	1.703
3.	1.732	1.761	1.789	1.817	1.844	1.871	1.897	1.924	1.949	1.975
4.	2.000	2.025	2.049	2.074	2.098	2.121	2.145	2.168	2.191	2.214
5.	2.236	2.258	2.280	2.302	2.324	2.345	2.366	2.387	2.408	2.429
6.	2.449	2.470	2.490	2.510	2.530	2.550	2.569	2.588	2.608	2.627
7.	2.646	2.665	2.683	2.702	2.720	2.739	2.757	2.775	2.793	2.811
8.	2.828	2.846	2.864	2.881	2.898	2.915	2.933	2.950	2.966	2.983
9.	3.000	3.017	3.033	3.050	3.066	3.082	3.098	3.114	3.130	3.146

come to the conclusion that a square root of an approximate number contains the same number of significant digits as the number under the radical sign $\sqrt{}$.

In order to eliminate much computational work in the extraction of square roots it is very convenient to use a Table of Square Roots of Numbers. These are computed in advance. Such a table is shown on pages 256 and 257.

The only inconvenience in the Table of Square Roots of Numbers is that it consists of two parts. The reason is that when extracting square roots we divide the whole part of a number into groups of pairs of digits. Note that $\sqrt{3} = 1.732$, and $\sqrt{30} = 5.477$.

When we obtain square roots of numbers from the table we must always take note of the number of digits in the whole part of the number whose square root is obtained. Thus, if the number is 342.6 its square root is obtained from Part 1. If the number is 65.42 its square root is obtained from Part 2.

Part 2—Even Number of Digits in the Whole Part

	0.	1.	2.	3.	4.	5.	6.	7.	8.	9.
1	3.162	3.317	3.464	3.606	3.742	3.873	4.000	4.123	4.243	4.359
2	4.472	4.583	4.690	4.796	4.899	5.000	5.099	5.196	5.292	5.385
3	5.477	5.568	5.657	5.745	5.831	5.916	6.000	6.083	6.164	6.245
4	6.325	6.403	6.481	6.557	6.633	6.708	6.782	6.856	6.928	7.000
5	7.071	7.141	7.211	7.280	7.348	7.416	7.483	7.550	7.616	7.681
6	7.746	7.810	7.874	7.937	8.000	8.062	8.124	8.185	8.246	8.307
7	8.367	8.426	8.485	8.544	8.602	8.660	8.718	8.775	8.832	8.888
8	8.944	9.000	9.055	9.110	9.165	9.220	9.274	9.327	9.381	9.434
9	9.487	9.539	9.592	9.644	9.695	9.747	9.798	9.849	9.899	9.950

The square roots are located in the same manner as the squares. The first digit on the extreme left of the number whose square root is sought is located in the column of the extreme left of the Table. The second digit (counting from the left) is located in the line in the top line of the Table. A horizontal line drawn through the first digit and a vertical line drawn through the second digit intersect in a cell where the square root is obtained. Thus, $\sqrt{13}$ is found in Part 2 of the table, and it is 3.606. $\sqrt{1.3}$ is found in Part 1 of the table, and it is 1.140.

Note that the indicating vertical column and top horizontal line have decimal points. In Part 1 the decimal points are in the vertical column. In Part 2 the decimal points are in the top horizontal line. This arrangement enables us to take care of the two kinds of numbers whose squares roots are to be obtained, as indicated by the headings of the two parts of the table.

The two parts of the table give square roots of numbers with one digit in the whole part of the number (Part 1) and numbers with two digits in the whole part of the number (Part 2). Suppose that the whole part of a number whose square root is to be obtained has three digits in the whole part, that is, the decimal point is moved two places to the right. The square root as read from the table should have its decimal point moved *one* place to the right. If the number whose square root is to be obtained has four digits in the whole part, the decimal point in the square root as obtained from the table should be moved *one* place to the right.

Generally, the following rule should be observed. Whenever we move the decimal point an even number of places, the decimal point in the square root of that number should be moved one half the number of places in the same direction. Thus

$$\sqrt{12} \ = 3.464, \quad \sqrt{1,200} = 34.64, \quad \sqrt{12,000,000} = 346.4.$$
$$\sqrt{1.2} = 1.095, \quad \sqrt{120} \ \ = 10.95, \quad \sqrt{12,000} \ \ \ = 109.5.$$
$$\sqrt{45} \ \ = 6.708, \quad \sqrt{0.45} = 0.6708, \quad \sqrt{0.0045} \ \ = 0.06708.$$
$$\sqrt{6.9} = 2.627, \quad \sqrt{0.069} = 0.2627, \quad \sqrt{0.00069} \ = 0.02627.$$

Suppose that we wish to extract the square root of 5.48. In Part 1 of the table we find

$$\sqrt{5.4} = 2.324,$$
$$\sqrt{5.5} = 2.345.$$

We infer that $\sqrt{5.48}$ must be located somewhere between $\sqrt{5.4}$ and $\sqrt{5.5}$. The difference between these two square roots is

$$2.345 - 2.324 = 0.021.$$

Multiply this difference by 0.8 (because the next digit is 8 and it is located 8 tenths of the distance between the two known roots), and add this to 2.324 $= \sqrt{5.4}$.

We have then

$$2.324 + 0.8 \cdot 0.021 = 2.324 + 0.0168 = 2.3408.$$

Rounding, we obtain

$$\sqrt{5.48} = 2.341.$$

Similarly, $\sqrt{72.5}$ is obtained from Part 2 of the table as follows.

$$\sqrt{72} = 8.485,$$
$$\sqrt{73} = 8.544.$$

Then $\sqrt{73} - \sqrt{72}$ is

$$8.544 - 8.485 = 0.0059.$$

And

$$\sqrt{72.5} = \sqrt{72} + 0.5 \cdot 0.059 = 8.485 + 0.0295 = 8.5145.$$

Rounding, we find $\sqrt{72.5} = 8.515$.

Should all the above numbers be approximate numbers, then

$$\sqrt{5.48} = 2.34,$$

correctly rounded to three significant digits, and

$$\sqrt{72.5} = 8.51,$$

correctly rounded from 8.5145.

PROBLEMS

585. Find the square roots of the following exact numbers: 21; 45; 67; 83; 92; 75; 67; 42; 89; 35.

586. Find the square roots of the following exact numbers: 3.4; 5.7; 7.4; 8.5; 3.9; 2.1; 1.1; 6.9; 4.3; 0.8.

587. Find the square roots of the following exact numbers: 215; 37,500; 489; 452; 781; 893; 993; 10,500; 78,400; 15,600.

588. Find the square roots of the following exact numbers: 6,780; 867,000; 7,560; 31.5; 74.3; 8,900; 7,820; 883,000; 9,340; 146,000.

589. Find the square roots of the following approximate numbers: 12.5; 45.7; 51.6; 74.3; 87.9; 43.2; 35.2; 77.8; 90.5; 21.7.

590. Find the square roots of the following approximate numbers: 6.75; 5.39; 8.92; 9.17; 8.37; 6.45; 3.25; 7.35; 2.17; 1.08.

591. Find the square roots of the following approximate numbers: 0.673; 0.00894; 0.000635; 0.134; 0.0000876; 0.000004539; 0.000367; 0.548; 0.000765; 0.0000319.

17

Logarithms

What are logarithms?

In order to understand what service logarithms can perform in arithmetic computations, it is necessary to have some idea of their nature and their capacities. The name *logarithm* may sound very ponderous, but actually a logarithm is a very simple number and its nature is also very simple.

We know by this time what is meant by raising a number to a power. When we raise a number to a power we actually perform a repeated multiplication of a number by itself.

Let us write the powers of 2:

$$2^1 = 2 \qquad 2^5 = 32 \qquad 2^9 = 512 \qquad 2^{13} = 8,192$$
$$2^2 = 4 \qquad 2^6 = 64 \qquad 2^{10} = 1,024 \qquad 2^{14} = 16,384$$
$$2^3 = 8 \qquad 2^7 = 128 \qquad 2^{11} = 2,048 \qquad 2^{15} = 32,768$$
$$2^4 = 16 \qquad 2^8 = 256 \qquad 2^{12} = 4,096 \qquad 2^{16} = 65,536$$

Every number above can be identified by the exponent of 2. The method of identification is as follows:

2,048 can be obtained by raising 2 to the power of 11.

This long statement can be written in a compact form as follows:

$$\log_2 2,048 = 11;$$

that is, the logarithm of 2,048 to the base 2 is 11. Thus we have two statements,

$$2^{11} = 2,048 \qquad \text{and} \qquad \log_2 2,048 = 11,$$

and they express the same relationship between the three numbers 2, 11, and 2,048. The number indicating the base is always written as a subscript on the right of the abbreviation log.

260

Thus the logarithm of 2,048 to the base 2 is the exponent of 2 indicating the power to which 2 must be raised, that is, 11, in order to obtain 2,048.

In order to obtain a method for working with logarithms we shall introduce a relation which is to be accepted as a matter of definition: The zero power of any number except zero is equal to 1. That is $2^0 = 1$, $34^0 = 1$.

How logarithms are used

When we examined the process of the raising to a power we found that the product of two powers of the same numbers is also a power of that number. Furthermore, we found that the exponent of this product is equal to the sum of the exponents of the factors. For example,

$$3^2 \cdot 3^3 = 3^{2+3} = 3^5.$$

Now, if we apply this fact to the powers of 2 given on page 260 we can obtain additional powers of two by means of multiplication. For example,

$$2^{20} = 2^{16} \cdot 2^4 = 65,536 \cdot 16 = 1,048,576.$$

Note that here we obtained a very important result, namely: The product of two powers of the same base is also a power of this base having an exponent equal to the sum of the exponents of the factors. But this result can now be also stated in terms of the logarithms of 65,536 and 16 to the base 2. Accordingly we have

$$\log_2 1,048,576 = \log_2 (65,536 \cdot 16) = \log_2 65,536 + \log_2 16,$$
$$20 \qquad\qquad\qquad\qquad = \qquad 16 \ + \quad 4$$

Thus we have a very important rule: *The logarithm of the product of two (or more) numbers is equal to the sum of the logarithms of the several factors.* All these logarithms must have the same base.

Note that this rule checks with the fact that the zero power of any number except zero is equal to 1, that is, $2^0 = 1$. In other words, $\log_2 1 = 0$. Since the product of any number by 1 does not change the value of the number, that is, $128 \cdot 1 = 128$, this fact should check with the above rule for the logarithm of the product. We have, then,

$$\log_2 128 = \log_2 (128 \cdot 1) = \log_2 128 + \log_2 1 = 7 + 0 = 7.$$

PROBLEMS

592. By means of the values of the powers of 2 given on page 260, compute the values of: 2^{18}; 2^{24}; 2^{27}; 2^{30}; 2^{32}.

593. Write a table of powers of 3 up to 3^8, and list them as $3^{\text{to some power}}$ = the value.

594. By means of the table of the powers of 3 in Problem 593 compute the values of: 3^{10}; 3^{12}; 3^{15}.

Division and logarithms

In order to ascertain how we can apply logarithms to division, let us examine the following quotient of two powers of 2,

$$2^{10} \div 2^4 = 1,024 \div 16 = 64.$$

But $64 = 2^6$. Also note that $10 - 4 = 6$.

When a power of any base is divided by a power of the same base, the quotient is also a power of that base, and the exponent of the quotient maybe found by subtracting the exponent of the divisor from the exponent of the dividend.

Let us take another example,

$$2^{16} \div 2^9 = 65,536 \div 512 = 128 = 2^7,$$

and

$$16 - 9 = 7.$$

The result just obtained is as important as the result arrived at in the case of multiplication. The result for division can also be stated in terms of the logarithms of the dividend and the divisor.   We have then

$$\log_2 (1{,}024 \div 16) = \log_2 1{,}024 - \log_2 16 = \log_2 64,$$
$$10 \qquad - \qquad 4 \quad = \qquad 6.$$

$$\log_2 (65{,}536 \div 512) = \log_2 65{,}536 - \log_2 512 = \log_2 128.$$
$$16 \qquad - \qquad 9 \quad = \qquad 7.$$

Thus we have the rule for division: *The logarithm of the quotient of two numbers is equal to the difference obtained by subtracting the logarithm of the divisor from the logarithm of the dividend.*   All these logarithms must have the same base.

PROBLEMS

595. By means of the values of the powers of 2 given on page 260, perform the following divisions: (a) $2^{10} \div 2^7$; (b) $2^{14} \div 2^8$; (c) $2^{15} \div 2^{11}$; (d) $2^{16} \div 2^4$; (e) $2^{12} \div 2^3$.

596. By means of the values of the powers of 3 obtained in Problem 593 and Problem 594, perform the following divisions: (a) $3^8 \div 3^3$; (b) $3^{12} \div 3^7$; (c) $3^{15} \div 3^8$; (d) $3^{12} \div 3^4$; (e) $3^{10} \div 3^5$.

Logarithms of powers of numbers

We know that the raising of a number to a power is actually a repeated multiplication of a number by itself, and this number is taken as a factor as many times as is indicated by the exponent. For example,

$$5^4 = 5 \cdot 5 \cdot 5 \cdot 5 = 625.$$

This procedure is also applied when we raise a power to a power. For example,

$$(2^2)^3 = 2^2 \cdot 2^2 \cdot 2^2 = 2 \cdot 2 \cdot 2 \cdot 2 \cdot 2 \cdot 2 = 2^6.$$

But $6 = 2 \cdot 3$.   Then

$$(2^2)^3 = 2^{2 \cdot 3} = 2^6.$$

When we raise a power to a power we retain the same base, but the exponent of the new power is the product of the exponents. We can make this same statement in the form of logarithms.

We note that

$$\log_2 2^2 = 2,$$
$$\log_2 2^6 = 6,$$

and then write the logarithmic statement:

$$\log_2 (2^2)^3 = 2 \cdot 3 = 6.$$

From these observations we can form a rule for raising to a power: *The logarithm of a power of a number is equal to the product of the logarithm of the number multiplied by the exponent indicating the power to which this number is raised.*

PROBLEMS

597. Perform the following operations: (*a*) $(3^3)^2$; (*b*) $(2^3)^4$; (*c*) $(4^2)^2$; (*d*) $(5^2)^2$; (*e*) $(2^4)^5$.

598. Compute the powers of the numbers in Problem 597.

599. Refer to the values of the powers of 2 on page 260 and compute the following: (*a*) $(2^4)^4$; (*b*) $(2^2)^8$; (*c*) $(2^3)^6$; (*d*) $(2^7)^3$; (*e*) $(2^4)^5$.

Extraction of roots of numbers

In Chapter 16, page 252, we described the operation of the extraction of square roots. We noted there the fact that the extraction of a square root is an operation which reverses the raising of that number to the second power.

Just as a number can be raised to a power so we can have an operation of the extraction of a root that will reverse such an operation. Thus, if we have raised a number of the third power, the operation that will reverse the raising to the power will be the extraction of a root of the third degree. If we raise a number to the fifteenth power, the operation that will reverse this operation will be the extraction of a root of the fifteenth degree.

The problem that arises in the process of the extraction of a root of a given degree is as follows: We have a number, say 81. What number must be multiplied by itself, taken as a factor four times, so that 81 is obtained as a product? The answer to this problem is obtained by means of the extraction of a root of the fourth degree.

The general symbol for the extraction of a root is $\sqrt{}$, known as the radical, and the number from which the root is to be extracted is written under it. The number which indicates the degree is written at the upper left of the radical; it is called the *index* of the root. The index 2 is, by agreement, never written. Thus the fourth-degree root of 81 is written as

$$\sqrt[4]{81}.$$

If we write $\sqrt{81}$ we understand it to represent the second-degree root, or the square root, of 81. If we write $\sqrt[3]{27}$ we understand it to represent the third-degree root, or the cube root, of 27.

Let us extract the following root (consult the values of the powers of 2 on page 260):

$$\sqrt[3]{4{,}096}.$$

Note that $4{,}096 = 2^{12}$, and we can write

$$2^{12} = 2 \cdot 2 \cdot 2 \cdot 2 \cdot 2 \cdot 2 \cdot 2 \cdot 2 \cdot 2 \cdot 2 \cdot 2 \cdot 2.$$

According to the associative property of multiplication we can write

$$2^{12} = (2 \cdot 2 \cdot 2 \cdot 2) \cdot (2 \cdot 2 \cdot 2 \cdot 2) \cdot (2 \cdot 2 \cdot 2 \cdot 2),$$

or

$$2^{12} = 16 \cdot 16 \cdot 16.$$

From this observation we conclude that the cube root of 4,096 is equal to 16, because 16, when taken as a factor three times, gives 4,096 as a product. We then write

$$\sqrt[3]{4{,}096} = \sqrt[3]{2^{12}} = 16 = 2^4.$$

But consider the arithmetic relation between the exponents and the index:

$$12 \div 3 = 4.$$

Thus we arrive at another important fact, namely that to extract a root of a power of some number we divide the exponent of the power from which the root is to be extracted by the index of the root.

For another example,

$$\sqrt[8]{3^{24}} = 3^{24 \div 8} = 3^3.$$

Relations of this sort can be stated in terms of logarithms. Let us return to the problem of $\sqrt[3]{4,096}$:

$$\sqrt[3]{4,096} = \sqrt[3]{2^{12}} = 16 = 2^4 = 2^{12 \div 3}.$$

We eliminate those expressions which do not contain exponents, and get

$$\sqrt[3]{2^{12}} = 2^{12 \div 3} = 2^4.$$

That is,

$$\log_2 \sqrt[3]{2^{12}} = \log_2 2^{12 \div 3} = \log_2 2^4.$$

Then we have the following rule for the extraction of roots: *The logarithm of any root of a number is equal to the quotient obtained by taking as a dividend the logarithm of the number whose root is to be extracted and taking as a divisor the index of the root to be extracted.*

PROBLEMS

600. Write the following roots: (*a*) 12th root of 15; (*b*) 25th root of 7; (*c*) 8th root of 32; (*d*) 100th root of 10; (*e*) 57th root of 75.

601. Compute the following roots (consult the values of the powers of 2 on page 260): (*a*) $\sqrt[3]{512}$; (*b*) $\sqrt[4]{4,096}$; (*c*) $\sqrt[5]{32,768}$; (*d*) $\sqrt[7]{16,384^2}$; (*e*) $\sqrt[8]{65,536^3}$.

The rules for logarithms

The results obtained in the preceding sections are thus as follows:

A. When *multiplying* several numbers *add* the logarithms of the factors. The sum of the logarithms is the logarithm of the product. For example,

$$\log_2 (128 \cdot 512 \cdot 16,384) = \log_2 128 + \log_2 512 + \log_2 16,384.$$

$B.$ When *dividing* one number by another *subtract* the logarithm of the divisor from the logarithm of the dividend. This difference of the logarithms is the logarithm of the quotient. For example,

$$\log_2 (32,768 \div 128) = \log_2 32,768 - \log_2 128.$$

$C.$ When *raising a number to a power, multiply* the logarithm of the number by the exponent of the power. The product is the logarithm of the power. For example,

$$\log_2 (2,048)^5 = 5 \cdot \log_2 2,048.$$

$D.$ When *extracting a root* from a number *divide* the logarithm of the number by the indicator of the degree of the root. The quotient is the logarithm of the root. For example,

$$\log_2 \sqrt[8]{65,536} = \tfrac{1}{8} \log_2 65,536.$$

PROBLEMS

602. Compute $(32 \cdot 2,048 \cdot 16,384) \div (32,768 \div 512)$.

603. Compute $(16 \cdot 64)^5 \div 32^7$.

604. Compute $\sqrt[13]{(8,192 \cdot 1,024 \cdot 32,768 \cdot 65,536)^3}$.

Logarithms to the base 10

So far we examined the rules for the use of logarithms in computation by means of logarithms of base 2. However, 2 need not be the base. Any number can be used as a base.

The selection of a base is guided by considerations of economy and of practicability. It has been found that the most usable and most convenient base for everyday work is 10. The reason for this decision can be seen from the following considerations.

Let us examine the powers of 10:

$$10^0 = 1,$$
$$10^1 = 10,$$
$$10^2 = 100,$$
$$10^3 = 1,000,$$
$$10^4 = 10,000,$$
$$10^5 = 100,000.$$

These facts can be stated in terms of logarithms (of base 10) as follows:

$10^0 = 1,$	$\log_{10} 1 = 0,$
$10^1 = 10,$	$\log_{10} 10 = 1,$
$10^2 = 100,$	$\log_{10} 100 = 2,$
$10^3 = 1,000,$	$\log_{10} 1,000 = 3,$
$10^4 = 10,000,$	$\log_{10} 10,000 = 4,$
$10^5 = 100,000.$	$\log_{10} 100,000 = 5.$

Note that in the above logarithms the following properties are clearly observable:

i. The logarithms of all the powers of 10 are whole numbers.

ii. These whole numbers arrange themselves in the order we count, as we raise 10 to consecutive powers.

iii. The logarithms of the powers of 10 are always equal to the number of zeros in each power. Thus, $10^2 = 100$ has 2 zeros, and $\log_{10} 100 = 2$, $10^5 = 100,000$ has five zeros, and $\log_{10} 100,000 = 5$.

If we wish to obtain the logarithm of some number other than the whole-number power of 10 we must proceed as follows. Suppose that we wish to obtain $\log_{10} 6$. Now, the number 6 is somewhere between 1 and 10. We know that in order to obtain 1 we must raise 10 to the zero power, that is, $10^0 = 1$, and in order to obtain 10 we must raise 10 to the power 1, that is, $10^1 = 10$. But 6 is greater than 1 and is less than 10. Thus in order to obtain 6 we must raise 10 to a power greater than zero (0) but smaller than 1. In other words, this power must, from necessity, be a fraction.

Furthermore, suppose we wish to obtain $\log_{10} 60$. We observe that 60 is greater than 10, but 60 is less than 100. In order to obtain 10 we must raise 10 to the power 1, and in order to obtain 100 we must raise 10 to the power 2. But 60 is greater than 10 and is less than 100. Thus in order to obtain 60 we must raise 10 to a power greater than 1 but smaller than 2. In other words, this power must, from necessity, be a mixed number (or a mixed decimal) whose whole part is 1.

Note that our observation concerning the $\log_{10} 60$ can be checked by means of the rule for multiplication given on page 266. We can represent 60 as a product $60 = 6 \cdot 10$. Let $\log_{10} 6 = 0.778$. Then

$$\log_{10} 60 = \log_{10} (6 \cdot 10) = \log_{10} 6 + \log_{10} 10 = 0.778 + 1 = 1.778.$$

In a similar manner we can obtain $\log_{10} 600$, $\log_{10} 6,000$. We have

$$\log_{10} 600 = \log_{10} (6 \cdot 100) = \log_{10} 6 + \log_{10} 100 = 0.778 + 2 = 2.778,$$
$$\log_{10} 6,000 = \log_{10} (6 \cdot 1,000) = \log_{10} 6 + \log_{10} 1,000 = 0.778 + 3 = 3.778.$$

From the above consideration we obtain a rule for finding the whole part of a logarithm of a number, when the number is greater than 1. *The whole part of the logarithm of a number, when the number is greater than 1, is obtained as follows: Subtract 1 from the number of digits in the whole part of the number. The number of digits remaining is the whole part of the logarithm.* This whole part of the logarithm is called the *characteristic*. It determines the character of the number whose logarithm is given, that is, the number of digits in its whole part.

For example, a number with 7 digits in its whole part (say 1,286,754 or 3,465,218.9) will have 6 as the characteristic of its logarithm, because $7 - 1 = 6$.

If we have a logarithm with a characteristic, we can determine the number of digits in the whole part of the number by adding 1 to the characteristic. Thus the characteristic 6 tells that the whole part of the number has 7 digits, because $6 + 1 = 7$. A characteristic 0 indicates that the whole part of the number has one digit, because $0 + 1 = 1$.

Now, suppose we wish to obtain the logarithm of a pure decimal fraction. Let this decimal fraction be 0.6. We know the logarithm of 6 (base 10). The pure decimal fraction 0.6 can be obtained by dividing 6 by 10, that is, $0.6 = 6 \div 10$. Let us apply the rule for division given on page 267. We have then

$$\log_{10} 0.6 = \log_{10} (6 \div 10) = \log_{10} 6 - \log_{10} 10 = 0.778 - 1.$$

In the same manner we can obtain the logarithms (base 10) of 0.06, 0.006, 0.0006.

$$\log_{10} 0.06 \ \ = \log_{10} (6 \div 100) \ \ = \log_{10} 6 - \log_{10} 100 \ \ = 0.778 - 2,$$
$$\log_{10} 0.006 \ = \log_{10} (6 \div 1,000) \ = \log_{10} 6 - \log_{10} 1,000 \ = 0.778 - 3,$$
$$\log_{10} 0.0006 = \log_{10} (6 \div 10,000) = \log_{10} 6 - \log_{10} 10,000 = 0.778 - 4.$$

The above examples show that the logarithm of a pure decimal fraction is a difference. The minuend is the logarithm of the significant number that goes into the making of the decimal fraction and determines its magnitude (for example, in 0.016 this significant number is 16; in 0.00008954 the significant number is 8954). The subtrahend in base 10 logarithms is the number representing the number of decimal places in the pure decimal fraction (for example, in 0.016 the subtrahend is 3; in 0.00008954 the subtrahend is 8). [This direction is a practical rule; in exact theory, the subtrahend is the logarithm of the denominator of the decimal fraction—see the three examples above.]

PROBLEMS

In the following problems use the following values:

$$\log_{10} 2 = 0.301, \quad \log_{10} 3 = 0.477, \quad \log_{10} 5 = 0.699, \quad \log_{10} 7 = 0.845.$$

605. Write the logarithms of the following numbers: 20; 300; 5,000; 700,000; 2,000.

606. Write the logarithms of the following numbers: 12; 14; 15; 210; 1,800; 25; 350.

Hint: Use the rule for multiplication given on page 266.

607. Write the logarithms of the following numbers: 1.5; 2.5; 3.5; 7.5; 10.5. *Hint:* Use the rule for division given on page 267.

608. Write the logarithms of the following numbers: 8; 16; 32; 64; 128; 27; 81; 125; 625; 2,430; 12.5; 6.25.

Hint: Use the rule for raising to a power given on page 267.

609. Write the logarithms of the following numbers: 0.12; 0.024; 0.0025; 0.0125; 0.243.

Table of logarithms

The fractional part of a logarithm is called the *mantissa.* It may contain as many decimal places as desired or as may be necessary. For many practical problems of everyday nature a logarithm with three decimal places in its mantissa is sufficient. Below is a table of such mantissas. Since they represent the fractional part of a logarithm, the decimal point is omitted.

By means of the table shown on pages 272–273 we can obtain the fractional portions of logarithms, that is, the mantissas. The whole parts of the logarithms must be determined according to the rules explained on page 269.

This table is good for four-place numbers in the part up to the numbers 199 and the remainder of the table is useful for three-place numbers only. Also, only mantissas with three decimal places can be obtained by means of this table.

Note that the above table consists of two parts. Up to and including the number 199 we can read the mantissas directly from the table. We locate the mantissa as follows. The first two digits of a number are located in the column on the extreme left of the table. The third digit is located in the first line on the top of the table. Draw a horizontal line and a vertical line through the vertical column and the horizontal line on the top of the table where the digits are located. Where these two lines intersect is the cell with the mantissa of the logarithm of the number. For example, the mantissa of the logarithm of 168 is found by following horizontally through the number 16 and vertically through the number 8 on the top of the table. We find then the mantissa **225.** The logarithm of 168 is 2.225. The logarithm of 16.8 is 1.225. The logarithm of 0.168 is 2.225 − 3.

	0	1	2	3	4	5	6	7	8	9
10	000	004	009	013	017	021	025	029	033	037
11	041	045	049	053	057	061	064	068	072	076
12	079	083	086	090	093	097	100	104	107	111
13	114	117	121	124	127	130	134	137	140	143
14	146	149	152	155	158	161	164	167	170	173
15	176	179	182	185	188	190	193	196	199	201
16	204	207	210	212	215	217	220	223	225	228
17	230	233	236	238	241	243	246	248	250	253
18	255	258	260	262	265	267	270	272	274	276
19	279	281	283	286	288	290	292	294	297	299
2	301	322	342							

Differences

1	2	3	4	5	6	7	8	9
2	4	6	8	10	12	14	16	18
1	2	3	4	5	6	7	8	9

Differences

1	2	3	4	5	6	7	8	9
2	4	5	7	9	11	12	14	16
2	3	5	6	8	10	11	13	14
1	3	4	6	7	8	10	11	12
1	2	4	5	6	7	8	10	11
1	2	3	4	5	6	7	8	9
1	2	3	4	5	6	6	7	8
1	2	2	3	4	5	6	6	7
1	1	2	3	3	4	5	5	6
1	1	2	2	3	3	4	5	5
1	1	2	2	3	3	4	4	5
0	1	1	2	2	3	3	4	4
1	2	3	4	5	6	7	8	9

Main table

	0	1	2	3	4	5	6	7	8	9
2				362	380	398	415	431	447	462
2	477	491	505	519						
3					531	544	556	568	580	591
3	602	613	623	633	643	653				
4							663	672	681	690
4	699	708	716	724	732	740	748	756	763	771
5	778	785	792	799	806	813	820	826	833	839
6	845	851	857	863	869	875	881	886	892	898
7	903	908	914	919	924	929	935	940	944	949
8	954	959	964	968	973	978	982	987	991	996
9										
	0	1	2	3	4	5	6	7	8	9

Beginning with the number 200 we obtain the mantissas in the following manner. The lower portion of the table gives mantissas for two-place numbers such as 20, 21, 35, and the like. But we can employ the method of interpolation. Furthermore, the table is so printed that no additional computation is required. On the right we have in the table a small table of differences already computed. We locate the first two digits of the number whose logarithm is to be obtained in the same manner as described in the preceding paragraph. Then, for the third digit we consult the same horizontal line in which the first digit of the number is located. Under the number indicating the third digit we locate the difference which must be added to the mantissa already found. For example, the logarithm of 481 is found as follows: Where the horizontal line through 4 intersects with the vertical line through 8 we find 681. Further on the right where the horizontal line through 4 intersects with the vertical line through 1 we find 1. Then the mantissa is equal to 681 + 1 = 682. The logarithm is then 2.682.

The logarithm of 4.81 is 0.682. The logarithm of 481,000 is 5.682. The logarithm of 0.000481 is 2.682 − 6.

PROBLEMS

610. Find the logarithms of the following numbers: 136; 1.89; 17.3; 3.45; 89.3; 76,400; 65.4; 3.47; 2.84; 489.

611. Find the logarithms of the following numbers: 0.367; 0.00735; 0.0895; 0.105; 0.0000562; 0.000121; 0.426; 0.268; 0.0592; 0.00675.

Computations with logarithms

Since we shall be using logarithms of base 10 exclusively, we shall omit the writing of the base from now on. Thus instead of writing $\log_{10} 15$ we shall write log 15, and we shall understand that we use 10 as the base.

Before we proceed with the practical application of logarithms to computations we must examine the method of finding the number whose logarithm is given.

Suppose the given logarithm is 1.266. For the time being we shall pay no attention to the characteristic. By means of the mantissa 266 we shall find the sequence of the digits in the number. We locate this mantissa in the table. It is not there, but we have 265 and 267. We take 265. The horizontal line passing through the cell in which this mantissa 265 is located passes through the digits 18 in the vertical column on the extreme left. The vertical line passes through the digit 4. Thus for the mantissa 265 we have the sequence 184. For the mantissa 267 the sequence is 185. The mantissa 266 is halfway between 265 and 267. The sequence of the digits must then be also halfway between 184 and 185, which is, 1845.

Now we must take into consideration the characteristic of the logarithm. It is 1. Therefore, the whole part of the number has 2 digits. Thus the number whose logarithm is 1.266 is 18.45.

Suppose the logarithm is 3.266 − 5; then the number is a pure decimal fraction. It has five decimal places, and the number sequence is 1845, that is it has four digits. In other words, there is one zero to the left of 1, and the number is 0.01845.

Suppose that the logarithm is 3.684. Again we pay no attention for the time being to the characteristic. We find that the nearest mantissa in the table is 681, and it belongs to the number 48. The difference 684 − 681 = 3. In the same horizontal line with 681, in the table of the differences we find the difference 3 determines the digit 3 (follow the vertical line that passes through 3). Then the sequence of the digits is 483. Since the characteristic is 3, the number must have 4 digits, and we conclude that the number whose logarithm is 3.684 is 4,830.

If the logarithm is 2.684 − 6, then the number is a pure decimal fraction with six decimals, and there will be 6 − 3 = 3 zeros after the decimal point. The number whose logarithm is 2.684 − 6 is therefore 0.000483.

Let us consider the following examples.

EXAMPLE 1. Obtain the product $3.52 \cdot 1.746$. We have

$$\log 3.52 = 0.546,$$
$$\log 1.746 = 0.242.$$

Note the log 1.74 = 0.241 and log 1.75 = 0.243.   The difference is 0.002, and adding to 0.241 for 0.006, we must take 0.6 of 0.002, which is 0.6 · 0.002 = 0.0012; when this difference is rounded to 0.001, and added to 0.241 we obtain 0.242.   Then the sum is

$$\log 3.52 + \log 1.746 = 0.546 + 0.242 = 0.788.$$

Now, by means of the table we find that the nearest mantissas to 788 that can be found are 785 and 792, and the difference 788 − 785 = 3.   By means of the difference table we find two digits 4 and 5.   Now recall that we dropped a digit 2; hence the digit 5 is closer.   Finally, we find that the product is 6.25.

EXAMPLE 2.   The product 0.0412 · 1.95 is obtained as follows:

$$\begin{aligned}
\log 0.0412 &= 2.615 - 4 \\
\log 1.95 &= 0.290 \\
\hline
\text{sum} &= 2.905 - 4
\end{aligned}$$

Then, the number whose logarithm is 2.905 − 4 is the pure decimal fraction 0.0803.

EXAMPLE 3.   Perform the division 0.136 ÷ 2.06.

$$\begin{aligned}
\log 0.136 &= 2.134 - 3 \\
\log 2.06 &= 0.313 \\
\hline
\text{difference} &= 1.821 - 3
\end{aligned}$$

Finally, by means of the table, we find that the quotient is 0.0661. Note that in the logarithm of the quotient, that is, in 1.821 − 3, we can add 1 to 1.821, and increase the minuend 3 by 1:

$$1.821 + 1 - 3 - 1 = 2.821 - 4.$$

The object of this change is to obtain a three-place significant number.   This change of form does not change the value of the difference, and we obtain the correct quotient.

EXAMPLE 4.   Suppose that we wish to perform the following division:

$$2.06 \div 0.136.$$

Note that this can be written as

$$2.06 \div \frac{136}{1,000}.$$

According to the rule for the division of a number by a common fraction, we have then

$$\frac{2.06 \cdot 1,000}{136}.$$

Also, the logarithm of the division

$$\log 2.06 + \log 1,000 - \log 136 = 0.313 + 3 - 2.134.$$

We get the logarithm of the quotient,

$$0.313 + 3 - 2.134 = 0.179,$$

and the quotient $2.06 \div 0.136 = 1.51$.

EXAMPLE 5. Extract the following root:

$$\sqrt[4]{14.6}.$$

We have

$$\log \sqrt[4]{14.6} = \tfrac{1}{4} \cdot 1.164 = 0.291,$$

and from the table we find that

$$\sqrt[4]{14.6} = 1.955$$

EXAMPLE 6. Extract the following root:

$$\sqrt[5]{0.0736}.$$

We have

$$\log \sqrt[5]{0.0736} = \tfrac{1}{5}(2.866 - 4).$$

Note that we must always have a whole number that must be subtracted because this whole number indicates the number of decimal places in the pure decimal fraction. However, the division of 4 by 5 will not give a whole number as a quotient. This difficulty can be remedied. Add 1 to 2.866 and to 4, thus keeping the difference unchanged. We have then the logarithm of the required root:

$$\frac{1}{5}(3.866 - 5) = \frac{2.866}{5} - 1 = 0.573 - 1.$$

Change $0.573 - 1$ into $2.573 - 3$, and we find that

$$\sqrt[5]{0.0736} = 0.374.$$

EXAMPLE 7. In Chapter 15 it was mentioned that compound interest can be computed by means of logarithms. Suppose that $1,500 was deposited in a bank and the interest is 2% compounded annually. What will this deposit amount to at the end of five years?

At the end of the first year it will amount to

$$\$1,500 \cdot (1 + 0.02) = \$1,500 \cdot 1.02.$$

At the end of the second year it will amount to

$$\$1,500 \cdot 1.02 \cdot (1 + 0.02) = \$1,500 \cdot 1.02^2.$$

At the end of the third year it will amount to

$$\$1,500 \cdot 1.02^2 \cdot (1 + 0.02) = \$1,500 \cdot 1.02^3.$$

At the end of the fourth year it will amount to

$$\$1,500 \cdot 1.02^3 \cdot (1 + 0.02) = \$1,500 \cdot 1.02^4.$$

Finally, at the end of the fifth year it will amount to

$$\$1,500 \cdot 1.02^4 \cdot (1 + 0.02) = \$1,500 \cdot 1.02^5.$$

This is then computed as follows:

$$\log (1,500 \cdot 1.02^5) = \log 1,500 + 5 \log 1.02,$$
$$\log (1,500 \cdot 1.02^5) = 3.176 + 5 \cdot 0.009 = 3.176 + 0.045 = 3.221.$$

Then, from the table we find that this amount is equal to $1,663.33.

Generally, the formula for the computation of an amount whose interest is compounded in a certain period is

$$A = K \left(1 + \frac{r}{100} \right)^n,$$

where K is the capital, r is the rate for a given period, and n is the number of periods during which interest is compounded. For example, if the yearly rate is 6% compounded quarterly, then

$$r = \frac{6}{4 \cdot 100} = \frac{3}{200}.$$

And if the capital is left to accumulate interest for 12 years, then

$$n = 12 \cdot 4 = 48 \text{ periods.}$$

PROBLEMS

Perform the following computations:

612. (a) $87.6 \cdot 1.45$;
(b) $12.4 \cdot 3.67$;
(c) $0.875 \cdot 34.5$;
(d) $0.562 \cdot 1.75$;
(e) $0.369 \cdot 0.152$.

613. (a) $10.7 \div 4.65$;
(b) $4.73 \div 12.6$;
(c) $55.6 \div 0.873$;
(d) $0.312 \div 12.4$;
(e) $0.712 \div 0.893$.

614. (a) 7.35^3;
(b) 3.56^4;
(c) 11.2^3;
(d) 1.06^8;
(e) 1.06^{12};
(f) 0.152^4;
(g) 0.0892^6.

615. (a) $\sqrt{89.6}$;
(b) $\sqrt[3]{112}$;
(c) $\sqrt[8]{17.5}$;
(d) $\sqrt[9]{0.000456}$;
(e) $\sqrt[12]{2}$.

616. (a) $\dfrac{7.84 \cdot 13.6}{56.8}$;

(b) $\dfrac{89.6}{15.4 \cdot 0.125}$;

(c) $6.84^4 \div (25.6 \div 0.00739)$;
(d) $\sqrt[3]{(18.9 \cdot 1.75)} \div 0.562$;
(e) $\dfrac{\sqrt[4]{8.95}}{14.2}$.

18

The Slide Rule

What is a slide rule?

When computations must be performed with numbers that may require a considerable amount of work, any simplification of the numerical work is a welcome time saver and labor saver. The reader, after having studied the use of logarithms in computation in Chapter 17, will readily agree that logarithms reduce even tedious multiplication, division, extraction of roots, and raising to a power to simple arithmetic computations. Furthermore, when we deal with approximate numbers, logarithms eliminate much numerical work in carrying out the computations to many unnecessary digits, digits that will have to be discarded as useless, anyway.

However, the work with logarithms still involves a considerable amount of numerical computations. Naturally, we may ask whether we can further reduce the amount of computational work.

The answer to this question is *yes!*

In place of a printed table of logarithms we use a simple instrument which is actually a graph of logarithms. This instrument is known as *the slide rule.*

A man who can operate the slide rule can perform very long multiplications and divisions faster than a man who operates an efficient calculating machine that is nowadays considered as standard office equipment. Furthermore, the slide rule does something that the calculating machine cannot do. A slide rule will give the answer to a problem with that number of significant digits (see Chapter 16) which is in agreement with the rules for the work with approximate numbers. A calculating machine will give all the digits, and then it becomes necessary to discard those that are unreliable.

In order to understand how a slide rule works the reader should consult pages 266–267 of Chapter 17.   The mechanical idea of the slide rule will be described in the next section.

A simple addition and subtraction machine

In the description below we chose to use a centimeter ruler because a centimeter is divided in tenths (known as millimeters), and thus we can use such a ruler for the purpose of counting according to our decimal system of notation.

If we wish to add two numbers we use the arithmetic operation of addition.   If we wish to add two lengths (say 1 meter and 3 meters) we take one length and attach to one of its ends the other length; the sum of the two lengths is then the total distance from the beginning of the first length to the end of the second length, as shown in Figure 6.

FIGURE 6

Using this fact, and employing two centimeter rulers, we can perform additions of numbers by sliding one ruler along the second.   Thus, in Figure 7, the addition

$$35 + 45 = 80$$

is shown.   Note that we place the zero (0) mark of the second ruler over the 35 mark of the first ruler.   Then the 45 mark of

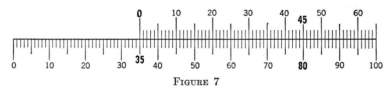

FIGURE 7

the second ruler will indicate the required sum on the first ruler, namely 80.

In a similar manner we can perform subtractions of numbers. Figure 8 illustrates the subtraction

$$115 - 53 = 62.$$

Note that we place the 53 mark of the second ruler under the 115 mark on the first ruler.   Then, at the zero (0) mark on the second

FIGURE 8

ruler will be the mark on the first ruler indicating the difference of the two numbers, namely 62.

The fundamental idea of a slide rule

The slide rule resembles this addition-and-subtraction instrument, with a distinct modification.   The lines on it are graduated not at equally spaced intervals but at intervals determined by the magnitudes of the mantissas of logarithms.   If the reader has examined carefully the table of logarithms on pages 272-273, he will have observed that the steps from the mantissas of numbers from one to another are not all equal throughout the table.

The scales on a slide rule are logarithmic scales.   When we propose to work with a slide rule we still employ the processes of addition and subtraction.   But we do not add or subtract natural numbers; we add and subtract logarithms.

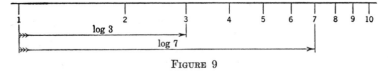

FIGURE 9

The starting point on a slide rule is 0, just as is the starting point on any other ruler.   However, this starting point is not marked 0 on the slide rule.   It is marked 1, because any number raised to the zero power is 1 (see page 268) and log 1 = 0.   This meaning of a scale on the slide rule is illustrated in Figure 9.

The addition of logarithms leads to the logarithm of a product (see page 266); this operation on the slide rule appears as shown in Figure 10.

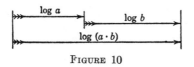

FIGURE 10

The subtraction of logarithms leads to the logarithm of a quotient (see page 267), and this operation on the slide rule appears as shown in Figure 11.

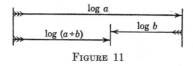

FIGURE 11

All other uses of the slide rule are different arrangements of these two basic operations.   Thus, in order to operate a slide rule we must remember two facts only: (1) we either subtract or add, or (2) we read directly on two scales.

The construction of a slide rule

The slide rule consists of three parts.

> *i.* A rule, or ruler.
> *ii.* A slide.
> *iii.* A runner.

A ruler and a slide contain various kinds of scales (all based on the logarithms), and the act of computing by means of a slide rule consists in the correct setting of these scales.

A runner is a piece of glass or celluloid set in a frame which slides along the rule.   Usually a runner has one or more hairlines which are used for the purpose of locating certain graduation marks on the rule, or for temporarily fixing such graduations in the process of computation when partial results must be temporarily kept unchanged until they can be used in further computations.

The logarithmic scale

The main scale of a slide rule is a table of logarithms, except that instead of having the mantissas listed we have them represented by a set of lengths (measured from the starting point of the slide rule marked by 1).

This scale (Figure 12) is divided into 9 main divisions. The division marked 2 indicates that the distance from 1 to 2 repre-

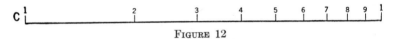

FIGURE 12

sents log 2. The division 3 indicates that the distance from 1 to 3 represents log 3. The division 6 indicates that the distance from 1 to 6 represents log 6, and so do all other divisions.

The distances between the main divisions are subdivided into ten smaller divisions, known as *secondary divisions* (none of them of equal length—remember we are dealing with a logarithmic scale). These secondary divisions are shown in Figure 13.

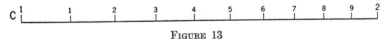

FIGURE 13

These divisions are not numbered except (sometimes) between 1 and 2.

The introduction of the secondary divisions increases the power of the logarithmic scale tenfold. Now, we can consider the distance between 1 and 2 as log 20, the distance between 1 and 3 as log 30, and so on. Furthermore, reading these divisions, we can find a point between the main divisions 2 and 3 which may be read as 25, and the distance between 1 and 25 is then a representation of log 25.

The final construction of the main scale utilizes further sub-divisions as shown (enlarged) in Figure 14. These divisions are known as *tertiary divisions*. The secondary divisions between 1 and 2 are each subdivided into 10 tertiary parts. These

FIGURE 14

tertiary parts are not equal to one another. The distances between the secondary divisions which are located between the main divisions 2 and 3, and 3 and 4 are too small to contain 10 tertiary parts each. Here the distances between the secondary divisions are divided into 5 tertiary parts. Further, beyond the main division 4, the distances between the secondary divisions are so small that they are subdivided into two tertiary parts only.

The graduation into tertiary parts completes the construction of the main logarithmic scale. But with this introduction the logarithmic scale enables us to read three-place numbers. Thus the mark 2 now indicates that the distance between 1 and 2 represents log 200, mark 3 indicates that the distance between 1 and 3 represents log 300, and so on.

The reading of the main scale then consists of three distinct steps of reading the divisions:

    i. First, we read the main division, and the number so read gives the first digit on the left of a number (say 2).

    ii. Secondly, we read the secondary division, and the number so read gives the second digit (counting from the left) of a number (say 3). Thus we might have 23.

    iii. Finally, we read the tertiary division. If we read between the main divisions 1 and 2 we can obtain every tertiary division (1, 2, 3, 4, 5, 6, 7, 8, and 9). If we read between the main divisions 2 and 4 we can obtain only the even digits (2, 4, 6, and 8), but with practice we can learn to estimate the odd digits with sufficient precision. When we read between the main divisions 4 and those beyond 4 to the end of the scale we can read only the digit 5, but we may attempt to estimate (although caution should be exercised). Thus, continuing our reading, we might complete it as 236.

PROBLEMS

617. Locate on the main scale the following points: 118; 128; 135; 147; 214; 318; 374; 425; 545; 685; 725; 775; 865; 945.

The scales on a slide rule

Figure 15 shows the face of a slide rule. The various scales, which will be described presently, are marked (for our convenience) by capital letters. It is well to study the various scales so that they will be recognized readily.

The strip that contains the capital letters B, CI, and C is the slide. It fits snugly into the rule, and it is moved whenever the rule is set for the purpose of computation.

The main scales are C and D. They are identical in every respect. The main scale was described on page 284. These two scales C and D are the most used on a slide rule.

The A and B scales are also identical in all respects. They are also logarithmic scales. They are similar (in construction) to the C and D scales. But, and this remark is important, scales A and B consist of two identical halves: in order to make scale A (or scale B), scale C (or D) was contracted to one-half its size. By this arrangement the range of the numbers that can be read on scales A and B is multiplied by 10. The reader will recall that on scale C (see page 285) we can read numbers from 1 to 1,000. On scale A (or B) we can read numbers from 1 to 1,000 on the left half; then numbers from 1,000 to 10,000 follow on the right half.

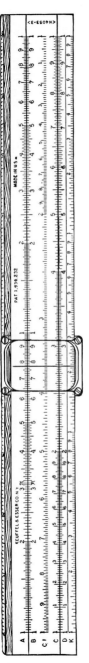

FIGURE 15.—*Polyphase* Slide Rule. (Illustration by courtesy of Keuffel & Esser Company.)

Scales A and B are used for reading the squares of numbers that are on scales C and D. For example, note that above the number 2 on scale C the number 4 appears on scale A, above the number 3 on scale C the number 9 appears on scale A, above the number 4 on scale C the number 16 appears on scale A. Moreover, we can reverse the process of reading. If we take a number on scale A (or B), then its square root will be below it on scale D (or C). We take the number 25 on scale A (second half); then below it, on scale D, we find the number 5. Again, we take the number 36 on the B scale (second half); below it, on scale C, we find the number 6.

In the preceding paragraph it has been assumed that the slide rule is *closed*, that all the number graduations 1 are aligned; in this condition the slide rule is said to be in its initial position. Yet even if the slide is moved, still by means of the runner we can read the squares and square roots if we set the runner's hairline over the given number on scale D and read its square on scale A, or set the runner's hairline on a given number on scale A and read its square root on scale D. Scales A and D are stationary.

At the lower edge of the slide rule is the K scale. It consists of three identical parts. It is also a logarithmic scale, similar to the main scale C. Since it is actually a logarithmic scale contracted to one-third the size of the main C scale, the K scale is used for obtaining the cubes of the numbers read on scales C or D. Also, scales C or D are used for the reading of the cube roots of the numbers read on scale K.

The division of the scale K into three identical parts enables us to read numbers on it as follows. In all the readings we start from the left of the scale.

If we read the first part as	Then the second part is	And then the third part is
1 to 10	10 to 100	100 to 1,000
1 to 100	100 to 1,000	1,000 to 10,000

In the center of the slide is a scale CI, the scale of the reciprocals of the numbers on scale C (or D). (A reciprocal of a number is a fraction whose numerator is 1 and whose denominator is the number itself: the reciprocal of 2 is $\frac{1}{2}$ or 0.5, the reciprocal of 4 is $\frac{1}{4}$ or 0.25.) On the other hand, scale C (or D) is also the reciprocal of the scale CI. For example, the reciprocal of 25 is $\frac{1}{25}$ or 0.04.

The slide rule does not offer any means for locating the decimal point either in a pure decimal fraction or in a mixed decimal fraction. The method used for the determination of the decimal point will be described presently.

Multiplication on the slide rule

For multiplication on the slide rule we use the scales C and D.

In order to describe the methods for the multiplication in general let us denote the two factors by a and b. Thus the product of the two numbers represented by these letters will be

$$a \cdot b.$$

Find the number designated by a on the scale D (Figure 16). Then move the slide to the right so that the number 1 of scale C

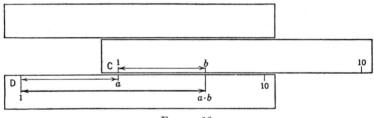

FIGURE 16

is set over the number a (which is on scale D). Locate on scale C the number designated by the letter b. Then on scale D below the number b (on scale C) is the product $a \cdot b$.

For example, the product $16 \cdot 4$ is obtained as follows: Locate 16 on the scale D. Move the slide so that 1 on scale C is over

16 (on scale D). Look for the number 4 on scale C. Below it read on scale D the product 64.

Note that this same setting of the slide rule gives us the products of other numbers multiplied by 16. For example, $16 \cdot 4.5 = 72$, $16 \cdot 5.5 = 88$.

Should we want to obtain the product $16 \cdot 8$ as above, we find that the number 8 on the C scale is moved out too far to the right, and it is beyond the D scale. In order to perform such a multiplication we set the number 10 of the C scale over the number designated by the letter a on the D scale (Figure 17). Then we

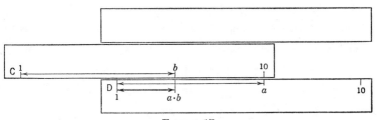

FIGURE 17

locate on the C scale the number designated by the letter b, and under it on the D scale we read the product.

For example, to obtain the product $16 \cdot 8$, locate 16 on scale D. Move the slide to the left so that 10 on the scale C is over the 16 (on scale D). Look for the number 8 on scale C. Below it read on scale D the product 128.

Suppose that we have several factors, say a, b, and c. The product of these is obtained in the same manner. First we obtain the product of a and b. After the product is obtained we are left with two numbers only: the product $(a \cdot b)$ and c. Now, in order to keep the product $(a \cdot b)$ on the scale D and not lose it, we set the runner's hairline over it, and then set the 1 of the C scale to coincide with the hairline. We look on the C scale for the third number c, and under it, on the D scale we find the product of the three numbers.

For example, to find the product of 5, 8, and 9, set the 1 of scale C over the 5 on scale D. Note that the 8 on scale C is too far out to the right. Then set the 10 of scale C over the 5 on scale D. Move the runner so that its hairline is over the 8 on scale C. Then move the 10 of scale C to coincide with the runner's hairline and read, under the 9 of scale C, 72 on scale D. The product is 720, and the fact that it is 720 and not 72 is determined by the observation of the three factors, 5, 8, and 9.

PROBLEMS

618. Perform the following multiplications: (a) $6 \cdot 9$; (b) $22 \cdot 15$; (c) $35 \cdot 46$; (d) $1.5 \cdot 2.8$; (e) $7.2 \cdot 3.5$.

619. Perform the following multiplications: (a) $15 \cdot 4.2 \cdot 8$; (b) $3 \cdot 7 \cdot 8 \cdot 12$; (c) $2.5 \cdot 8.5 \cdot 15$.

Division on the slide rule

Division on the slide rule is performed by means of scales C and D. Let us denote the quotient by $a \div b$ or $\frac{a}{b}$.

Find the number designated by a (the dividend, or the numerator) on scale D. Also find the number designated by b

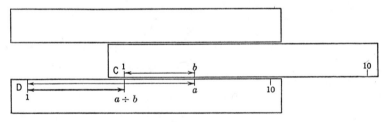

FIGURE 18

(the divisor, or the denominator) on scale C. Then move the slide so that the number mark of b (on scale C) is over the number mark of a (on scale D) as shown in Figure 18. Then read on scale D, under the number 1 on scale C, the quotient $a \div b$.

For example, to divide $85 \div 5$, find 85 on scale D. Find 5 on scale C. Set 5 (on scale C) over 85 (on scale D). Read on scale D, under the 1 of the scale C, the quotient 17.

If the setting of the slide is such that the 1 of scale C is too far to the left of the end of the slide rule, and the quotient cannot be read under the 1 of the C scale, the quotient is found under the 10 of scale C as shown in Figure 19.

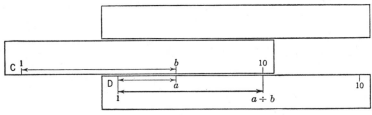

FIGURE 19

For example, to divide $26 \div 4$, set the 4 of scale C over the 26 of scale D. Then read on scale D, under the 10 of scale C, the quotient 6.5.

PROBLEMS

620. Perform the following divisions: (a) $55 \div 22$; (b) $65 \div 2.6$; (c) $42 \div 1.4$; (d) $1.7 \div 8.5$; (e) $256 \div 8$.

The location of the decimal point in the product and quotient of two numbers

In order to locate the correct place of the decimal point in the product or quotient of two numbers we shall make use of the property of the moving of the decimal point in a fraction. This property was discussed in detail on page 111, and this section may be worth rereading now.

Suppose that we multiply 856 by 41.2. In order to determine the location of the decimal point, let us change the two factors into numbers that contain only one digit in the whole part, that is, 8.56 and 4.12. By doing this we divide 856 by 100 or 10^2, and we divide 41.2 by 10. Thus the product is divided by 10^3. To restore the correct product, after we find the digit sequence, we shall have to multiply it by 10^3, that is, move the decimal point three places to the right. The product $8 \cdot 4 = 32$, that is, it has two places in the whole part. Thus with the restored three places, the product will have five places or digits.

Suppose that we multiply 18.56 by 0.00378. Again let us change the two factors into numbers with only one digit in the whole parts, that is, 1.856 and 3.78. The first factor was divided by 10, and the second factor was multiplied by 1,000 or 10^3. Thus the product was multiplied by 10^2. In order to correct for this we shall have to divide the product by 10^2 after we find the digit sequence; that is, the decimal point will have to be moved two places to the left. The product of 1 and 3 is a one-digit number. Moving the decimal point two places to the left will result in one zero to the right of the decimal point.

The slide-rule operator should carefully examine the digits that follow the decimal point in the changed factors. For example, $2.35 \cdot 4.56$ might lead us to think that since $2 \cdot 4 = 8$ we shall have one digit in the whole part. But we actually get two digits.

Let us consider the division $864 \div 415$. We can change the two numbers into 8.64 and 4.15, and the quotient will not be affected by this because the divisor and dividend are both divided by the same number, 100. The quotient $8 \div 2 = 4$ gives one digit in the whole part of the quotient of the division $864 \div 415$.

Let us perform the division $0.0864 \div 91.2$. Changing the two numbers into 8.64 and 9.12 we multiply the quotient by $1,000 = 10^3$ (0.0864 was multiplied by 100, and the division of the divisor 91.2 multiplied the quotient by 10). Thus, in order to restore the quotient we must divide the quotient $8 \div 9$ by 1,000, that is, we shall have to move the decimal point three places to the left. In other words, there will be three zeros to the right of the decimal point.

The above examples illustrate the procedure for determining the location of the decimal point: *Change the numbers so that they contain one digit in the whole part. Perform the multiplication or division with the numbers in this form. Note what correction must be made to restore the decimal point to its proper place in the product or quotient; finally make this correction.*

There are other rules for the locating of the decimal point, but all of them are very complicated. The above procedure is the simplest of all.

Multiplication with the reciprocal scale CI

Note that the reciprocal scale CI is read from right to left. This fact should be always remembered.

The product of two numbers a and b, that is, $a \cdot b$, can be obtained by using the D scale and the reciprocal scale CI, as follows:

Move the runner so that its hairline is set over the number represented by a on the scale D. Then move the slide so that the number indicated by b on the reciprocal scale CI is also under the hairline of the runner. This position is shown in Figure 20. Then, if the slide was moved to the right (Figure 20) the product

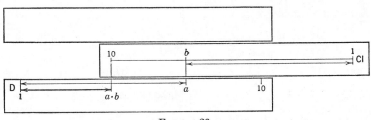

FIGURE 20

is read on scale D under the number 1 of the scale C (which is the same as 10 on the scale CI). If the slide was moved to the left (Figure 21) the product is read on scale D under the number 10 on scale C (which is the same as 1 on the scale CI).

For example, to find the product $3.5 \cdot 5.2$, locate 3.5 on scale D. Move the runner over it so that the hairline coincides with its graduation. Move the slide so that 5.2 on the reciprocal scale coincides with the runner's hairline. Then read on scale D, under the 1 of scale C (or 10 of scale CI), the product 18.2.

To find the product $2.82 \cdot 2.5$, locate 2.82 on scale D. Move the runner over it so that the hairline coincides with its gradua-

tion.   Move the slide so that 2.5 on the reciprocal scale coincides
with the runner's hairline.   Then read on scale D, under the 10
of scale C (or 1 of scale CI), the product 7.05.

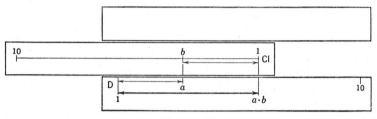

FIGURE 21

PROBLEMS

621. Perform the following multiplications: (a) 12.4 · 3.6; (b) 37.5 · 0.54;
(c) 8.85 · 0.0246; (d) 0.98 · 1.25; (e) 0.258 · 0.405.

Division with the reciprocal scale CI

The division of numbers by means of the reciprocal scale is
performed as follows:

Let the quotient be $a \div b$, or $\frac{a}{b}$.   Locate on the scale D the
dividend (or numerator) a and slide the reciprocal scale CI so

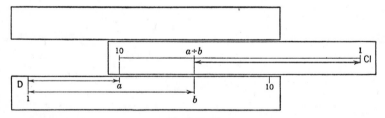

FIGURE 22

that one of its ends is over the dividend a.   In case a is smaller
than b the slide is moved to the right, and the 10 of the reciprocal
scale CI (or 1 of the scale C) is over it, as shown in Figure 22.   If
a is greater than b then the slide is moved to the left, and the 1

of the reciprocal scale CI (or 10 of the scale C) is over it, as shown in Figure 23. After the setting has been obtained, move the runner until its hairline will be over the divisor (or denominator) b on scale D. Read scale CI (the reciprocal scale) where the runner's hairline crosses it. This reading is the quotient.

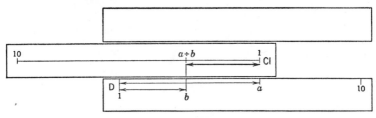

FIGURE 23

For example, to perform the division 4.6 ÷ 9.4, locate 4.6 on the D scale. Move this slide so that the 10 on the reciprocal scale is over the 4.6 on scale D. Move the runner until its hairline is over 9.4 on scale D. Read on the reciprocal scale CI, where the hairline crosses it, the quotient 0.49.

To perform the division 8.75 ÷ 3.6, locate 8.75 on the scale D. Move slide so that the 1 on the reciprocal scale is over the 8.75 on the D scale. Move runner until its hairline is over 3.6 on the D scale. Read on the reciprocal scale CI, where the hairline crosses it, the quotient 2.43.

PROBLEMS

622. Perform the following divisions: (*a*) 2.84 ÷ 0.185; (*b*) 17.6 ÷ 482; (*c*) 9.05 ÷ 18.6; (*d*) 0.0075 ÷ 1.46; (*e*) 0.0167 ÷ 0.135.

Squaring and extraction of square roots

The squaring and the extraction of square roots of numbers are performed by means of the runner. Its hairline is used for aligning a number found on scale D and its square which is found on scale A. Similarly, if we take a number on scale A, then the hairline of the runner will align with its square root on scale D.

For example, the square of 4.2 (4.2 is located on scale D) is found on scale A by means of the runner, and $4.2^2 = 17.6$.

The square root of 15.4 is found on scale D (15.4 is located on scale A), and it is $\sqrt{15.4} = 3.92$.

PROBLEMS

623. Find the squares of the following numbers: 15.8; 9.85; 0.345; 4.56; 2.75; 7.34; 8.25; 6.54; 4.12; 5.46.

624. Find the square roots of the following numbers: 2.34; 7.89; 0.895; 0.0658; 4.05; 1.76; 17.6; 9.25; 0.000984; 10.6.

Problems with squares of numbers

The following illustrations of typical slide-rule computations in which the square of a number occurs will assume that the reader has learned how to multiply and how to divide by means of the slide rule.

The computations should always begin on the scales C or D. The final result will always appear on scale A.

The computation of $(a \cdot b)^2$. On page 288 the multiplication of two numbers is described. After the product is obtained, and

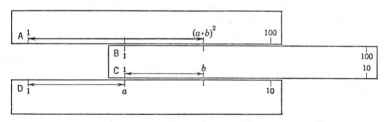

FIGURE 24

it need not be read immediately, bring the runner so that its hairline is over it, read the square of the product on scale A, as illustrated in Figure 24.

For example, to compute $(2.45 \cdot 8.64)^2$, locate 2.45 on scale D. Move the slide so that the 10 on scale C is over the 2.45. Now, using the runner, locate 8.64 on scale C and place the runner's hairline over it. Follow the hairline to scale A and read 448.

PROBLEMS

625. Perform the following computations: (a) $(2.4 \cdot 6.9)^2$; (b) $(1.35 \cdot 1.76)^2$; (c) $(0.89 \cdot 1.65)^2$; (d) $(0.75 \cdot 0.45)^2$; (e) $(0.016 \cdot 3.65)^2$.

The computation of $(a \div b)^2$. The division of two numbers is described on page 290. After the quotient is obtained, and it need not be read now, bring the runner so that its hairline is over it, and read the square of the quotient on scale A, as illustrated in Figure 25.

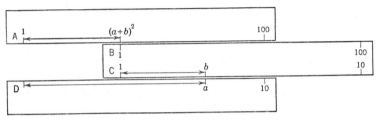

FIGURE 25

For example, to compute $(8.72 \div 4.84)^2$, locate 8.72 on scale D. Move the slide so that 4.84 found in scale C is over the 8.72. Now, using the runner, move it so that its hairline is over the 1 of the scale C. Read where the hairline crosses the scale A the number 3.25.

PROBLEMS

626. Perform the following computations: (a) $(1.46 \div 2.78)^2$; (b) $(0.894 \div 2.35)^2$; (c) $(15.6 \div 7.75)^2$; (d) $(11.5 \div 34.5)^2$; (e) $(0.078 + 0.0065)^2$.

The computation of $a^2 \cdot b$. Locate a on scale D. Then bring the runner over so that the runner's hairline crosses the scale D where a is located. Move the slide so that the 1 on scale B is under the runner's hairline as shown in Figure 26. Then locate the number b on scale B. Read on scale A over the place where b is located the product $a^2 \cdot b$. The drawing in Figure 26 shows that the slide was moved to the right. It may happen that the number b on scale B will be too far to the right. If so, then the slide must be moved to the left so that the 100 on scale B is under the hairline.

For example, to compute $4.56^2 \cdot 8.9$, locate 4.56 on scale D. Move the runner so that its hairline is over the 4.56. Then move

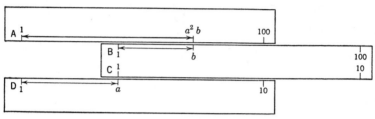

FIGURE 26

the slide so that the 100 on scale B is under the hairline. Then move the runner until 8.9 on the scale B is under the hairline. Read scale A where the hairline crosses it. The number is 185.

PROBLEMS

627. Perform the following computations: (a) $2.34^2 \cdot 0.568$; (b) $0.875^2 \cdot 1.64$; (c) $69.6^2 \cdot 0.0025$; (d) $18.7^2 \cdot 11.5$; (e) $0.572^2 \cdot 0.125$.

The computation of $a^2 \div b$. Locate the number a on the D scale. Place the runner so that its hairline is over the number a. Move the slide so that the number b on the B scale is also under

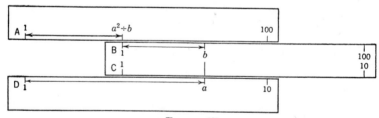

FIGURE 27

the runner's hairline. Read on scale A the number which is over the 1 of the B scale. If the number 1 on the B scale is outside the rule, then read the place that is over the 100 on the B scale. The scheme is shown in Figure 27.

For example, $25.8^2 \div 4.75$ is performed as follows: Locate 25.8 on the D scale. Move the runner so that its hairline is over it. Then move the slide so that 4.75 on the B scale is also under the runner's hairline. Then read on scale A the number which is over the 1 on scale B. It is 140.

PROBLEMS

628. Perform the following computations: (a) $1.34^2 \div 4.5$; (b) $0.65^2 \div 1.25$; (c) $8.75^2 \div 45.2$; (d) $9.87^2 \div 145$; (e) $0.456^2 \div 0.078$.

The computation of $a \div b^2$. Locate a on the A scale. Move the runner so that its hairline is over the a. Then move the slide so that the number b, located on scale C, is under the hairline also, as shown in Figure 28. Then read on scale A the number

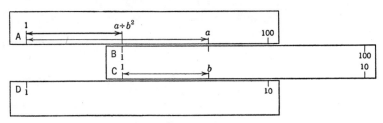

FIGURE 28

which is over the 1 on scale B. If the number 1 on the B scale is outside the rule, read the place on scale A that is over the 100 on scale B.

For example, to compute $5.65 \div 4.15^2$, locate 5.65 on the scale A. Move the runner so that its hairline is over the 5.65. Then move the slide so that 4.15, located on scale C, is also under the hairline. Read the result on scale A at the point where 100 on scale B is under scale A. The number on scale A which is over the 100 on scale B is 0.327.

PROBLEMS

629. Perform the following computations: (a) $45.3 \div 7.75^2$; (b) $7.54 \div 4.75^2$; (c) $0.895 \div 0.653^2$; (d) $13.4 \div 6.75^2$; (e) $11.4 \div 0.458^2$.

Problems with square roots of numbers

The computations which involve square roots must begin on the A or B scales, in order to permit finding the square root on scale D or C. The reader should consult pages 284–287 for the method of reading on the scales A and B. He should also consult pages 252–259 regarding the extraction of square roots.

The computation of $\sqrt{a \cdot b}$. For the computation of the product $a \cdot b$ refer to page 288. In the case of the extraction of a square root of a product the computation of the product must be performed on scales A and B.

Locate the number a on scale A. Move the slide so that the 1 of scale B is directly under the a on scale A. Then locate the number b on scale B. Move the runner so that its hairline is over the graduation mark of b. Follow the hairline to scale D. Where the hairline intersects scale D we read $\sqrt{a \cdot b}$. The scheme is shown in Figure 29.

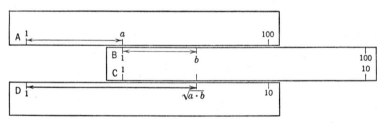

FIGURE 29

For example, $\sqrt{24.5 \cdot 8.65}$ is computed as follows: Locate 24.5 on scale A. If we move the slide so that the 1 on scale B falls under the 24.5 we shall find that 8.65 on the B scale will be outside the rule. We reverse then the direction and place the 100 on the B scale under 24.5. Placing the hairline of the runner over the 8.65 we read on scale D, where the hairline crosses it, 14.5.

PROBLEMS

630. Extract the square roots of the following: (*a*) 6.78 · 0.785; (*b*) 0.758 · 0.895; (*c*) 1.78 · 0.0438; (*d*) 96.4 · 12.5; (*e*) 10.7 · 0.875.

The computation of $\sqrt{a \div b}$. Locate *a* on the A scale. Move the slide so that the number *b*, located on scale B, is then directly under the number *a* (which is on scale A). Move the runner so that its hairline is over the 1 on the scale B. Where the hairline crosses scale D we read $\sqrt{a \div b}$. If desired it is not necessary to move the runner at all. The square root will be read where the 1 on the scale C is over the graduation on the scale D. This computation is shown in Figure 30.

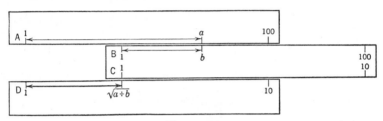

FIGURE 30

For example, to compute $\sqrt{13.5 \div 2.65}$, locate 13.5 on scale A. Move the slide so that 2.65 on the B scale is under 13.5 (which is on the scale A). Where the 1 on scale C is over scale D, read on scale D the root 2.26.

Note. Should the 1 on scale B be outside the rule, then read the root under the 100 on the B scale.

PROBLEMS

631. Extract the square roots of the following: (*a*) 89.3 ÷ 7.42; (*b*) 76.3 ÷ 168; (*c*) 0.483 ÷ 2.54; (*d*) 0.988 ÷ 0.437; (*e*) 56.9 ÷ 0.684.

The computation of $a \cdot \sqrt{b}$. Locate *a* on the D scale. Move the slide so that the 1 of the C scale is over the number *a* on the D scale. Locate the number *b* on the B scale. Place the runner's hairline over the number *b* and read $a \cdot \sqrt{b}$ on the D scale where the runner's hairline intersects the D scale, as shown in Figure 31. Should the graduation of the number *b* on scale B fall outside the rule, the direction of the slide should be reversed; that is, 10 of the C scale should be placed over *a* on the D scale.

For example, to compute $7.84 \cdot \sqrt{65.3}$, locate 7.84 on the scale
D. Move the slide so that the 100 of the B scale (or the 10 of
the C scale) is directly over the 7.84. (*Note.* We have reversed
the direction of the slide here.) Locate 65.3 on scale B. Place

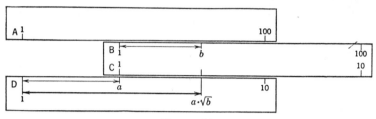

FIGURE 31

the hairline of the runner over this 65.3 mark, and read on scale
D, where the hairline crosses it, the number 63.6.

PROBLEMS

632. Perform the following computations: (*a*) $56.5 \cdot \sqrt{4.68}$; (*b*) 0.675
$\cdot \sqrt{0.995}$; (*c*) $1.37 \cdot \sqrt{26.4}$; (*d*) $3.16 \cdot \sqrt{0.0452}$; (*e*) $78.5\sqrt{68.15}$.

The computation of $\sqrt{a} \div b$. Locate a on the A scale. Place
the runner so that its hairline is over the number a. Move the
slide so that the number b, which is located on the C scale, is under
the hairline. Where the 1 of the C scale is directly over the D

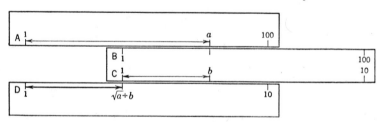

FIGURE 32

scale read $\sqrt{a} \div b$. Should the 1 on the C scale fall outside the
rule, the direction of the slide should be reversed. The scheme
of the computation is shown in Figure 32.

For example, to compute $\sqrt{76.5} \div 5.75$, locate 76.5 on the A scale. Move the runner so that its hairline is over 76.5. Move the slide so that 5.75 on the C scale is directly under the runner's hairline. Read on the D scale, directly under the 1 of the C scale, the solution 1.52.

PROBLEMS

633. Perform the following computations: (a) $\sqrt{1.45} \div 2.34$; (b) $\sqrt{54.2} \div 3.15$; (c) $\sqrt{0.00845} \div 12.5$; (d) $\sqrt{0.605} \div 1.07$; (e) $\sqrt{38.2} \div 7.55$.

The computation of $a \div \sqrt{b}$. Locate a on scale D. Place the runner so that its hairline is over the number a. Move the slide so that the number b, which is located on the scale B, is also under the runner's hairline. Where the 1 of the scale B (or the 1 of scale C) is directly over scale D, read the value of $a \div \sqrt{b}$, as shown in Figure 33. Should the 1 of the scale B fall outside the

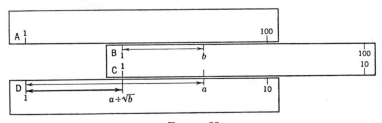

FIGURE 33

rule, the reading should be done at the point where the 100 of scale B (or 10 of scale C) is directly over the scale D.

For example, to compute $34.8 \div \sqrt{28.5}$, locate 34.8 on the scale D. Move the runner so that its hairline is over the 34.8. Move the slide so that 28.5 on the B scale is also under the hairline. Where the 10 of the C scale is directly over the D scale, read on the D scale the result 6.52.

PROBLEMS

634. Perform the following computations: (a) $13.4 \div \sqrt{69.5}$; (b) $0.725 \div \sqrt{3.56}$; (c) $1.56 \div \sqrt{0.785}$; (d) $0.125 \div \sqrt{0.225}$; (e) $11.8 \div \sqrt{894}$.

Cubing and the extraction of cube roots of numbers

To cube a number, read the number on the D scale. Then place the runner so that its hairline is directly over this number. Following this hairline to the K scale, read the cube of the number where the hairline crosses the K scale.

For example, $2^3 = 8$, $2.5^3 = 15.6$.

The extraction of cube roots is the reverse of the procedure stated above. First locate the number whose cube root is to be obtained on scale K. Then place the runner so that its hairline passes over that number. Where the hairline crosses the D scale the cube root is found.

For example, $\sqrt[3]{50} = 3.68$, $\sqrt[3]{142} = 5.77$.

PROBLEMS

635. Find the cubes of the following numbers: 6.25; 1.36; 0.345; 7.84; 18.6.

636. Find the cube roots of the following numbers: 1.86; 0.562; 3.45; 56.7; 289.

Appendix I

Tables

UNITS OF LENGTH

Unit	Inches	Feet	Yards	Rods	Miles	Centi-meters	Meters
1 inch	1	0.083	0.028	0.00505	0.000016	2.540	0.0254
1 foot	12	1	0.333	0.0606	0.000189	30.480	0.3048
1 yard	36	3	1	0.182	0.000568	91.440	0.9144
1 rod	198	16.3	5.5	1	0.00313	502.92	5.0292
1 cm.	0.394	0.0328	0.0109	0.00199	0.000006	1	0.01
1 m.	39.37	3.281	1.094	0.199	0.000621	100	1

UNITS OF AREA

Unit	Square inches	Square feet	Square yards	Acres	Square miles	Square centimeters	Square meters
1 sq. in.	1	0.00694	0.000772	0.00000016	0.0000000002	6.452	0.000645
1 sq. ft.	144	1	0.111	0.000023	0.0000000359	929.03	0.092903
1 sq. yd.	1,296	9	1	0.000207	0.000000323	8,361.307	0.83613
1 acre	6,272,640	43,560	4,840	1	0.001563	40,468,726	4,046.873
1 sq. mi.	4,014,489,600	27,878,400	3,097,600	640	1	25,899,984,703	2,589,998
1 sq. cm.	0.155	0.001076	0.00012	0.0000000247	0.00000000000039	1	0.0001
1 sq. m.	1,550	10.764	1.196	0.000247	0.000000386	10,000	1

UNITS OF VOLUME

Unit	Cubic inches	Cubic feet	Cubic yards	Cubic centimeters	Cubic meters
1 cu. in.	1	0.000579	0.0000214	16.387	0.000016387
1 cu. ft.	1,728	1	0.037	28,317.016	0.028317
1 cu. yd.	46,656	27	1	764,559.4	0.7645594
1 cu. cm.	0.06102	0.0000353	0.00000131	1	0.000001
1 cu. m.	61,023.38	35.314	1.308	1,000,000	1

UNITS OF CAPACITY (LIQUID MEASURE)

Unit	Fluid ounces	Gills	Liquid pints	Liquid quarts	Gallons	Liters	Cubic inches
1 fluid ounce	1	0.25	0.0625	0.03125	0.0078125	0.0296	1.805
1 gill	4	1	0.25	0.125	0.03125	0.1183	7.219
1 liquid pint	16	4	1	0.5	0.125	0.473	28.875
1 liquid quart	32	8	2	1	0.25	0.946	57.75
1 gallon	128	32	8	4	1	3.785	231
1 liter	33.815	8.454	2.113	1.057	0.264	1	61.025
1 cu. in.	0.554	0.139	0.0346	0.0173	0.00433	0.0164	1

UNITS OF CAPACITY (DRY MEASURE)

Unit	Dry pints	Dry quarts	Pecks	Bushels	Liters	Cubic inches
1 dry pint	1	0.5	0.625	0.015625	0.551	33.6
1 dry quart	2	1	0.125	0.03125	1.101	67.2
1 peck	16	8	1	0.25	8.81	537.6
1 bushel	64	32	4	1	35.24	2,150.4
1 liter	1.816	0.908	0.114	0.0284	1	61.025
1 cu. in.	0.0298	0.0149	0.00186	0.000465	0.0164	1

UNITS OF WEIGHT

Unit	Ounces	Pounds	Short tons	Long tons	Kilograms
1 ounce	1	0.0625	0.00003125	0.0000279	0.02834
1 pound	16	1	0.0005	0.000446	0.4536
1 short ton	32,000	2,000	1	0.8929	907.185
1 long ton	35,840	2,240	1.12	1	1,016.05
1 kilogram	35.274	2.205	0.001102	0.000984	1
1 metric ton	35,274	2,204.6	1.102	0.9842	1,000

CONVERSION FORMULAS FOR FAHRENHEIT AND CENTIGRADE DEGREES

$$C = \frac{5}{9}(F - 32°),$$

$$F = \frac{9}{5}C + 32°,$$

where

C is the number of degrees Centigrade

and

F is the number of degrees Fahrenheit.

PRIME NUMBERS

1	2	3	5	7	11	13	17	19	23	29	31	37
41	43	47	53	59	61	67	71	73	79	83	89	97
101	103	107	109	113	127	131	137	139	149	151	157	163
167	173	179	181	191	193	197	199	211	223	227	229	233
239	241	251	257	263	269	271	277	281	283	293	307	311
313	317	331	337	347	349	353	359	367	373	379	383	389
397	401	409	419	421	431	433	439	443	449	457	461	463
467	479	487	491	499	503	509	521	523	541	547	557	563
569	571	577	587	593	599	601	607	613	617	619	631	641
643	647	653	659	661	673	677	683	691	701	709	719	727
733	739	743	751	757	761	769	773	787	797	809	811	821
823	827	829	839	853	857	859	863	877	881	883	887	907
911	919	929	937	941	947	953	967	971	977	983	991	997

Appendix II

Formulas From Geometry

SQUARE

Perimeter = $4a$
Area   = a^2
Diagonal = $a\sqrt{2}$ or $1.41a$

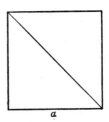

RECTANGLE

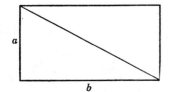

Perimeter = $2a + 2b$
Area   = $a \cdot b$
Diagonal = $\sqrt{a^2 + b^2}$

TRIANGLE

Perimeter = $a + b + c$
Area   = $\frac{1}{2}a \cdot h$, when h is the height or altitude of the vertex opposite side a

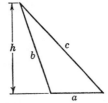 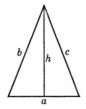

CIRCLE

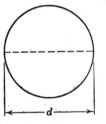

Circumference $= 2\pi r$ or $6.28\ r$

or πd or $3.14\ d$

Area $= \pi r^2$ or $3.14\ r^2$

or $\frac{1}{4}\pi d^2$ or $0.79\ d^2$

$d =$ diameter $= 2r;\ r =$ radius

CYLINDER

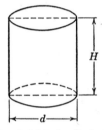

Side area $= \pi dH$ or $3.14\ dH$

or $2\pi rH$ or $6.28\ rH$

Volume $= \pi r^2H$ or $3.14\ r^2H$

or $\frac{1}{4}\pi d^2H$ or $0.79\ d^2H$

$H =$ height of cylinder
$d\ =$ diameter of base $= 2r$
$r\ =$ radius of the base

CONE

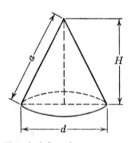

Side area $= \pi ra$ or $3.14\ ra$

or $\frac{1}{2}\pi da$ or $1.57\ da$

Volume $= \frac{1}{3}\pi r^2H$ or $1.05\ r^2H$

or $\frac{1}{12}\pi d^2H$ or $0.26\ d^2H$

$H =$ height of cone
$a\ =$ side of cone
$d\ =$ diameter of base $= 2r$
$r\ =$ radius of the base

SPHERE

Area of surface $= \pi d^2$ or $3.14\ d^2$
or $4\pi r^2$ or $12.56\ r^2$
Volume $= \frac{4}{3}\pi r^3$ or $4.19\ r^3$
or $\frac{1}{6}\pi d^3$ or $0.53\ d^3$

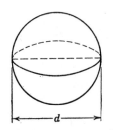

$d =$ diameter of the sphere $= 2r$
$r =$ radius of the sphere

Appendix III

Simple Trigonometry

The sum of the angles of any triangle is equal to 180° (180 degrees).

A degree is equal to $\frac{1}{360}$ of the angular measure of a circle.

An angle of 90° (90 degrees) is known as a *right angle*.

The most useful triangle that is used in measuring heights and distances is the right triangle, that is, a triangle one of whose angles is a right angle as shown.

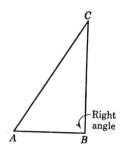

In order to measure distances and heights by means of a right triangle the following facts are used. We must know one of the angles (not the right one) and the length of one of the sides. We then employ the following ratios:

$$\frac{\text{length of side } BC}{\text{length of side } AB} = \text{sine of angle } A.$$

Note that the side AB is opposite the right angle.

$$\frac{\text{length of side } AC}{\text{length of side } AB} = \text{cosine of angle } A.$$

312

By means of either of these two ratios we can find the angle A. We do so by computing the ratio and consulting the table of the ratios given on page 314.

If the angle A is given and the side AB is given we change the above ratios into

length of side BC = (length of side AB) · (sine of angle A),
length of side AC = (length of side AB) · (cosine of angle A).

For example, angle $A = 35°$ and $AB = 16$ in. Then

$$BC = 16 \cdot 0.574 = 9.184 \text{ inches,}$$
$$AC = 16 \cdot 0.819 = 13.104 \text{ inches.}$$

If the two smaller sides of the right triangle are given we employ the ratio

$$\frac{\text{length of side } BC}{\text{length of side } AC} = \text{tangent of angle } A.$$

If the side AC is given and the angle A is given we change the ratio into

length of side BC = (length of side AC) · (tangent of angle A).

For example, angle $A = 56°$ and $AC = 24$ in. Then

$$BC = 24 \cdot 1.48 = 35.52 \text{ inches.}$$

VALUES OF TRIGONOMETRIC RATIOS

Angle	Sine	Cosine	Tangent	Angle	Sine	Cosine	Tangent
1°	0.017	1.000	0.017	46°	0.719	0.695	1.04
2°	0.035	0.999	0.035	47°	0.731	0.682	1.07
3°	0.052	0.999	0.052	48°	0.743	0.669	1.11
4°	0.070	0.998	0.070	49°	0.755	0.656	1.15
5°	0.087	0.996	0.087	50°	0.766	0.643	1.19
6°	0.105	0.995	0.105	51°	0.777	0.629	1.23
7°	0.122	0.993	0.123	52°	0.788	0.616	1.28
8°	0.139	0.990	0.141	53°	0.799	0.602	1.33
9°	0.156	0.988	0.158	54°	0.809	0.588	1.38
10°	0.174	0.985	0.176	55°	0.819	0.574	1.43
11°	0.191	0.982	0.194	56°	0.829	0.559	1.48
12°	0.208	0.978	0.213	57°	0.839	0.545	1.54
13°	0.225	0.974	0.231	58°	0.848	0.530	1.60
14°	0.242	0.970	0.249	59°	0.857	0.515	1.66
15°	0.259	0.966	0.268	60°	0.866	0.500	1.73
16°	0.276	0.961	0.287	61°	0.875	0.485	1.80
17°	0.292	0.956	0.306	62°	0.883	0.469	1.88
18°	0.309	0.951	0.325	63°	0.891	0.454	1.96
19°	0.326	0.946	0.344	64°	0.899	0.438	2.05
20°	0.342	0.940	0.364	65°	0.906	0.423	2.14
21°	0.358	0.934	0.384	66°	0.914	0.407	2.25
22°	0.375	0.927	0.404	67°	0.921	0.391	2.36
23°	0.391	0.921	0.424	68°	0.927	0.375	2.48
24°	0.407	0.914	0.445	69°	0.934	0.358	2.61
25°	0.423	0.906	0.466	70°	0.940	0.342	2.75
26°	0.438	0.899	0.488	71°	0.946	0.326	2.90
27°	0.454	0.891	0.510	72°	0.951	0.309	3.08
28°	0.469	0.883	0.532	73°	0.956	0.292	3.27
29°	0.485	0.875	0.554	74°	0.961	0.276	3.49
30°	0.500	0.866	0.577	75°	0.966	0.259	3.73
31°	0.515	0.857	0.601	76°	0.970	0.242	4.01
32°	0.530	0.848	0.625	77°	0.974	0.225	4.33
33°	0.545	0.839	0.649	78°	0.978	0.208	4.70
34°	0.559	0.829	0.675	79°	0.982	0.191	5.14
35°	0.574	0.819	0.700	80°	0.985	0.174	5.67
36°	0.588	0.809	0.727	81°	0.988	0.156	6.31
37°	0.602	0.799	0.754	82°	0.990	0.139	7.12
38°	0.616	0.788	0.781	83°	0.993	0.122	8.14
39°	0.629	0.777	0.810	84°	0.995	0.105	9.51
40°	0.643	0.766	0.839	85°	0.996	0.087	11.43
41°	0.656	0.755	0.869	86°	0.998	0.070	14.30
42°	0.669	0.743	0.900	87°	0.999	0.052	19.08
43°	0.682	0.731	0.933	88°	0.999	0.035	28.64
44°	0.695	0.719	0.966	89°	1.000	0.017	57.29
45°	0.707	0.707	1.000	90°	1.000	0.000	...

Answers to Problems

Page 8   **11.** 1,165   **12.** 2,910   **13.** 5,670   **14.** 124,154
15. 2,705,824   **16.** 2,382   **17.** 59,657   **18.** 29,940   **19.** 1,005
20. 2,302

Page 13   **29.** 201,820   **30.** 413,160

Page 17   **32.**(*a*) 2,124; (*b*) 13,431; (*c*) 21,245; (*d*) 83,441;
(*e*) 343,333   **33.**(*a*) 482; (*b*) 855; (*c*) 1,887; (*d*) 27,687;
(*e*) 267,787   **34.**(*a*) 362; (*b*) 359,725; (*c*) 6,159,439;
(*d*) 2,218,983; (*e*) 697,188,552   **35.** 9,356   **36.** 31,126
37. 289,436   **38.** 102.783   **39.** 9,000,000

Page 27   **51.** $3,230   **52.** Increase by 77   **53.** Decrease by 212
54. Increase by 65   **55.** Increase by 256

Page 31   **56.** 124   **57.** 135   **58.** 188   **59.** 374

Page 37   **66.**(*a*) 144; (*b*) 384; (*c*) 112   **67.** $80   **68.**(*a*) 150;
(*b*) 864; (*c*) 672

Page 40   **71.**(*a*) 900; (*b*) 600; (*c*) 735; (*d*) 1,300
72. 8,000 hours   **73.** 12,600   **74.** 43,200

Page 45

81. 2,268	**85.** 2,768,580
56,637	4,821,201
3,980	19,299,682
44,515	9,974,326
69,618	86,316,111
82. 450	**86.** 491,737,326
1,700	72,847,459,862
67,000	477,474,270
807,000	900,526,669
6,070,900	3,703,875,288
83. 23,200	**87.** 466,894,296
70,200	602,135,007
2,472,000	1,871,581,306
343,800	881,974,890
7,020,000	1,042,656,021
84. 17,361	**88.** 5,402,300
59,704	4,446,000
453,152	48,151,600
726,791	467,078,000
88,890,085	36,867,885,600

89. 539,246,592
4,713,827,400
2,846,482,207
36,933,045
5,080,730,580

90. 584,564,706
48,979,989,050
24,246,972
4,844,077,335
5,560,695,000

Page 47   **91.** 80 days **92.** 13,600 lines **93.** 1,440 minutes
94. 172,800 seconds **95.** 90 miles **96.** 27,500 feet
97. 27,840 parts

Page 48   **98.** 3,750 gallons **99.** 65,000,000 times **100.** 500 miles

Page 63   **101.**(*a*) 4,393; (*b*) 6,295; (*c*) 94,062; (*d*) 611,696;
(*e*) 93,091

Page 64   **102.**(*a*) 15,686; (*b*) 1,568,721; (*c*) 2,152,970;
(*d*) 3,580; (*e*) 207,250 **103.**(*a*) 691; (*b*) 543; (*c*) 818;
(*d*) 298; (*e*) 868 **104.**(*a*) 497; (*b*) 908; (*c*) 458; (*d*) 53,800;
(*e*) 95,880 **105.**(*a*) 20,499; (*b*) 641; (*c*) 8,003; (*d*) 1,602;
(*e*) 909 **106.**(*a*) 200,752; (*b*) 29; (*c*) 25,083; (*d*) 947; (*e*) 86
107. 497; **108.** 792; **109.** 378; **110.**(*a*) 263,105;
(*b*) 31,152,240; (*c*) 658,497; (*d*) 2,948,374; (*e*) 340,102,237
111.(*a*) 199,137; (*b*) 2,271,753; (*c*) 25,059; (*d*) 194,133;
(*e*) 241,016 **112.**(*a*) 9,135; (*b*) 271,518; (*c*) 17,949,060;
(*d*) 2,024,513; (*e*) 174,111,200 **113.**(*a*) 1,154; (*b*) 6,923;
(*c*) 9,339; (*d*) 5,972; (*e*) 6,273 **114.**(*a*) 5,797; (*b*) 4,776;
(*c*) 24,810; (*d*) 78,206,040; (*e*) 32,554,708
115.(*a*) 24,530,223; (*b*) 18,760,738; (*c*) 185,358; (*d*) 469,982;
(*e*) 3,312,828 **116.**(*a*) 6,642; (*b*) 3,892,097; (*c*) 96,080,394;
(*d*) 13,214,048; (*e*) 10,084,761 **117.**(*a*) 26,560,164;
(*b*) 254,501,527; (*c*) 49,740,829; (*d*) 80,905,663; (*e*) 49,901,497
118.(*a*) 14,680,367; (*b*) 458,502,751; (*c*) 73,504,410;
(*d*) 286,001,144; (*e*) 15,480,387 **119.** 528 **120.** 950,616
121. 28,243

Page 65   **122.** 1,273,792 **123.** 375 miles per hour **124.** 39
125. 426,854

Page 69   **126.** Multiplied by 12 **127.** Divided by 9
128. Multiplied by 35 **129.** Multiplied by 75
130. Multiplied by 27 **131.** Divided by 30
132. Multiplied by 3 **133.** Divided by 2
134.(*a*) Multiplied by 5; (*b*) Multiplied by 10;
(*c*) Divided by 15; (*d*) Divided by 20; (*e*) Multiplied by 2

Page 72   **136.** Multiplied by 5 **137.** Multiplied by 7
138. Divided by 6 **139.** Divided by 8 **142.** 90 **143.** 25
144. 8 **145.** 7

Page 79   **150.** (a) $5^6 = 15,625$; (b) $4^7 = 16,384$;
(c) $10^9 = 1,000,000,000$; (d) $6^7 = 279,936$; (e) $2^{12} = 4,096$
151. (a) 400; (b) 74,088; (c) 50,625; (d) 1,764; (e) 1,728,000

Page 81   **152.** 150 138 155 105 147 84 168

Page 83   **153.** 39,780 127,635 45,000 49,852 19,354,335
123,531

Page 84   **154.** 178 594 36 825 20,729 665,635,646 **155.** 8
396 36 960 358 **156.** 46,284 **157.** 100 **158.** 16 **159.** 48
160. 602

Page 86   **161.** (a) 1, 2, 3, 6, 41, 82, 123, 246;
(b) 1, 2, 4, 8, 16, 23, 46, 92, 184, 368; (c) 1, 479;
(d) 1, 2, 3, 6, 9, 12, 18, 36, 54, 108;
(e) 1, 2, 3, 4, 6, 8, 12, 13, 16, 24, 26, 32, 48, 52, 78, 96, 104, 156,
192, 208, 312, 382, 416, 624, 1,248 **162.** (a) 5; (b) 27; (c) 495
163. The sum of even numbers is even and is, therefore, divisible
by 2. **164.** Yes **165.** (a) 2, 3, 5; (b) 2, 5; (c) 2, 77;
(d) 2, 79; (e) 2, 3, 5, 29

Page 90   **166.** 40, 42, 44, 46, 48, 50, 52, 54, 56, 58, 60
167. 75, 77, 79, 81, 83, 85, 87, 89
168. Divisible by 2: 11,210; 7,638; 992,536; 809,234;
8,876,458; 3,426,378; 445,672; 6,095,432
Divisible by 4: 992,538; 445,672; 6,095,432
Divisible by 5: 773,645; 10,635
169. Divisible by 3: 67,775,895; 2,538,756,225
Divisible by 9: 67,775,895
Divisible by 25: 11,345,675
170. 2,221 **171.** 74,988 **172.** 4,680; 6,480; 8,640; 8,460;
4,860; 6,840 **173.** 37,512 **174.** 10,115 **175.** Divisible by 2.
Divisible by 3. Not divisible by 9

Page 91
176. Divisible by 12: 645,312; 489,276; 5,089,572; 94,367,232
Divisible by 18: 489,276; 57,870; 5,089,572; 94,367,232;
748,926
Divisible by 15: 73,845
177. 73,845 **178.** 648,936 **179.** 32,670
180. 4,657,320; 4,673,025

Page 95   **181.** 838 boxes

Page 96   **182.** 12,814 feet **183.** \$2,447,039 **184.** \$4.71
185. 604,800 seconds **186.** 48,000 tons **187.** 51,720 tons

Page 96   **188.** 960 miles, 240 miles **189.** 3,010 gallons
190. 21,900 gallons

Page 98   **191.** $5,224   **192.** 4,889 feet   **193.** 1,435 tables
    194. 3 times   **195.** 88 acres   **196.** 4 hours   **197.** 4 times

Page 99   **198.** 171 miles   **199.** 108 soldiers   **200.** 108 men
    201. 544 revolutions
    202. 235,629 tons of gasoline; 152,100 tons of crude oil
    203. 30 days

Page 104   **204.** (*a*) 25 square feet; (*b*) 100 square inches;
    (*c*) 225 square yards; (*d*) 225 square inches; (*e*) 900 square feet
    205. (*a*) 375 square inches; (*b*) 432 square feet;
    (*c*) 540 square inches; (*d*) 36 square feet;
    (*e*) 2,772 square inches

Page 105   **206.** 5,184 cubic inches   **207.** 45 square feet
    208. (*a*) 3,375 cubic inches; (*b*) 27 cubic feet; (*c*) 8 cubic yards;
    (*d*) 512 cubic inches; (*e*) 1,000 cubic feet   **209.** 6 inches
    210. 234 square feet   **211.** (*a*) 2,400 cubic inches;
    (*b*) 16 cubic feet; (*c*) 7,776 cubic inches; (*d*) 24 cubic feet;
    (*e*) 18 cubic feet   **212.** 1,200 cubic feet
    213. 120 square feet and 80 square feet   **214.** 5,184 cubic inches
    215. 77,760 cubic inches

Page 106   **217.** 10 days   **218.** 27 hours   **219.** $625
    220. 10 hours   **221.** 1,200 miles   **222.** 464 books and 392 books
    223. 590 pounds, 410 pounds and 560 pounds

Page 107   **224.** 384 men, 192 women and 96 children
    225. In the first section 1,300 workers;
    in the second section 260 workers;
    in the third section 4,080 workers
    226. Nine 5-pound weights and fifteen 3-pound weights
    227. 8 days. The first bindery—4,800 books;
    the second bindery—3,200 books; the third bindery—1,600 books
    228. 1,964 dies, 1,964 dies, and 1,919 dies   **229.** 45 days
    230. The car costs $2,800 and the truck costs $5,660
    231. 24 tons

Page 110   **233.** (*a*) 105.67; (*b*) 0.4631; (*c*) 0.011; (*d*) 0.0057;
    (*e*) 7.682

Page 113   **234.** 43720   98   875.4   1.23   0.46
         0.0036   560.02   8923.04   417,809   0.000045
    235. 5600   80900   120   1230   13.5
         700.89   0.025   0.562   89007.2   0.0076
    236. 8000   789000   3400   15670   130
         4.5   0.743   89765   70030.5   0.00642

237. 0.5   5.6   78.3
         0.47   5.687   67.8352
         0.0165   0.00754   0.0000056
         80.900045   0.2000001
238. 0.04   0.73   9.34
         0.034   0.0547   0.893354
         51.739023   0.0057   0.00683
         0.0000453   0.000000723   0.8000035
239. 0.0007   0.035   0.702
        8.365   0.0073   0.0894
        0.46324   0.0036872   4.080756
        0.000634   0.00000809
        0.0000005072   0.0000000063
240. By 1,000   **241.** By 10,000   **242.** By 100,000
243. By 100,000   **244.** Multiply by 100
245. Divide by 10,000

Page 115   **246.**(a) 15.6; (b) 706.1; (c) 18.3; (d) 0.7; (e) 1.1
247.(a) 9.20; (b) 66.57; (c) 0.03; (d) 0.01; (e) 8,345.21
248. 17.60   17.92
        4.78   15.51
     46.177
     38.002

Page 116   **249.**(a) 48.52; (b) 25.88; (c) 0.22; (d) 12.259;
    (e) 5.524   **250.** 7.62   7.21   12.530
    251. Difference will decrease by 28.92   **252.** 9.89 miles
    253. 257.6 feet   **254.** 1,780.757

Page 118   **255.**(a) 6.12; (b) 16.1226; (c) 32.8335; (d) 113.40084;
    (e) 155.12564   **256.** 0.000378   61.050   20.676960   1.8432
    0.00037625   **257.**(a) 80; (b) 44.25; (c) 129; (d) 18.690;
    (e) 26.862   **258.** 2.25 square inches   **259.** 15.625 cubic inches
    260.(a) 15.072 inches; (b) 15.700 feet; (c) 95.456 inches;
    (d) 40.192 feet; (e) 954.56 inches
    261.(a) 1,808.64 square inches; (b) 19.6250 square feet;
    (c) 725.4656 square inches; (d) 128.6144 square feet;
    (e) 72,546.56 square inches   **262.**(a) 15.700 square inches;
    (b) 3,278.160 square inches; (c) 413.224 square inches;
    (d) 61.2300 square feet; (e) 2,580.3264 square inches

Page 119   **263.**(a) 19.6250 cubic inches;
    (b) 23,767.4450 cubic inches; (c) 971.0764 cubic inches;
    (d) 549.2250 cubic feet; (e) 12,385.56672 cubic inches

264.(*a*) 162.7776 square inches; (*b*) 1,962.5000 square inches; (*c*) 563.8184 square inches; (*d*) 128.6144 square feet; (*e*) 2,978.7296 square inches

Page 122   **266.** 24.1   5.82
                     29.7   4.97
                     47.0   9.62
                     63.7   8.62
                     74.8   8.08
         267.   4.12   747.
                     0.411   79.7
                     70.4   897.
                     23.2   8.82
                     18.7   8.960.
         268.   0.912   0.086
                     0.777   0.31
                     0.0677   0.059
                     0.676   0.084
                     0.885   0.32

Page 125   **269.** 20.512   3,294.44   0.373   1.722   0.129
         270. 0.041   54.668
                 24.   1.004
                 250.07
                 0.242
                 9.06 feet

Page 129   **272.**(*a*) 0.34036 meters; (*b*) 13.920216 meters; (*c*) 109.728 meters; (*d*) 4.3842 meters; 1,207.0155 meters
273.(*a*) 5.91 inches; (*b*) 62.992 inches; (*c*) 2.6595 inches; (*d*) 54.1844 inches; (*e*) 68.8975 inches
274.(*a*) 147,645 feet; (*b*) 492.15 feet; (*c*) 2.490 feet; (*d*) 123.0375 feet; (*e*) 4.7888 feet
Note: The answers to Problems 272 to 274 should be rounded to hundredths and thousandths.

Page 130   **275.**(*a*) 0.000456 square meters;
(*b*) 2.3876071 square meters; (*c*) 15.1332712 square meters; (*d*) 0.0564375 square meters; (*e*) 0.334408 square meters.
276.(*a*) 12.667 square feet; (*b*) 173.9 square feet; (*c*) 726.3916 square feet; (*d*) 0.3146224 square feet; (*e*) 8.989 square feet   **277.**(*a*) 7.178 square inches; (*b*) 489.6 square inches; (*c*) 2,315 square inches; (*d*) 453.6 square inches; (*e*) 0.04185 square inches
Note: The answers in the Problems 275 to 278 should be rounded to tenths, hundredths, and thousandths.

Page 131   *Note:* All the answers are rounded, wherever possible, to thousandths, or to hundredths if thousandths are not obtainable.

278. (a) 0.0001675 cubic meters; (b) 2.594 cubic meters;
(c) 27.218 cubic meters; (d) 0.006301 cubic meters;
(e) 15.999 cubic meters   **279.** (a) 2.794 cubic feet;
(b) 207.36 cubic feet; (c) 5,456.013 cubic feet;
(d) 0.05523 cubic feet; (e) 98.162 cubic feet
280. (a) 8.238 cubic inches; (b) 13.064 cubic inches;
(c) 113,739.746 cubic inches; (d) 40,590.72 cubic inches;
(e) 95,534.07 cubic inches

Page 132   *Note:* All the answers are rounded wherever possible, to hundredths or thousandths.

281. (a) 0.02575 pounds; (b) 1,508 pounds; (c) 3,494.40 pounds;
(d) 7,604.87 pounds; (e) 125.035 pounds
282. (a) 3.829 kilograms; (b) 1,524.075 kilograms;
(c) 2,743.335 kilograms; (d) 197.107 kilograms;
(e) 510.745 kilograms   **283.** 32.124 cubic feet

Page 133   *Note:* All the answers are rounded to thousandths, wherever possible.

284. (a) 2.838 liters; (b) 1.419 liters; (c) 123.013 liters;
(d) 0.444 liters; (e) 10.879 liters   **285.** (a) 173.774 cubic inches;
(b) 86.574 cubic inches; (c) 7,506.223 cubic inches;
(d) 26,969.998 cubic inches; (e) 663.836 cubic inches

Page 134   *Note:* All the answers are rounded, wherever possible, to hundredths or thousandths.

286. (a) 2,838 cubic centimeters; (b) 1,419 cubic centimeters;
(c) 123,012.5 cubic centimeters; (d) 443.625 cubic centimeters;
(e) 10,879 cubic centimeters   **287.** (a) 2.63 gallons;
(b) 0.592 liquid quarts; (c) 10.441 gills; (d) 11.513 fluid ounces;
(e) 1.585 liquid pints   **288.** (a) 33.753 cubic inches;
(b) 34.126 cubic inches; (c) 75.371 cubic inches;
(d) 20.781 cubic inches; (e) 45.760 cubic inches
289. (a) 553.110 cubic centimeters; (b) 559.197 cubic centimeters;
(c) 1,235.110 cubic centimeters; (d) 340.541 cubic centimeters;
(e) 749.853 cubic centimeters

Page 135   *Note:* All the answers are rounded to hundredths or thousandths, wherever possible.

290. (a) 85.956 liters; (b) 63.658 liters; (c) 576.174 liters;
(d) 23,787 liters; (e) 26.43 liters   **291.** (a) 524.16 cubic inches;
(b) 3,884.16 cubic inches; (c) 35,159.04 cubic inches;
(d) 1,451,520 cubic inches; (e) 1,612.8 cubic inches

292.(*a*) 4,986.510 cubic centimeters;
(*b*) 62,549.730 cubic centimeters;
(*c*) 576,151.188 cubic centimeters;
(*d*) 23,786,058.24 cubic centimeters;
(*e*) 26,428.954 cubic centimeters   **293.**(*a*) 9.902 dry pints;
(*b*) 21.293 dry quarts; (*c*) 17.841 pecks; (*d*) 35.074 bushels;
185.217 bushels   **294.**(*a*) 0.193 cubic feet; (*b*) 0.828 cubic feet;
(*c*) 5.553 cubic feet; (*d*) 42.187 cubic feet; (*e*) 222.830 cubic feet
295.(*a*) 0.00401 cubic meters; (*b*) 0.0135 cubic meters;
(*c*) 0.157 cubic meters; (*d*) 1.195 cubic meters;
(*d*) 6.310 cubic meters

Page 138   **297.**(*a*) $\dfrac{7}{13}$; (*b*) $\dfrac{8}{27}$; (*c*) $\dfrac{1}{50}$; (*d*) $\dfrac{5}{32}$; (*e*) $\dfrac{7}{64}$

Page 139   **298.** Proper fractions: (*a*) $\dfrac{4}{5}$; (*e*) $\dfrac{116}{125}$; (*i*) $\dfrac{63}{64}$

Improper fractions: (*b*) $\dfrac{7}{6}$; (*c*) $\dfrac{19}{19}$; (*d*) $\dfrac{17}{16}$; (*f*) $\dfrac{33}{32}$; (*g*) $\dfrac{49}{48}$;

(*h*) $\dfrac{56}{55}$; (*j*) $\dfrac{32}{32}$ **299.** $\dfrac{3}{7}, \dfrac{3}{9}, \dfrac{3}{11}, \dfrac{7}{9}, \dfrac{7}{11}, \dfrac{9}{11}$ **300.** $\dfrac{24}{12}$; 2

301. $\dfrac{6}{2}, \dfrac{8}{2}, \dfrac{15}{3}, \dfrac{18}{3}$.   Other forms are also possible.   **302.** 5

303. When $10m = n$

Page 141   **304.** $14\dfrac{3}{7}$; $14\dfrac{11}{16}$; $87\dfrac{3}{13}$; $23\dfrac{1}{8}$; $73\dfrac{23}{32}$ **305.**(*a*) $\dfrac{79}{9}$;

(*b*) $\dfrac{286}{25}$; (*c*) $\dfrac{2995}{64}$; (*d*) $\dfrac{593}{32}$; (*e*) $\dfrac{1555}{48}$ **306.** In 5: 80.

In 8: 128. In 10: 160. In 15: 240.   **307.** In 5: 25.

In 12: 60. In 81: 405. In 143: 715.   **308.** In $\dfrac{1}{2}$: 2.

In $\dfrac{3}{2}$: 6.   **309.** In $\dfrac{1}{3}$: 2.   In $\dfrac{7}{3}$: 14.   In $6\dfrac{2}{3}$: 40.

310. $\dfrac{ac + b}{c}$

Page 144   **311.** $\dfrac{2}{97}, \dfrac{3}{97}, \dfrac{8}{97}, \dfrac{19}{97}, \dfrac{31}{97}, \dfrac{47}{97}, \dfrac{67}{97}, \dfrac{91}{97}$ **312.** $\dfrac{13}{14}, \dfrac{13}{17},$

$\dfrac{13}{18}, \dfrac{13}{28}, \dfrac{13}{29}, \dfrac{13}{77}, \dfrac{13}{85}, \dfrac{13}{93}$ **313.** $\dfrac{115}{137}, \dfrac{81}{137}, \dfrac{72}{137}, \dfrac{49}{137}, \dfrac{37}{137}, \dfrac{27}{137},$

$\dfrac{13}{137}, \dfrac{5}{137}$ **314.** $\dfrac{57}{239}, \dfrac{57}{137}, \dfrac{57}{112}, \dfrac{57}{91}, \dfrac{57}{89}, \dfrac{57}{71}, \dfrac{57}{65}, \dfrac{57}{59}$ **315.** $\dfrac{115}{137}$,

$\dfrac{81}{137}, \dfrac{72}{137}, \dfrac{49}{137}, \dfrac{37}{137}, \dfrac{27}{137}, \dfrac{13}{137}, \dfrac{5}{137}$ **316.** $\dfrac{17}{18}, \dfrac{24}{25}, \dfrac{32}{33}, \dfrac{34}{35}$,

$\dfrac{44}{45}, \dfrac{56}{57}, \dfrac{64}{65}, \dfrac{71}{72}, \dfrac{78}{90}$ **317.** $\dfrac{137}{138}, \dfrac{107}{108}, \dfrac{91}{92}, \dfrac{74}{75}, \dfrac{67}{68}, \dfrac{63}{64}, \dfrac{51}{52}, \dfrac{35}{36}$,

$\dfrac{15}{16}$ **318.** One sixteenth   **319.** 50 centimeters in 0.5 meter

25 centimeters in 0.25 meter   75 centimeters in 0.75 meter
320. 30 minutes in half an hour; 10 minutes in one-sixth hour;
6 minutes in one-tenth hour.   **321.** One quire is one-twentieth of
a ream; 5 quires are one-fourth of a ream; 10 quires are one-half
of a ream.

Page 145   **322.** The length should be divided into 36 equal parts.
Every six of these parts will be equal to one-sixth of the length.
Every four of these parts will be equal to one-ninth of the length.
Every three of these parts will be equal to one-twelfth of the length.

323. One half   **324.** 5 kilograms are $\dfrac{1}{200}$ of a metric ton.

60 kilograms are $\dfrac{3}{50}$ of a metric ton.   200 kilograms are $\dfrac{1}{5}$ of a

metric ton.   **325.** 100 pounds are $\dfrac{1}{20}$ of a short ton.   500 pounds

are $\dfrac{1}{4}$ of a short ton.   1000 pounds are $\dfrac{1}{2}$ of a short ton.

326. 2, 3, 4, 5, 10, 15   **327.** Multiplied by: 4, 5, 13, 7, 25

Page 148   **328.** (a) $\dfrac{28}{73}$; (b) $\dfrac{48}{35}$; (c) $\dfrac{105}{26}$; (d) $\dfrac{357}{100}$; (e) $\dfrac{187}{105}$

329. (a) $\dfrac{5}{66}$; (b) $\dfrac{18}{125}$; (c) $\dfrac{18}{245}$; (d) $\dfrac{13}{1605}$; (e) $\dfrac{29}{1636}$ **330.** (a) $\dfrac{5}{6}$;

(b) $\dfrac{5}{64}$; (c) $\dfrac{45}{32}$; (d) $\dfrac{3}{13}$; (e) $\dfrac{17}{8}$ **331.** (a) $26\dfrac{1}{2}$; (b) $42\dfrac{12}{25}$;

(c) $92\dfrac{5}{8}$; (d) $34\dfrac{7}{8}$; (e) $49\dfrac{19}{32}$ **332.** (a) $1\dfrac{5}{28}$; (b) $\dfrac{139}{200}$; (c) $\dfrac{167}{400}$;

(d) $\dfrac{57}{256}$; (e) $1\dfrac{403}{512}$

Page 151   **334.** The fraction is multiplied by $\dfrac{5}{27}$

335. $\dfrac{a \cdot m}{b \cdot m}$; $\dfrac{\dfrac{a}{m}}{\dfrac{b}{m}}$; $\dfrac{a \cdot m}{b \cdot m}$

Page 152   **336.** $\dfrac{65}{91}$ **337.** $\dfrac{154}{238}$

Page 154   **338.** 28, 39, 119, 599, 605; 39, 72, 215;
72, 119, 599, 605

339. Of 180: 1, 2, 3, 5; of 400: 1, 2, 5; of 550:
1, 2, 5, 11; of 1,712: 1, 2, 107; of 8,146:
1, 2, 4,073; of 2,864: 1, 2, 179; of 1,984:
1, 2, 31; of 4,608: 1, 2, 3

340.
$$100 = 1 \cdot 2 \cdot 2 \cdot 5 \cdot 5$$
$$1,000 = 1 \cdot 2 \cdot 2 \cdot 2 \cdot 5 \cdot 5 \cdot 5$$
$$10,000 = 1 \cdot 2 \cdot 2 \cdot 2 \cdot 2 \cdot 5 \cdot 5 \cdot 5 \cdot 5$$
$$100,000 = 1 \cdot 2 \cdot 2 \cdot 2 \cdot 2 \cdot 2 \cdot 5 \cdot 5 \cdot 5 \cdot 5 \cdot 5$$
$$300 = 1 \cdot 2 \cdot 2 \cdot 3 \cdot 5 \cdot 5$$
$$5,220 = 1 \cdot 2 \cdot 2 \cdot 3 \cdot 3 \cdot 5 \cdot 29$$
$$15,360 = 1 \cdot 2 \cdot 2 \cdot 2 \cdot 2 \cdot 2 \cdot 2 \cdot 2 \cdot 2 \cdot 2 \cdot 3 \cdot 5$$
$$3,240 = 1 \cdot 2 \cdot 2 \cdot 2 \cdot 3 \cdot 3 \cdot 3 \cdot 3 \cdot 5$$
$$10,368 = 1 \cdot 2 \cdot 2 \cdot 2 \cdot 2 \cdot 2 \cdot 2 \cdot 2 \cdot 3 \cdot 3$$
$$2,257 = 1 \cdot 2,257$$
$$1,902 = 1 \cdot 2 \cdot 3 \cdot 317$$
$$10,395 = 1 \cdot 3 \cdot 3 \cdot 3 \cdot 5 \cdot 73$$
$$41,472 = 1 \cdot 2 \cdot 2 \cdot 2 \cdot 2 \cdot 2 \cdot 2 \cdot 2 \cdot 2 \cdot 2 \cdot 3 \cdot 3 \cdot 3$$

Page 155   **341.**   First line: $2 \cdot 3 \cdot 3 = 18$
Second line: $2 \cdot 2 \cdot 2 \cdot 2 \cdot 2 \cdot 2 \cdot 2 \cdot 3 = 384$
Third line: 7
Fourth line: None
Fifth line: $2 \cdot 3 \cdot 7 = 42$

Page 156   **342.**   First line: Common divisors: 1, 2, 3, and 6;
greatest common divisor: 6
Second line: Common divisors: 1 and 5;
greatest common divisor: 5
Third line: Common divisors: 3 and 9;
greatest common divisor: 9
Fourth line: Common divisors: 2, 3, 4, 6, 9, 18, 36;
greatest common divisor: 36

Fifth line: Common divisors: 2, 4, 7, 8, 14, 28, 56; greatest common divisor: 56

343. $\dfrac{23}{93}$, $\dfrac{39}{104}$, $\dfrac{215}{634}$

Page 157 **344.** $\dfrac{2}{3}$, $\dfrac{2}{5}$, $\dfrac{3}{7}$, $\dfrac{11}{70}$, $\dfrac{1}{20}$, $\dfrac{25}{71}$, $\dfrac{3}{7}$, $\dfrac{4}{9}$, $\dfrac{5}{6}$, $\dfrac{3}{7}$ **345.** $\dfrac{4}{5}$, $\dfrac{11}{13}$,

$\dfrac{51}{57}$, $\dfrac{4}{5}$, $\dfrac{2}{3}$, $\dfrac{40}{1687}$, $\dfrac{9}{13}$, $\dfrac{14}{17}$, $\dfrac{4}{5}$ **346.** $1\dfrac{1}{2}$, $1\dfrac{1}{2}$, $1\dfrac{1}{5}$, $2\dfrac{2}{3}$, $1\dfrac{6}{13}$, $1\dfrac{9}{41}$,

$1\dfrac{4}{7}$, 5, $16\dfrac{7}{13}$ **347.** 9 inches are one fourth of a yard; 12 inches are one third of a yard; 16 inches are $\dfrac{4}{9}$ of a yard; 24 inches are $\dfrac{2}{3}$ of a yard; 30 inches are $\dfrac{5}{6}$ of a yard **348.** 100 pounds are $\dfrac{5}{112}$ of a long ton; 56 pounds are $\dfrac{1}{40}$ of a long ton; 280 pounds are $\dfrac{1}{8}$ of a long ton **349.** 4 ounces are $\dfrac{1}{4}$ of a pound; 6 ounces are $\dfrac{3}{8}$ of a pound; 8 ounces are $\dfrac{1}{2}$ of a pound; 12 ounces are $\dfrac{3}{4}$ of a pound **350.** 3 hours are $\dfrac{1}{8}$ of a day; 6 hours are $\dfrac{1}{4}$ of a day; 8 hours are $\dfrac{1}{3}$ of a day **351.** 125 grams are $\dfrac{1}{8}$ of a kilogram; 450 grams are $\dfrac{9}{20}$ of a kilogram; 750 grams are $\dfrac{3}{4}$ of a kilogram **352.** 132 feet are $\dfrac{1}{40}$ of a mile; 3960 feet are $\dfrac{3}{4}$ of a mile; 1980 feet are $\dfrac{3}{8}$ of a mile **353.** $\dfrac{1}{2} = \dfrac{2}{4} = \dfrac{4}{8} = \dfrac{8}{16} = \dfrac{16}{32}$ **354.** $\dfrac{25}{28}$

355. 75 kilograms are $\dfrac{3}{40}$ of a metric ton; 125 kilograms are $\dfrac{1}{8}$ of a metric ton; 390 kilograms are $\dfrac{39}{100}$ of a metric ton; 750 kilograms are $\dfrac{3}{4}$ of a metric ton; 800 kilograms are $\dfrac{4}{5}$ of a metric ton

Page 159   **356.**   50   2,016

               180   4,050

               480   540

               165   1,080

               480   2,310

               140   60

               144   504

                      2,420

357. The product of these three numbers.   **358.** 12 times.

Page 161   **359.** $\dfrac{6}{8}, \dfrac{15}{20}, \dfrac{18}{24}, \dfrac{24}{32}, \dfrac{27}{36}, \dfrac{33}{44}, \dfrac{36}{48}, \dfrac{39.5}{54}, \dfrac{48}{64}, \dfrac{57}{72}, \dfrac{60}{80},$

$\dfrac{66}{88}, \dfrac{72}{96}$

Page 162   **360.** $\dfrac{4}{10}, \dfrac{6}{15}, \dfrac{10}{25}, \dfrac{14}{35}, \dfrac{18}{45}, \dfrac{22}{55}, \dfrac{26}{65}, \dfrac{28}{70}, \dfrac{34}{85}, \dfrac{40}{100}$

361. $\dfrac{50}{100}, \dfrac{75}{100}, \dfrac{140}{100}, \dfrac{45}{100}, \dfrac{52}{100}, \dfrac{90}{100}, \dfrac{85}{100}$

362. (a) $\dfrac{5}{9}, \left[\dfrac{3}{5}, \dfrac{9}{15}\right], \dfrac{2}{3}, \dfrac{3}{4}$; (b) $\dfrac{11}{18}, \dfrac{23}{36}, \dfrac{47}{60}, \dfrac{17}{20}, \dfrac{7}{8}$;

(c) $\dfrac{11}{21}, \dfrac{23}{42}, \dfrac{7}{12}, \dfrac{9}{14}$; (d) $\dfrac{5}{14}, \dfrac{13}{32}, \dfrac{20}{45}, \dfrac{11}{21}$ **363.** (a) $\dfrac{4}{48}, \dfrac{3}{48}$;

(b) $\dfrac{25}{80}, \dfrac{64}{80}$; (c) $\dfrac{114}{133}, \dfrac{119}{133}$; (d) $\dfrac{65}{75}, \dfrac{64}{75}$; (e) $\dfrac{6}{12}, \dfrac{4}{12}, \dfrac{3}{12}, \dfrac{2}{12}$;

(f) $\dfrac{75}{360}, \dfrac{140}{360}, \dfrac{27}{360}, \dfrac{234}{360}$; (g) $\dfrac{48}{320}, \dfrac{280}{320}, \dfrac{64}{320}, \dfrac{140}{320}$;

(h) $\dfrac{93}{180}, \dfrac{65}{180}, \dfrac{116}{180}, \dfrac{110}{180}$; (i) $\dfrac{168}{816}, \dfrac{48}{816}, \dfrac{459}{816}, \dfrac{238}{816}$;

(j) $\dfrac{490}{1000}, \dfrac{962}{1000}, \dfrac{425}{1000}, \dfrac{740}{1000}$ **364.** $\dfrac{1}{16}, \dfrac{1}{20}, \dfrac{1}{24}$,   or,

$\dfrac{15}{240}, \dfrac{12}{240}, \dfrac{10}{240}$

Page 165   **365.** (a) $\dfrac{9}{16}$; (b) $\dfrac{100}{143}$; (c) $\dfrac{73}{50}$; (d) $\dfrac{97}{180}$; (e) $\dfrac{59}{45}$

366. (a) $\dfrac{8}{15}$; (b) $\dfrac{199}{132}$; (c) $\dfrac{193}{180}$; (d) $\dfrac{7}{5}$; (e) $\dfrac{56}{45}$

Page 166 **367.** (a) $\dfrac{19}{6}$; (b) $\dfrac{107}{45}$; (c) $\dfrac{9187}{5040}$; (d) $\dfrac{101}{30}$; (e) $\dfrac{323}{80}$

368. (a) $4\dfrac{11}{12}$; (b) $5\dfrac{15}{16}$; (c) $12\dfrac{103}{144}$; (d) $13\dfrac{53}{60}$; (e) $34\dfrac{67}{90}$

369. (a) $30\dfrac{89}{112}$; (b) $21\dfrac{31}{45}$; (c) $27\dfrac{11}{180}$; (d) $49\dfrac{59}{360}$; (e) $113\dfrac{11}{30}$

370. (a) $89\dfrac{13}{20}$; (b) $40\dfrac{37}{80}$; (c) $92\dfrac{569}{720}$; (d) $22\dfrac{13}{100}$; (e) $198\dfrac{2}{3}$

372. $\dfrac{37}{180}$ **373.** $402\dfrac{1}{2}$ feet   **374.** $22\dfrac{22}{25}$ grams   **375.** $\dfrac{113}{360}$

376. Increase by $33\dfrac{17}{36}$ **377.** $90\dfrac{9}{16}$ pounds

Page 168   **378.** (a) $\dfrac{5}{36}$; (b) $\dfrac{17}{99}$; (c) $\dfrac{46}{105}$; (d) $\dfrac{41}{96}$; (e) $\dfrac{13}{24}$

379. (a) $\dfrac{22}{45}$; (b) $\dfrac{1}{12}$; (c) $\dfrac{1}{168}$; (d) $\dfrac{1}{66}$; (e) $\dfrac{361}{546}$ **380.** (a) $18\dfrac{13}{28}$;

(b) $11\dfrac{19}{24}$; (c) $63\dfrac{3}{10}$; (d) $3\dfrac{7}{108}$; (e) $6\dfrac{181}{448}$ **381.** $19\dfrac{49}{120}$; $1\dfrac{193}{360}$;

$13\dfrac{159}{230}$; $18\dfrac{3}{40}$; $23\dfrac{13}{180}$

Page 169   **382.** $3\dfrac{41}{50}$ kilograms   **383.** $\dfrac{4}{10}$ or $\dfrac{2}{5}$ **384.** $1\dfrac{50}{63}$

385. $25\dfrac{319}{240}$; $18\dfrac{5}{36}$; $9\dfrac{125}{144}$ **386.** 1 foot.   **387.** $26\dfrac{1}{2}$ yards

388. $\dfrac{29}{60}$ **389.** $\dfrac{1}{40}$ **390.** Decrease by $5\dfrac{13}{80}$

391. Increase by $24\dfrac{3}{40}$ **392.** Decrease by $15\dfrac{43}{80}$

Page 174   **393.** (a) $\dfrac{14}{7}$; (b) $\dfrac{15}{2}$; (c) $\dfrac{175}{9}$; (d) $\dfrac{3}{5}$; (e) $\dfrac{11}{3}$; (f) $\dfrac{15}{4}$;

(g) $\dfrac{42}{5}$; (h) $\dfrac{110}{3}$; (i) $\dfrac{81}{7}$; (j) $\dfrac{45}{2}$ **394.** (a) $26\dfrac{1}{2}$; (b) $19\dfrac{1}{3}$;

(c) $56\frac{1}{2}$; (d) $159\frac{1}{7}$; (e) $41\frac{1}{2}$ 395.(a) $\frac{15}{16}$; (b) $\frac{51}{5}$; (c) $\frac{23}{7}$;

(d) $\frac{95}{4}$; (e) $\frac{25}{3}$ 396.(a) $17\frac{5}{6}$; (b) $56\frac{1}{3}$; (c) $326\frac{5}{8}$; (d) $63\frac{1}{5}$;

(e) $3\frac{17}{27}$ 397.(a) $\frac{2}{21}$; (b) $\frac{2}{15}$; (c) $\frac{3}{20}$; (d) $\frac{36}{325}$; (e) $\frac{32}{75}$

398.(a) $4\frac{1}{3}$; (b) $17\frac{1}{3}$; (c) $21\frac{2}{3}$; (d) 41; (e) $61\frac{1}{7}$; (f) $252\frac{5}{7}$;

(g) $109\frac{277}{512}$

Page 175   399. $\frac{2}{5}$; $\frac{9}{100}$; $29\frac{41}{65}$; $12\frac{83}{125}$; $122\frac{8}{11}$ 400. $5\frac{1}{12}$; $51\frac{9}{10}$;

$5\frac{16}{21}$; $6\frac{241}{3132}$; $7\frac{5}{8}$

Page 176   401. 5,150 gallons   402. $1,471\frac{11}{19}$ short tons

403. 117 Fahrenheits   404. $6\frac{2}{7}$ feet; $111\frac{4}{7}$ feet   405. $7\frac{1}{3}$ miles

406. $16\frac{3}{4}$ yards; $46\frac{4}{9}$ yards; $5\frac{29}{36}$ yards   407. 280 gallons

408. $\frac{3}{40}$ 409. $\frac{13}{36}$

Page 180   410.(a) $\frac{2}{11}$; (b) $\frac{1}{18}$; (c) $\frac{3}{224}$; (d) $\frac{3}{50}$; (e) $\frac{1}{54}$

411.(a) $\frac{2}{3}$; (b) $\frac{2}{9}$; (c) $\frac{2}{3}$; (d) $\frac{29}{24}$; (e) $\frac{2}{9}$ 412.(a) 16; (b) $\frac{61}{3}$;

(c) $\frac{100}{3}$; (d) $\frac{56}{5}$; (e) $\frac{225}{4}$ 413.(a) $\frac{2}{5}$; (b) 8; (c) $\frac{16}{3}$; (d) $\frac{25}{2}$;

(e) 21 414.(a) $\frac{45}{32}$; (b) $\frac{42}{11}$; (c) $\frac{10}{9}$; (d) $\frac{225}{256}$; (e) $\frac{145}{21}$

415.(a) $\frac{10}{21}$; (b) $\frac{529}{25}$; (c) $\frac{8}{15}$; (d) 5; (e) $\frac{3059}{18544}$ 416. $\frac{32}{9}$; $\frac{5}{2}$;

$\frac{50}{9}$; $\frac{2051}{4560}$

Page 181   **417.** $13\dfrac{1}{2}$ **418.** $\dfrac{329}{41}$ **419.** $\dfrac{9}{2}$ **420.** 160 pieces

421. \$294   **422.** $\dfrac{7}{10}$ short tons   **423.** $\dfrac{305}{28}$; $\dfrac{183}{56}$

Page 185   **424.** 0.2; 0.12; 0.76; 0.94; 0.625; 0.875; 0.4375;

0.43875; 0.253125; 0.165; 0.116; 0.5675   **425.** $\dfrac{12}{25}$ and $\dfrac{15}{32}$

426. 0.09999...; 0.2461538...; 0.142857...; 0.714275...;
0.2778...; 0.2667...; 0.171717...; 0.235235235...;
0.1271...; 1.294...; 0.841...

Page 189   **427.** $0.34 = \dfrac{17}{50}$; $0.06 = \dfrac{3}{50}$; $0.075 = \dfrac{3}{40}$; $0.375 = \dfrac{3}{8}$;

$0.6738 = \dfrac{3369}{5000}$; $0.7575 = \dfrac{303}{400}$; $0.0085 = \dfrac{17}{2000}$; $0.9125 = \dfrac{73}{400}$;

$0.12567 = \dfrac{12567}{100000}$ **428.** $0.4444... = \dfrac{4}{9}$; $0.7777... = \dfrac{7}{9}$;

$0.15555... = \dfrac{7}{45}$; $0.045666... = \dfrac{401}{9990}$; $0.30444... = \dfrac{1507}{4950}$;

$23.555... = 23\dfrac{5}{9}$; $3.74777... = 3\dfrac{7403}{9900}$

429. $0.565656... = \dfrac{56}{99}$; $0.3474747... = \dfrac{172}{495}$;

$0.045878787... = \dfrac{2276}{49500}$; $1.34585858... = 1\dfrac{856}{2475}$;

$34.0898989... = 3\dfrac{9}{110}$; $15.3424242... = 15\dfrac{113}{330}$;

$92.078676767 = 92\dfrac{7789}{99000}$; **430.** $0.235235235... = \dfrac{235}{999}$;

$0.2563563563... = \dfrac{2561}{9990}$; $0.3892892892... = \dfrac{3889}{9990}$;

$1.0478478478... = 1\dfrac{236}{4995}$; $45.2378378378... = 45\dfrac{1189}{4995}$;

$210.12745745745... = 210\dfrac{12733}{99900}$; $15.479479479... = 15\dfrac{479}{999}$

431. $1.457245724572... = 1\dfrac{508}{1111}$;

$$16.683468346834\ldots = 16\frac{2278}{3333};$$

$$982.634563456345\ldots = 982\frac{705}{1111};$$

$$0.893548935489354\ldots = \frac{89354}{99999};$$

$$0.142857142857142857\ldots = \frac{1}{7};$$

$$0.384615384615384615\ldots = \frac{42735}{111111}$$

Page 195   **432.**(a) Greater by 22; (b) Smaller by 8.7;
(c) Greater by 1.22; (d) Greater by 5.75; (e) Greater by 856;

(f) Smaller by $\frac{1}{36}$; (g) Smaller by $\frac{23}{75}$; (h) Greater by $3\frac{78}{80}$;

(i) Smaller by $2\frac{1}{12}$; (j) Greater by 0.975   **433.**(a) 13 to 1;

(b) 1 to 23; (c) 1 to 2; (d) 3 to 2; (e) 6 to 1; (f) 8 to 15;
(g) 3 to 2; (h) 10 to 81; (i) 13 to 10; (j) 48 to 31
434.(a) 2 to 1; (b) 72 to 43; (c) 23,412 to 50,000;
(d) 2,000 to 4,402; (e) 10 to 11.025   **435.**(a) 24 to 1;
(b) 3 to 3; (c) 15 to 64.52; (d) 15 to 7.72; (e) 12 to 53.82
436.(a) 1.11 to 1; (b) 248.805 to 5; (c) 1.5 to 2.616;
(d) 25 to 176.57; (e) 2.6475 to 10

Page 197   **439.** 7.56 kilograms   **440.** Copper: 1 to 6.
Tin: 7 to 12.   Antimony: 1 to 4.   The sum of the ratios is equal
to 1   **441.** 25 to 18

Page 201   **442.** 382.84 ft²   **443.** 8.82 pounds   **444.** 48.984 inches
445. 1 to 10   **446.** 32.4 kilograms   **447.** 6.8 inches

Page 202   **448.** 600,000,000 square inches or 4,166,667 square feet
449. $1\frac{1}{9}$ ounces of hydrogen   **450.** 14,240,000 calories

451. 37 feet and $5\frac{1}{2}$ inches

Page 204   **452.**(a) Yes; (b) No; (c) No; (d) Yes; (e) No

Page 205   **454.** (*a*) $3 \div 8 = 9 \div 24$; (*b*) $0.5 \div 2 = 5 \div 20$;
(*c*) $5 \div 3 = 20 \div 12$; (*d*) $3.8 \div 0.1 = 76 \div 2$;

(*e*) $\dfrac{3}{4} \div \dfrac{5}{12} = \dfrac{9}{25} \div \dfrac{1}{5}$ **455.** No   **456.** (*a*) 405; (*b*) 480;

(*c*) 75; (*d*) 512; (*e*) $\dfrac{8}{7}$; (*f*) 4.2; (*g*) $\dfrac{7}{27}$; (*h*) 26.1; (*i*) 1;

(*j*) 0.9

Page 208   **457.** (*a*) Direct proportionality;
(*b*) Inverse proportionality; (*c*) Inverse proportionality;
(*d*) Direct proportionality; (*e*) Inverse proportionality;
(*f*) Inverse proportionality   **458.** When the side of the square is doubled, the area of the square is quadrupled.   When the side of the square is tripled, the area of the square is increased nine-fold. When the side of the square is quadrupled, the area of the square is increased 16 times.   **459.** When the edge of the cube is doubled, the volume of the cube is increased 8 times.   When the edge of the cube is tripled, the volume of the cube is increased 27 times. When the edge of the cube is quadrupled, the volume of the cube is increased 64 times.

Page 209   **460.** In 3 hours 20 minutes
461. 122 hours 38.4 minutes   **462.** Approximately 153.2 days
463. 199.2 revolutions per minute
464. Approximately 199.4 inches   **465.** 3 hours 30 minutes

466. $\dfrac{7}{9}$ ft long

Page 212   **467.** 16 pounds of tin and 8 pounds of lead
468. 4,200 and 3,000   **469.** 320 and 160   **470.** 390 and 360
471. 90 and 15   **472.** 495, 605, 715   **473.** 24, 36, 40
474. 540, 180, 90   **475.** 42 and 70   **476.** 570, 57, and 5.7
477. 17, 34, 51, 68, 85   **478.** \$2,250, \$2,000, and \$3,200
479. 9 pounds of sulphur, 58.5 pounds of nitrate, and 7.5 pounds of carbon   **480.** \$24, \$30, and \$16   **481.** 24 ft, 40 ft, and 60 ft

Page 214   **485.** 200 percent; 400 percent   **486.** 1,200 percent;
2,500 percent   **487.** 0.01, 0.07, 0.10, 0.32, 0.57, 1.36, 3.62, 1.00,
2.00, 10.00   **488.** 0.025, 0.057, 0.075, 0.086, 0.175, 0.289, 0.004,
0.0014, 0.0028, 0.016, 5.325, 1.065, 24.505   **489.** 0.015, 0.0075,
0.07, 0.0816, 0.333, 0.667, 1.2717   **490.** $\dfrac{1}{50}, \dfrac{9}{100}, \dfrac{3}{25}, \dfrac{27}{100},$

$\dfrac{7}{20}$, $\dfrac{11}{20}$, $\dfrac{3}{4}$, $\dfrac{1}{4}$, $\dfrac{1}{2}$, $1\dfrac{1}{4}$, $1\dfrac{1}{2}$, $1\dfrac{3}{4}$, $2\dfrac{1}{2}$, $4\dfrac{3}{4}$ **491.** $\dfrac{1}{40}$, $\dfrac{1}{400}$, $\dfrac{7}{400}$,

$\dfrac{7}{4000}$, $\dfrac{11}{2000}$, $\dfrac{3}{400}$, $\dfrac{1}{4000}$, $\dfrac{7}{40}$, $\dfrac{272}{1000}$, $\dfrac{3}{2000}$, $5\dfrac{107}{2000}$, $1\dfrac{13}{200}$

492. $\dfrac{5}{300}$, $\dfrac{11}{400}$, $\dfrac{91}{600}$, $\dfrac{2}{3}$, $\dfrac{43}{600}$, $1\dfrac{331}{600}$, $1\dfrac{49}{800}$

Page 215 **493.** 10%, 70%, 12%, 27%, 75%, 99%, 1%, 5%, 0.1%, 0.7%, 1.5%, 7.5%, 8.9%, 12.5%, 35.5%, 49.9%, 50.1%, 75.5%, 99.9% **494.** 110%, 150%, 190%, 125%, 175%, 255%, 106%, 475%, 501%, 725%, 766%, 833%, 957%, 999%, 10,125%, 25,075%

Page 216 **495.** 1%, 50%, 25%, 20%, 10%, 5%, 4%, 2.5%, 2%, 12.5%, 6.25%, 3.125%, 1.5625%, 75%, 62.5%, 32%, 13.6%, 51%, 19.6%, 17.8%, 9.9%, 36.25%, 1.0625%, 17.8125% **496.** 1550%, 71.25%, 980%, 1768%, 575%,

646.875%, 1634%, 3523.4375%, 1029.6% **497.** $66\dfrac{1}{3}\%$, $57\dfrac{1}{7}\%$,

$55\dfrac{5}{9}\%$, $63\dfrac{7}{11}\%$, $54\dfrac{2}{7}\%$, $55\dfrac{5}{49}\%$, $91\dfrac{19}{41}\%$, $120\dfrac{15}{28}\%$, $89\dfrac{1}{11}\%$,

$91\dfrac{5}{7}\%$, $68\dfrac{1}{7}\%$ **498.** $142\dfrac{6}{7}\%$, $344\dfrac{4}{9}\%$, $745\dfrac{5}{11}\%$, $646\dfrac{2}{3}\%$,

$938\dfrac{2}{21}\%$, $1514\dfrac{22}{27}\%$, $517\dfrac{1}{7}\%$, $727\dfrac{7}{12}\%$ **499.** 28.57%,

55.56%, 88.89%, 59.24%, 65.22%, 85.19%, 51.43%. 73.27%, 28.89%, 49.33%, 59.76%, 75.78% **500.** 283.33%, 177.78%, 372.73%, 423.08%, 513.333%, 727.78%, 623.21%, 111.43%, 411.90%

Page 218 **501.** 165.25 grams **502.** 105 short tons of carbon; 110 short tons of manganese; 20 short tons of silicon; 9765 short tons of pure iron. **503.** 875 short tons of carbon; 375 short tons of silicon; 250 short tons of manganese; 100 short tons of phosphorus; 2.5 short tons of sulphur; 23,397.5 short tons of pure iron **504.** $165 **505.** $306.25

Page 219 **506.** $11.25 **507.** $30.05 **508.** $3.50

Page 220 **509.** $2.70 **510.** $22.50

Page 221 **511.** $161 **512.** $41.16 **513.** $242.28 **514.** $1,410.39 **515.** $984.34

Page 223   **516.** $54.90 + $1,500 = 1,554.90   **517.** $2,018.33
518. $61,351.74   **519.** $339   **520.** $5,128.47

Page 225   **521.** $318.51   **522.** $5,286.96   **523.** $828.28
524. $152.26   **525.** $337.85

Page 227   **526.** $88.25   **527.** $147.83   **528.** $4.17   **529.** $12.75
530. $2.68   **531.**(*a*) 1,800; (*b*) 1,080; (*c*) 675; (*d*) 450;
(*e*) 270; (*f*) 162; (*g*) 81; (*h*) 43.2; (*i*) 30.8; (*j*) 21.6
532.(*a*) 1,200; (*b*) 50; (*c*) 200; (*d*) 2,000; (*e*) 60; (*f*) 75;
(*g*) 450; (*h*) 72; (*i*) 68.44; (*j*) 60   **533.** 375   **534.** 516⅔

Page 228   **535.** 1,024 parts beyond the daily quota. The daily
quota: 800 parts.   **536.** 40 pounds   **537.** $725.33   **538.** $525
539. $240   **540.** 205.7 pounds   **541.** 724.6 pounds

Page 229   **542.**(*a*) 1.56%; (*b*) 5.156%; (*c*) 0.85%; (*d*) 4.65%;
(*e*) 6.85%   **543.**(*a*) 2.83%; (*b*) 33.33%; (*c*) 16.92%;
(*d*) 77.8%; (*e*) 21.06%   **544.** 94%

Page 230   **545.** 15.02%   **546.** 70%   **547.** 28.33%   **548.** 7.8%
549. Increased by 14.6%   **550.** Decreased by 20%
551. 5.24%   **552.** 0.028%   **553.** 3.4%   **554.** 11.3%
555. 2.85%   **556.** 9.9%

Page 234   **557.** 14%   **558.** 32.76% per annum

Page 235   **559.** 25.2%   **560.** 38.33%   **561.** 95.52%   **562.** 5.83%
563. 20%   **564.** 41.5%

Page 239   **565.**(*a*) 0.1 inch; (*b*) 0.001 meter; (*c*) 0.01 kilogram;
(*d*) 1 ounce; (*e*) 0.1 millimeter; (*f*) 0.001 foot;
(*g*) 0.001 kilogram; (*h*) 0.1 mile; (*i*) 0.01 meter
566.(*a*) 0.333, error: −0.0003; (*b*) 0.833, error: +0.0003;
(*c*) 3.778, error: −0.001; (*d*) 5.846, error: +0.0001;
(*e*) 6.267, error: +0.001   **567.**(*a*) 0.0003; (*b*) 0.0003;
(*c*) 0.0002; (*d*) 0.0002; (*e*) 0.0007

Page 241   **568.**(*a*) 0.004%; (*b*) 0.0013%; (*c*) 0.0018%;
(*d*) 0.0019%; (*e*) 0.004%; (*f*) 0.000009%; (*g*) 0.000006%;
(*h*) 0.0011%; (*i*) 0.00004%   **569.**(*g*) 0.000006%;
(*f*) 0.000009%; (*i*) 0.0004%; (*h*) 0.0011%; (*b*) 0.0013%;
(*c*) 0.0018%; (*d*) 0.0019%; (*a*) and (*e*) 0.004.   The most accurate measure is 78.450 kilograms.   The least accurate measure is
12.7 inches.

Page 242   **570.**(*a*) 3; (*b*) 4; (*c*) 3; (*d*) 4; (*e*) 5
571.(*a*) 0.6667; (*b*) 0.5556; (*c*) 0.6364; (*d*) 0.08333;
(*e*) 0.04166

Page 243   **572.**(a) 56.576; (b) 3.028; (c) 1227.96; (d) 2.842;
(e) 24.270   **573.**(a) 231.04; (b) 0.678; (c) 2.756; (d) 1.47;
(e) 4.738

Page 245   **574.** 8.650 square inches   **575.** 18,000 cubic inches
576.(a) 60; (b) 952; (c) 17300; (d) 164,000; (e) 29.8

Page 249   **578.**(a) 18.7; (b) 0.34357; (c) 3.667; (d) 0.175;
(e) 12.2   **579.**(a) 1.79; (b) 2.80; (c) 0.856; (d) 0.564;
(e) 4.02; (f) 2.620; (g) 2.68; (h) 0.915; (i) 4.10; (j) 5.09;
(k) 2.64; (l) 3.74

Page 251   **580.** $53^2 = 2,890$; $26.8^2 = 718$; $78.4^2 = 6,150$;
$45.3^2 = 2,050$; $17.5^2 = 307$; $22.6^2 = 511$; $36.9^2 = 1,360$;
$71.6^2 = 5,130$; $37.8^2 = 1,430$ **581.** $1.56^2 = 2.44$; $7.89^2 = 62.2$;
$0.0653^2 = 0.00433$; $9.34^2 = 89.2$; $8.21^2 = 67.4$;
$0.00108^2 = 0.00000117$; $0.562^2 = 0.316$; $6.34^2 = 40.2$;
$1.74^2 = 3.03$; $0.0458^2 = 0.00210$

Page 255   **582.** $\sqrt{467,856} = 684$; $\sqrt{118,336} = 344$;
$\sqrt{150,544} = 388$; $\sqrt{62,001} = 249$; $\sqrt{779,689} = 883$;
$\sqrt{2,085,136} = 1,444$; $\sqrt{4,879,681} = 2,209$; $\sqrt{34,012,224} = 5,832$;
$\sqrt{594,823,321} = 24,389$; $\sqrt{244,140,625} = 15,625$
583. $\sqrt{438,976} = 662.55$; $\sqrt{74,088} = 272.19$;
$\sqrt{830,584} = 911.36$; $\sqrt{8,998,912} = 2,999.82$;
$\sqrt{12,649,337} = 3,556.59$; $\sqrt{15,438,249} = 3,929.14$;
$\sqrt{143,877,824} = 11,996.17$; $\sqrt{174,676,879} = 13,216.54$;
$\sqrt{814,780,504} = 28,544.34$; $\sqrt{893,871,739} = 29,897.69$
584. $\sqrt{6.16441} = 2.48253$; $\sqrt{96.9536} = 9.64650$;
$\sqrt{1.84119} = 1.35690$; $\sqrt{231.0844} = 15.20113$;
$\sqrt{2791.057} = 52.83045$; $\sqrt{30.4795} = 5.52981$;
$\sqrt{99.0959} = 9.95469$; $\sqrt{8.80627} = 2.96753$;
$\sqrt{0.96332} = 0.98199$; $\sqrt{0.098991} = 0.31463$

Page 259   **585.** $\sqrt{21} = 4.583$; $\sqrt{45} = 6.708$; $\sqrt{67} = 8.185$;
$\sqrt{83} = 9.110$; $\sqrt{92} = 9.592$; $\sqrt{75} = 8.660$; $\sqrt{67} = 8.185$;
$\sqrt{42} = 6.481$; $\sqrt{89} = 9.434$; $\sqrt{35} = 5.916$ **586.** $\sqrt{3.4} = 1.844$;
$\sqrt{5.7} = 2.387$; $\sqrt{7.4} = 2.720$; $\sqrt{8.5} = 2.915$; $\sqrt{3.9} = 1.975$;
$\sqrt{2.1} = 1.449$; $\sqrt{1.1} = 1.049$; $\sqrt{6.9} = 1.627$; $\sqrt{4.3} = 2.074$;
$\sqrt{0.8} = 0.8944$ **587.** $\sqrt{215} = 14.66$; $\sqrt{37,500} = 195.6$;
$\sqrt{489} = 22.12$; $\sqrt{452} = 21.26$; $\sqrt{781} = 27.95$; $\sqrt{893} = 29.88$;
$\sqrt{10,500} = 102.5$; $\sqrt{78.400} = 280.0$; $\sqrt{15.600} = 124.9$

588. $\sqrt{6,780} = 82.34$; $\sqrt{867.000} = 931.1$; $\sqrt{7,560} = 86.95$;
$\sqrt{31.5} = 5.613$; $\sqrt{74.3} = 8.619$; $\sqrt{8.900} = 94.34$;
$\sqrt{7.820} = 88.43$; $\sqrt{883,000} = 939.7$; $\sqrt{9.340} = 96.64$;
$\sqrt{146,000} = 382.1$ **589.** $\sqrt{12.5} = 3.54$; $\sqrt{45.7} = 6.76$;
$\sqrt{51.6} = 7.18$; $\sqrt{74.3} = 8.62$; $\sqrt{87.9} = 9.38$; $\sqrt{43.2} = 6.57$;
$\sqrt{35.2} = 5.93$; $\sqrt{77.8} = 8.73$; $\sqrt{90.5} = 9.51$; $\sqrt{21.7} = 4.66$
590. $\sqrt{6.75} = 2.60$; $\sqrt{5.39} = 2.32$; $\sqrt{8.92} = 2.99$;
$\sqrt{9.17} = 3.03$; $\sqrt{8.37} = 2.89$; $\sqrt{6.45} = 2.54$; $\sqrt{3.25} = 1.80$;
$\sqrt{7.35} = 2.71$; $\sqrt{2.17} = 1.47$; $\sqrt{1.08} = 1.04$
591. $\sqrt{0.673} = 0.820$; $\sqrt{0.00894} = 0.0946$; $\sqrt{0.000635} = 0.0252$;
$\sqrt{0.134} = 0.366$; $\sqrt{0.0000876} = 0.00936$;
$\sqrt{0.000004539} = 0.00213$; $\sqrt{0.000367} = 0.0192$;
$\sqrt{0.548} = 0.740$; $\sqrt{0.000765} = 0.0279$; $\sqrt{0.0000319} + 0.00565$

Page 262 **592.** $2^{18} = 262,144$; $2^{24} = 16,777,216$;
$2^{27} = 134,217,728$; $2^{30} = 1,073,741,824$; $2^{32} = 4,294,967,296$
593. $3^1 = 3$ $3^2 = 9$ $3^3 = 27$ $3^4 = 81$ $3^5 = 243$ $3^6 = 729$
$3^7 = 2.187$ $3^8 = 6,561$ $3^9 = 19,683$ **594.** $3^{10} = 59.049$;
$3^{12} = 531,441$; $3^{15} = 14,348,907$

Page 263 **595.** (a) $2^3 = 8$; (b) $2^6 = 64$; (c) $2^4 = 16$;
(d) $2^{12} = 4,096$; (e) $2^9 = 512$ **596.** (a) $3^5 = 243$; (b) $3^5 = 243$;
(c) $3^7 = 2,187$; (d) $3^8 = 6.561$; (e) $3^5 = 243$

Page 264 **597.** (a) 3^6; (b) 2^{12}; (c) $4^4 = 2^8$; (d) 5^4; (e) 2^{20}
598. (a) 729; (b) $4,096$; (c) 256; (d) 625; (e) $1,048,476$
599. (a) $2^{16} = 65,536$; (b) $2^{16} = 65,536$; (c) $2^{18} = 262,144$;
(d) $2^{21} = 2,097,152$; (e) $2^{20} = 1,048,576$

Page 266 **600.** (a) $\sqrt[12]{15}$; (b) $\sqrt[25]{7}$; (c) $\sqrt[8]{32}$; (d) $\sqrt[100]{10}$; (e) $\sqrt[57]{75}$
601. (a) 8; (b) 8; (c) 8; (d) 16; (e) 64

Page 267 **602.** $16,777,216$ **603.** $32,768$ **604.** 512

Page 270 **605.** $\log 20 = 1.301$; $\log 300 = 2.477$;
$\log 5,000 = 3.699$; $\log 700,000 = 5.845$; $\log 2,000 = 3.301$
606. $\log 12 = 1.079$; $\log 14 = 1.146$; $\log 15 = 1.176$;
$\log 210 = 2.322$; $\log 1,800 = 3.255$; $\log 25 = 1.398$;
$\log 350 = 2.544$

Page 271 **607.** $\log 1.5 = 0.176$; $\log 2.5 = 0.398$;
$\log 3.5 = 0.544$; $\log 7.5 = 0.875$; $\log 10.5 = 1.021$
608. $\log 8 = 0.903$; $\log 16 = 1.204$; $\log 32 = 1.505$;
$\log 54 = 1.806$; $\log 128 = 2.107$; $\log 27 = 1.431$;
$\log 81 = 1.908$; $\log 125 = 2.097$; $\log 625 = 2.796$;
$\log 2,430 = 3.385$; $\log 12.5 = 1.097$; $\log 6.25 = 0.796$

609. $\log 0.12 = 1.079 - 2$; $\log 0.024 = 1.380 - 3$;
$\log 0.0025 = 1.398 - 4$; $\log 0.0125 = 2.097 - 4$;
$\log 0.243 = 2.385 - 3$

Page 274   **610.** $\log 136 = 2.134$; $\log 1.89 = 0.276$;
$\log 17.3 = 1.238$; $\log 3.45 = 0.537$; $\log 89.3 = 1.951$;
$\log 76,400 = 4.883$; $\log 65.4 = 1.816$; $\log 3.47 = 0.539$;
$\log 2.84 = 0.453$; $\log 489 = 2.689$ **611.** $\log 0.367 = 2.564 - 3$;
$\log 0.00735 = 2.866 - 5$; $\log 0.0895 = 2.952 - 4$;
$\log 0.105 = 2.021 - 3$; $\log 0.0000562 = 2.750 - 7$;
$\log 0.000121 = 2.083 - 6$; $\log 0.426 = 2.629 - 3$;
$\log 0.268 = 2.428 - 3$; $\log 0.0592 = 2.773 - 4$;
$\log 0.00675 = 2.829 - 5$

Page 279   **612.** (*a*) 12.7; (*b*) 45.4; (*c*) 30.2; (*d*) 0.985; (*e*) 0.0561
613. (*a*) 2.23; (*b*) 0.376; (*c*) 63.9; (*d*) 0.0251; (*e*) 0.795
614. (*a*) 397.; (*b*) 160.; (*c*) 1,405; (*d*) 1.59; (*e*) 2.00;
(*f*) 0.000535; (*g*) 0.000000501   **615.** (*a*) 9.46; (*b*) 4.83;
(*c*) 1.43; (*d*) 0.436; (*e*) 1.06   **616.** (*a*) 1.88; (*b*) 46.4;
(*c*) 0.640; (*d*) 5.70; (*e*) 0.122

Index